Subscribe to

Trust Watch

The Grantseekers Newsletter

today . . .

As a purchaser of one of the CAF **Focus Series** titles you are eligible to subscribe to **Trust Watch**. Only £7.95 for three editions.

Trust Watch, th[e] is published thr[ee] readers up-to-da[te] happening in the [...] The newsletter includes:

■ scores of newly registered trusts

■ latest trends in trust funding

■ lottery news

■ in-depth case studies of major funders

■ profiles of key people

If you don't have all the latest information others will get there first. **Trust Watch** is part of the lifeline to funding success.

D0491626

Please complete the form below in BLOCK LETTERS

Title	Name

Job title	Organisation

Address

Town/City	County	Postcode

Please note No photocopies of this form accepted. Only one subscription available per registration

All orders must be signed and dated and are subject to acceptance by the publisher. Please allow 30 days for delivery.

PLEASE COMPLETE AS APPROPRIATE

Tel

Fax

E-mail

Please charge £   to my MasterCard/Visa/American Express/Delta/Switch Card

Card number | | | | | | | | | | | | | | | | | | | | |

Expiry date   Issue number

OR

I enclose a cheque made payable to CAF for £

Date   Signature

PLEASE DETACH THIS CARD AND SEND IT TO

Petra Buckley, CAF, Kings Hill, West Malling, Kent ME19 4TA

1ST EDITION

The Directory of
Grant Making Trusts

FOCUS SERIES

Manchester, Liverpool
and the North West

EDITORIAL TEAM
Owen Bevan
Johanna Davis
David Moncrieff

REFERENCE ONLY

© **1999 CAF**

Published by CAF (Charities Aid Foundation)
Kings Hill
West Malling
Kent ME19 4TA

Telephone
+44 (0) 1732 520000

Fax
+44 (0) 1732 520001

Website
http://www.charitynet.org

E-mail
cafpubs@caf.charitynet.org

Database management
and typesetting
The Polestar Group
(Whitefriars) Ltd

Design
Eugenie Dodd Typographics

Printed and bound in Great
Britain by Bell & Bain Ltd,
Glasgow

A catalogue record for this book
is available from the British
Library.

ISBN 1–85934–099–7

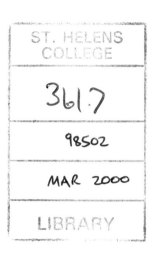

Contents

Introduction

It has been estimated that there are approximately 8,800 charitable grant makers in the UK. These are a major source of funding for the voluntary sector both in the UK and overseas. Figures published by CAF in the 1998 edition of *Dimensions of the Voluntary Sector* indicate that in 1997 the trust and foundation community had an income of approximately £2.1 billion and made grants of approximately £1.9 billion.

CAF published the first edition of *The Directory of Grant Making Trusts* (*DGMT*) in 1968. Since that time, the title has gained a notable reputation as a comprehensive guide to UK grant making trusts and their funding policies. Today it is hard to imagine the difficulties which must have been encountered in trying to obtain funds from trusts before the *DGMT* threw a spotlight on their existence.

Since the publication of the last edition of the *DGMT*, extensive research has been undertaken amongst both users of the directory, the grant seekers, and with the trusts themselves, the grant givers. One important message to come out of this research is that grant seekers want more information about trusts' policies. For their part trusts are desperate that applications should be targetted more accurately towards individual trusts' guidelines. It is the *DGMT*'s role to address these issues and bring the grant seekers and grant givers together to make the workload of both less onerous.

The *Directory of Grant Making Trusts Focus Series* was developed in response to demand from our readers. Many expressed the view that, while the main edition of the directory is extremely useful to larger organisations and reference libraries, smaller local bodies could benefit from a publication containing a smaller, more focused selection of trusts.

Features new to the *Focus Series* include:

- an easier to read layout;
- clear headings in the trust entries;
- an index of trusts by grant type to further enhance the searching process;
- the top ten grants made by many trusts.

It is hoped that this book will provide grant seekers working in Manchester, Liverpool and the North West of England with clear and accurate information on trusts most likely to be interested in funding their work.

The trusts we have listed

The details of trusts registered under the law of England and Wales are recorded on the public register at the Charity Commission and are consequently available for publication. As there is no register available in Scotland and Northern Ireland we have relied on either direct contact with the Scottish and Irish trusts listed or other published material in order to obtain the most up-to-date information.

Every trust in the directory was asked to update the information contained in its entry and to classify its grant-making activities for 1999–2000. Many of the trusts we contact are extremely helpful and provide us with comprehensive information on their funding policies.

However, not all trusts are so helpful and open. Where a trust did not respond to our request to amend its entry, the details have been updated using the information on its file at the Charity Commission. We have stated where we have been unable to find financial records on file for later than 1995. However, it should be noted that, in CAF's experience, records held by the Charity Commission in respect of accounts filed are not always accurate.

A new, more robust policy has been introduced to determine which trusts should be omitted from this listing. We believe that trust directories provide an invaluable bridge between the trust community and the rest of the voluntary sector, and that trusts in receipt of public funds through tax relief should not attempt to draw a veil of secrecy over their activities. Consequently, we have declined the majority of requests from trusts to be excluded from this directory.

In general we have included:

■ trusts which make grants to charities and voluntary organisations (including the National Lottery boards and Arts Councils).

We have excluded:

■ trusts which fund individuals only;
■ trusts which fund one organisation exclusively;
■ trusts whose funds are demonstrably fully committed for the life of the directory;
■ trusts which have ceased to exist.

Frequent users of our directories will note a change of policy regarding trusts that do not respond to unsolicited applications. These trusts are now being included because we believe that this gives fundraisers a broader overview of the grant making community and because the information could be important in supporting relationship fundraising activity.

The structure of the directory

This directory contains three indexes:

- Trusts by geographical area;
- Trusts by field of interest and type of beneficiary;
- Trusts by grant type.

Using these indexes, users should end up with a shortlist of trusts whose funding policies match their needs. They can then look at the individual trust details in the Alphabetical register of grant making trusts

Trusts by geographical area

This index enables you to see which trusts will consider applications from a charity or project in a particular geographical area.

These pages contain two separate listings:

LIST OF GEOGRAPHICAL AREA HEADINGS

This is a complete list of all the geographical area headings used in the directory. The page numbers relate to the second listing.

LIST OF TRUSTS BY GEOGRAPHICAL AREA

These pages list trusts under the geographical areas from which they will consider applications for funding.

Trusts by field of interest and type of beneficiary

This index enables you to see which trusts are likely to fund projects doing a particular type of work to benefit a particular type of person. These pages list trusts according to:

- the type of activity or work they are willing to fund – their 'fields of interest'
- who they want to benefit – their preferred 'beneficiaries'

These pages contain two separate listings:

CATEGORISATION OF FIELDS OF INTEREST AND TYPES OF BENEFICIARY

This lists all of the headings used in the directory to categorise fields of interest and types of beneficiary. This listing should help you match your project with one – or more – of the categories used. The page numbers relate to the second listing.

LIST OF TRUSTS BY FIELD OF INTEREST AND TYPE OF BENEFICIARY

These pages list trusts under the fields of interest and types of beneficiary they have indicated they might be willing to support.

Trusts were asked to indicate whether projects working in a field of interest/for a type of beneficiary:

- are a **funding priority**, ie the area is one which the trust is particularly interested in funding;
- **will be considered**, ie the trust may consider funding in the area but it is not one of their priorities.

Trusts by grant type

This index enables you to see which trusts will consider making the types of grant you are looking for. Trusts are listed under the types of grant that they have indicated they are willing to make.

These pages contain two separate listings:

LIST OF GRANT TYPES

This lists all of the headings used in the directory to categorise grant types. Page numbers relate to the second listing.

LIST OF TRUSTS BY GRANT TYPE

These pages list trusts under the types of grant that they are willing to make.

Trusts were asked to indicate whether the grant types:

- are a **funding priority**, ie the type of grant the trust prefers to give;
- **will be considered**, ie the trust may consider making this type of grant.

Users should note that, although all trusts are listed under at least one geographical area and field of interest, not all trusts will be listed under type of beneficiary and grant type.

Alphabetical register of grant making trusts

The alphabetical register of grant making trusts contains the core data about the individual trusts held on the database.

In 1997 the Top 300 grant making trusts as defined by CAF gave away £1,132,877,000. In view of this total, we feel that it is important for these trusts to be covered in more detail than they have in previous directories.

For most of 1998 CAF's team undertook an extensive research exercise and personally contacted 300 major trusts in order to gain a greater understanding of their grant making policies. This information was then used to produce an in-depth commentary. The entries for these trusts are divided into two parts: the first part contains 'at a glance' details of the trusts' funding policies, and the second part contains the commentary. The number in brackets by the trust name indicates its position in the Top 300.

Each trust in the Top 300 was asked to send CAF a copy of their latest Annual Report and Accounts, which they are legally required to provide, upon request, to any person under section 47(2) of the Charities Act 1993. Fifty of these trusts did not send us a copy of their Annual Report and Accounts. As a result of this, we sent a team of researchers into the Charity Commission to find the most up-to-date information for these trusts. However, we were unable to find financial records later than 1995 on file for four trusts, and there was insufficient information to write a substantive commentary for a further 12 trusts.

A typical trust entry

A complete entry should contain information under the headings listed below. An explanation of the information which should appear in these fields appears on the alongside.

The types of project the trust will definitely not fund, eg expeditions, scholarships

Full details of the types of project or activity the trust plans to fund in 1999–2000

■ The Fictitious Trust

The village, town, borough, parish or other geographical area the trust is prepared to fund

WHAT IS FUNDED Education and training
WHAT IS NOT FUNDED No grants to individuals
WHO CAN BENEFIT Charities benefiting children
WHERE FUNDING CAN BE GIVEN UK
TYPE OF GRANT One-off, capital, running costs
RANGE OF GRANTS £250–£5,000

The people, animals, etc the trust wishes ultimately to benefit (although via charities and other voluntary organisations)

The smallest, largest and typical size of grant normally given

SAMPLE GRANTS £5,000 to a school; £1,000 to a university; £800 to a school library; £600 to a school; £500 to a community school; £500 to a grammar school; £500 for classroom equipment; £400 towards the building of a science block; £400 to a university appeal; £250 for a wheelchair ramp

The types of grant or loan the trust is prepared to give, eg one-off, recurring, interest-free loan

The top ten grants given by the trust in the last financial year

The trust's most recent financial figures including the total amount of grants given

FINANCES *Year* 1997 *Income* £55,000
Grants £50,000
TRUSTEES Peter Brown, BA (Chairman), Mrs Mary Brown, Alistair Johnson, Miss Natalie Jones

Names of the Trustees

Titles of publications the trust has produced which are of interest to grant seekers

PUBLICATIONS Annual Report and Accounts, *The Fictitious Trust – the first twenty years*
NOTES Owing to the large number of applications, some considerable time may elapse before a response is received

Any other information which might be useful to grant seekers

Any information which is useful to those preparing their grant application

HOW TO APPLY In writing to the address below. A sae should be included if an acknowledgement is required
WHO TO APPLY TO Peter Brown, Chairman, The Fictitious Trust, 1 The Street, Any Town, AT13 4LY
Tel 0171-000 0000 *Fax* 0171-000 0000
E-mail person@abc.efghijklmn.org
Website http://www.efghijklmn.co.uk

The name and address of the person to whom applications should be sent

Charity Commission number

CC NO 1234567   **ESTABLISHED** 1977

Year established

Glossary

Certain trust entries in this directory refer to headings which are no longer used in CAF's directories. The up-to-date headings used in their place are listed here.

Beneficial Area	→ **Where Funding Can Be Given**
Correspondent	→ **Who To Apply To**
Funding Priorities	→ **What Is Funded**
Restrictions	→ **What Is Not Funded**
Submission of Applications	→ **How To Apply**
Type of Beneficiary	→ **Who Can Benefit**

How to use the directory
key steps

This directory is designed to enable fundraisers to draw up a hit list of trusts which might support their cause in eight easy steps.

STEP 1

Define the project, programme or work for which you are seeking funding.

▼

STEP 2

Geographical area: find the area most local to your requirements. Note down the names of the trusts listed here.

▼

STEP 3

Field of interest and type of beneficiary: identify the categories that match your project. Note down the names of the trusts listed here.

▼

STEP 4

Grant type: identify the grant type that you are looking for. Note down the names of the trusts listed here.

▼

STEP 5

Compare the three lists of trusts to produce a list of trusts whose funding policies most closely match the characteristics of the project for which you are seeking funding.

▼

STEP 6

If your list of trusts is too short you could include trusts that have a general interest in funding in your area.

STEP 7

If your list of trusts is too long you could limit yourself to trusts that regard your area of work as a 'Funding priority', and leave out those that 'Will consider' applications.

▼ ▼

STEP 8

Look up the entries for the trusts identified, studying their details carefully and paying particular attention to 'What Is Funded' and 'What Is Not Funded'.

If you need additional information, please read the relevant note overleaf.

STEP 1

The following checklist will help you assemble the information you need:

■ What is the geographical location of the people who will benefit from any funding received?

■ What facilities or services will the funding provide?

■ What are the characteristics which best describe the people who will benefit from any funding received?

■ What type of grant are you looking for?

EXAMPLE

Funding is being sought for a project in Salford to enable unemployed young people to take part in an employment training scheme.

■ *The geographical location is:*
*UK → England → North West → **Salford***

■ *The service to be provided is: **Training for work***

■ *The key characteristic of the people to benefit is that they are: **Unemployed***

■ *The type of grant being sought is: **Project***

STEP 2

Look up the area where your project is based in the list of geographical area headings on page 2.

Turn to the relevant pages in the list of trusts by geographical area and note down the names of the trusts which have stated that they will consider funding projects in your area.

EXAMPLE

Look up the area most local to your requirements (Salford) in the list of geographical area headings. Then turn to the relevant page in the list of trusts by geographical area and look up the names of the trusts listed under Salford. You may want to look at the trusts listed under the broader region heading (North West) as well. Note down the names so that they can be compared with the lists produced through the field of interest and type of beneficiary and grant type indexes.

STEP 3 Using the categorisation of fields of interest and types of beneficiary on pages 12–16, identify all the categories that match the project, programme or work for which you are seeking funding.

Turn to the relevant pages in the list of trusts by field of interest and type of beneficiary and look up the headings identified. Look first at the trusts that appear under the heading 'Funding priority', then look under the heading 'Will consider'.

Note down the names of the trusts appearing under these headings so that you can compare them with the names identified through the geographical area and grant type indexes.

EXAMPLE *With a project to provide training for work, you will probably look first under the main heading 'Education & training'. Under this heading you will find the sub-heading 'Education & training' and under this you will find the heading 'Training for work'. Note down the page numbers beside 'Education & training' and 'Training for work'. Trusts that have expressed an interest in funding training for work may represent your best prospects, but trusts with a more general interest in funding education and training might be worth approaching – particularly if they like to fund projects in your area.*

If you look under 'Beneficiaries' you will find 'Unemployed' under 'Beneficiaries from all professional and economic groups'. Note down this page number too.

STEP 4 Look up the type of grant that you are seeking in the list of grant types on page 78.

Turn to the relevant pages in the list of trusts by grant type and note down the names of the trusts that will consider giving the type of grant that you are seeking, so that you can compare them with the names identified through the geographical area and field of interest and type of beneficiary indexes.

EXAMPLE *Look up the type of grant you are seeking (project) in the list of grant types. Then turn to the relevant page of the list of trusts by grant type and look at the names of the trusts listed under 'Project'. Note down the names of all these trusts.*

STEP 5 Compare the lists of trust names produced via steps 2, 3 and 4, and make a list of all the trusts which appear on more than one list. This will produce a list of trusts whose funding policies most closely match the characteristics of the project for which you are seeking funding.

In order to achieve a ranking, you could assign a certain number of points to each element of the criteria you have devised and then 'score' each trust on the basis of the number of 'matches'.

STEP 6 If the list turns out to be too short it can easily be adjusted.

EXAMPLE *You find that you have ended up with a list of five trusts. Going back to step 3, you could include the trusts which come under 'Education & training', or, going back to step 2, you could include trusts which will consider funding projects in the North West.*

STEP 7 If your list turns out to be too long it can easily be adjusted.

EXAMPLE *You find that you have ended up with a list of 150 trusts. Going back to step 3, you could limit yourself to trusts that regard your particular area of activity as a 'Funding priority' and leave out those that 'Will consider' applications. You could also discard the names of trusts that have a general interest in funding education and training and confine your list to trusts that are interested in funding training for work or projects for unemployed people.*

STEP 8 Look up the entries for the trusts identified and study their details carefully, paying particular attention to 'What Is Funded' and 'What Is Not Funded'.

If you feel that there is a good match between the characteristics of the project for which you require support and the funding policies of the trust identified, you could submit an application.

About CAF

CAF, Charities Aid Foundation, is a registered charity with a unique mission – to increase the substance of charity in the UK and overseas. It provides services that are both charitable and financial which help donors make the most of their giving and charities make the most of their resources.

Many of CAF's publications reflect the organisation's purpose: *Dimensions of the Voluntary Sector* offers the definitive financial overview of the UK voluntary sector, while the *Directory of Grant Making Trusts* provides the most comprehensive source of funding information available.

As an integral part of its activities, CAF works to raise standards of management in voluntary organisations. This includes the making of grants by its own Grants Council, sponsorship of the Charity Annual Report and Accounts Awards, seminars, training courses and the Charities Annual Conference, the largest regular gathering of key people from within the voluntary sector. In addition, Charitynet (www.charitynet.org) is now established as the leading Internet site on voluntary action.

For decades, CAF has led the way in developing tax-effective services to donors, and these are now used by more than 250,000 individuals and 2,000 of the UK's leading companies, between them giving £150 million each year to charity. Many are also using CAF's CharityCard, the world's first debit card designed exclusively for charitable giving. CAF's unique range of investment and administration services for charities includes the CafCash High Interest Cheque Account, two common investment funds for longer-term investment and a full appeals and subscription management service.

CAF's activities are not limited to the UK, however. Increasingly, CAF is looking to apply the same principles and develop similar services internationally, in its drive to increase the substance of charity across the world. CAF has offices and sister organisations in the United States, Bulgaria, South Africa, Russia, India and Brussels.

For more information about CAF, please visit www.charitynet.org/caf

Other publications from CAF

The Directory of Grant Making Trusts 1999–2000
16th Edition
ISBN 1–85934–078–4
£89.95 FOR THREE VOLUMES
Published January 1999

Grant making trusts represent a major source of support for charitable activity in the UK – in 1997 alone they contributed over £1.9 billion.

Grant making trusts support a wide variety of causes and their criteria for allocating funds are often very specific. *The Directory of Grant Making Trusts* (*DGMT*) keeps fundraisers in touch with changes in trusts' funding priorities. Its extensive indexing allows great precision in the targeting of trusts – thus reducing the flow of irrelevant applications and saving time and money at both ends.

The information published in the *DGMT* is the result of extensive research and close liaison with the trust community; it provides one of the most comprehensive pictures of UK trusts currently published. As well as listing over 3,500 trusts – of which 1,500 are new to this edition – this directory now features top 10 sample grants for hundreds of trusts and a new index by grant type. With the addition of the new third volume providing detailed commentaries on 250 of the major trusts, the *DGMT* now truly represents a complete, one-stop information shop for trust fundraisers.

And it works! Feedback from the fundraising community has been overwhelmingly positive. As essential tool for every trust fundraiser, in most cases it more than pays for itself – it does so many, many times over.

Grantseeker
The interactive CD-ROM for fundraisers
**£58.69 (INCL VAT)
FOR EACH
SIX-MONTHLY RELEASE**

Drawing on CAF's years of experience as a publisher of *The Directory of Grant Making Trusts*, *Grantseeker* is the tailor-made solution to the information needs of trust fundraisers in the electronic age. Published for the first time as a subscription service, users will receive a completely new updated edition every six months.

Fully interactive, *Grantseeker*'s specially designed search engine will quickly scan the entire *DGMT* database on the basis of a user's own selection criteria and generate a 'hit list' of trusts whose funding preferences match their project or cause. There are two additional search functions: the ability to search on trustees' names and a key word search by town or city which allows users a more closely defined geographical search. Users' bookmarks and notes automatically carry over to each new release.

Taking full advantage of the extra options available via an electronic search tool, *Grantseeker* offers a more sophisticated matching service than can be provided by traditional methods, enabling fundraisers to save weeks of effort and frustration. A simple hypertext link can provide them with a complete *DGMT* entry on a potential funder within moments of loading the CD. The days of ultimate dependence on a paper-based directory are over.

Designed for use by fundraisers with little or no experience of electronic directories, as well as the more technically minded, *Grantseeker* provides step-by-step instructions on every stage of the search process, backed by comprehensive help files. Even the most confirmed Luddite should not be intimidated!

Grantseeker runs under Windows 3.1 or above.

The Directory of Smaller Grant Making Trusts

1st Edition

ISBN 1–85934–062–8
£26.95
Published February 1998

For many years *The Directory of Grant Making Trusts*, known colloquially as the 'fundraiser's bible', has thrown a spotlight on the funding policies and preferences of the majority of the UK's leading trusts and foundations. Of necessity, however, space constraints have meant that many of the smaller trusts have not been listed. *The Directory of Smaller Grant Making Trusts*, which is to be published every two years, has been developed to remedy this situation and ensure that grant seekers have access to the information they need on these important sources of funding.

The Directory of Smaller Grant Making Trusts contains details of over 1,000 smaller trusts with an income of less than £13,000 per annum. Many of them have not previously been included in directory listings. The individual entries demonstrate that a large number of the trusts have a particular preference for funding activities in selected local, community-based arenas, which will make the directory of particular interest to fundraisers with a regional focus.

FOCUS SERIES

Designed to make the search for funds easier still, many directories from the *Focus Series* collect together, in individual volumes, details of trusts which have expressed an intention to support charitable activity in a particular field or in a particular geographical area.

In addition to comprehensive details of the funding policies of the trusts listed, information is also provided on recent grants they have made.

These directories will give grant seekers working in the relevant fields a head-start in identifying sympathetic trusts and presenting well-tailored funding applications.

Environment, Animal Welfare and Heritage

ISBN 1-85934-016-4
£19.95

Social Care

ISBN 1-85934-051-2
£16.95

International

ISBN 1-85934-052-0
£19.95

Schools, Colleges and Educational Establishments

ISBN 1-85934-053-9
£19.95

Children and Youth
2nd Edition

ISBN 1-85934-072-5
£19.95

Religion
2nd Edition

ISBN 1-85934-080-6
£19.95
Published April 1999

Older People

ISBN 1-85934-102-0
£19.95
Published April 1999

Cambridgeshire, Norfolk and the East Midlands

ISBN 1-85934-087-3
£19.95
Published April 1999

Yorkshire, Humberside and the North East

ISBN 1-85934-086-5
£19.95
Published April 1999

HOW TO SERIES

The *How To Series* has been developed for use by anyone working with smaller voluntary organisations. Whatever your background, this series is designed to provide practical one-stop guides on a variety of core activities to give both volunteers and inexperienced salaried staff essential information and guidance on good practice.

Each title provides a clear picture of the subject matter in a jargon-free format for non-specialists. The books include information on relevant legislation, contact details of useful organisations, examples of practical worksheets – all the necessary tools to help develop your understanding, step by step, of the topic being discussed.

Applying to a Grant Making Trust
Anne Villemur

ISBN 1-85934-033-4
£7.95

Effective Media Relations
Ian Gilchrist

ISBN 1-85934-063-6
£7.95

Payroll Giving
Willemina Bell

ISBN 1-85934-061-X
£7.95

Public Speaking and Presentations
Ian Gilchrist

ISBN 1-85934-064-4
£7.95

Running a Local Fundraising Campaign
Janet Hilderley

ISBN 1-85934-040-7
£9.95

Running a Public Collection
Jennie Whiting

ISBN 1-85934-060-1
£7.95

The Treasurer's Handbook
Ian Caulfeild Grant

ISBN 1-85934-018-0
£7.95

Promotional Materials
Karen Gilchrist

ISBN 1-85934-084-9
£9.95

Fundraising for Education
Karen Gilchrist

ISBN 1-85934-083-0
£9.95
Published April 1999

Fundraising using a Database
Peter Flory

ISBN 1-85934-082-2
£11.95
Published June 1999

To order any of the above publications, please ring Biblios Publishers' Distribution Services Ltd on 01403 710851 or you can order online using our website: http://www.charitynet.org/bookstore/

Trusts by geographical area

Geographical area headings

Trusts by geographical area

Eden's Foundation, James
114
Greater Manchester Police
Community Charity 120
Gurunanak 121
Hillards Charitable Trust, Gay &
Peter Hartley's 124
Holt Trust, The Edward 126
Hoover Foundation, The 127
Kershaw Trust, The Peter 130
Manchester Guardian Society
Charitable Trust, The 143
Mersey Basin Trust 146
Mersey Basin Trust – Greenlink
Awards, The 147
Mersey Basin Trust – Stream
Care Project 147
Mersey Basin Trust – Waterside
Revival Grants 148
National Lottery Charities Board
151
North and East Lancashire
Unitarian Mission 155
North West Arts Board 155
Provincial Insurance Company
Trust for Bolton 165
Rowbotham Charitable Trust,
The Christopher 177
Rycroft Children's Fund 178
Scott Trust, Sir James & Lady
182
Stanley Charitable Trust, The
185

Bury
Amelan Charitable Trust, The
Harold 88
BNFL Risley Medical, Research
and Charity Trust, The 89
Barnabas Charitable Trust 90
Beauland Ltd 91
Busby Charities Fund, Sir Matt
98
Cheshire Provincial Grand
Lodge of Mark Master
Mason's Fund of
Benevolence, The 103
Community Trust for Greater
Manchester, The 106
Davies Trust, The John Grant
109
Duchy of Lancaster Benevolent
Fund, The 111
Greater Manchester Police
Community Charity 120
Gurunanak 121
Hillards Charitable Trust, Gay &
Peter Hartley's 124
Holt Trust, The Edward 126
Kershaw Trust, The Peter 130
Manchester Guardian Society
Charitable Trust, The 143
Marks Foundation, The Ann and
David 145
Mersey Basin Trust 146

Mersey Basin Trust – Greenlink
Awards, The 147
Mersey Basin Trust – Stream
Care Project 147
Mersey Basin Trust – Waterside
Revival Grants 148
National Lottery Charities Board
151
North and East Lancashire
Unitarian Mission 155
North West Arts Board 155
Rycroft Children's Fund 178
Scott Charitable Trust, The
Francis C 180
Stanley Charitable Trust, The
185

Cheshire
Adlington Women's Institute
87
BNFL Risley Medical, Research
and Charity Trust, The 89
Baddiley Consolidated Charity
90
Barker Charity, Philip 90
Barnabas Charitable Trust 90
Birkenhead and Wirral Moral
Welfare Association 92
Britannia Building Society
Foundation 95
Brotherton Trust, The Charles
96
Capenhurst Medical and
Research Charity Trust Fund,
The 99
Cheadle Royal Industries
Charitable Trust 102
Cheshire Constabulary
Community Involvement
Fund of Northwich Division
102
Cheshire Constabulary
Involvement Fund for the
Northern Divisions, The
102
Cheshire Provincial Fund of
Benevolence, The 102
Cheshire Provincial Grand
Lodge of Mark Master
Mason's Fund of
Benevolence, The 103
Chester Diocesan Moral Aid
Charity 103
Clutterbuck Charitable Trust,
Robert 105
Congleton Inclosure Trust, The
106
Congleton Town Trust, The
107
Darnhill Exhibition Foundation,
The 109
Drugwatch Trust 111
Duchy of Lancaster Benevolent
Fund, The 111
Evans Trust, Mabel 115

Ferguson Benevolent Fund
Limited 116
Hale and Hale Barns Charitable
Trust 122
Historic Cheshire Churches
Preservation Trust 125
Holford's Charity, John 125
Kershaw Trust, The Peter 130
Keyes Trust, The Ursula 131
Knights House Charity 131
Leverhulme's Charitable Trust,
Lord 137
Llay Estate, The 140
Lord Mayor of Chester
Charitable Trust 141
Marks Foundation, The Ann and
David 145
Mayor of Hyde's Trust Fund
145
Mersey Basin Trust 146
Mersey Basin Trust – Greenlink
Awards, The 147
Mersey Basin Trust – ICI Green
Action Grants 147
Mersey Basin Trust – Stream
Care Project 147
Mersey Basin Trust – Waterside
Revival Grants 148
Nantwich and Acton Grammar
School Foundation 151
National Lottery Charities Board
151
North West Arts Board 155
North West Cancer Research
Fund 156
Overton Community Trust 160
Patients' Aid Association
Hospital and Medical
Charities Trust 160
Pennycress Trust, The 162
Rotary Club of Alderley Edge
and Bollin Valley Trust Fund
174
Rotary Club of New Mills Marple
and District Benevolent
Fund, The 174
Round Table, Sale and District,
Charitable Trust Fund 176
Rowbotham Charitable Trust,
The Christopher 177
Rowley Trust, The 177
Runcorn Community Action
Trust 178
Rycroft Children's Fund 178
Severn Trent Water Charitable
Trust Fund, The 183
Shaw Trust, Alfred 183
Timperley Educational
Foundation 189
Verdin Trust Fund, The 191
Warrington Animal Welfare 192
Warrington Church of England
Educational Trust 192
Westminster Foundation, The
194

Trusts by field of interest and type of beneficiary

Fields of interest and type of beneficiary

Social care & development

■ Community facilities
32

Art galleries & cultural centres *20*
Community centres & village halls *31*
Libraries & museums *51*
Parks *57*
Playgrounds *58*
Recreation grounds *60*
Sports centres *66*
Theatres & opera houses *69*

■ Community services
32

Adoption & fostering services *18*
Care in the community *27*
Clubs *30*
Community transport *33*
Counselling (social issues) *34*
Crime prevention schemes *35*
Day centres *36*
Emergency care, refugees, famine *40*
Holidays & outings *47*
Income support & maintenance *49*
Meals provision *52*
Playschemes *58*

■ Campaigning (social issues) *26*

Community issues *32*
Development proposals *36*
Gay & lesbian rights (campaigning) *42*
International rights of the individual *50*
Peace *57*
Penal reform *57*
Racial equality, discrimination, relations *60*
Transport proposals *70*
Unborn children's rights (campaigning) *70*

■ Advocacy (social issues) *18*

Equal opportunities *41*
Individual rights *49*

■ Advice & information (social issues) *18*

Advice centres *18*
Law centres *51*

Accommodation & housing

■ Residential facilities & services
61

Advice & information (housing) *18*
Almshouses *19*
Emergency & short-term housing *40*
Holiday accommodation *47*
Hostels *48*
Housing associations *48*
Residential facilities *61*
Respite *62*
Sheltered accommodation *64*

Arts, culture & recreation

■ Arts & arts facilities *21*

Architecture *20*
Combined arts *31*
Crafts *35*
Dance & ballet *36*
Film, video, multimedia broadcasting *42*
Fine art *42*
Literature *52*
Music *54*
Opera *56*
Residences *61*
Theatre *69*
Visual arts *73*

■ Community arts & recreation *31*

Arts activities *21*
Arts education *21*
Dance groups *36*
Opera companies, opera groups *56*
Orchestras *56*
Theatrical companies, theatre groups *69*

■ Cultural heritage (of national & historical importance) *35*

Cultural activity *35*
English literature *40*

Education & training

■ Schools & colleges *63*

Business schools *26*
Church schools *30*
Independent schools *49*
Junior schools *50*
Postgraduate education *58*
Pre-school education *59*
Primary schools *59*
Secondary schools *64*
Special schools *66*
Tertiary & higher education *69*

■ Education & training *39*

Cultural & religious teaching *35*
English as a second or foreign language – TESL & TEFL *40*
IT training *50*
Literacy *51*
Professional, specialist training *59*
Special needs education *66*
Speech therapy *66*
Textiles & upholstery *69*
Training for community development *69*
Training for personal development *70*
Training for work *70*
Vocational training *73*

■ Costs of study *34*

Bursaries & fees *26*
Fellowships *42*
Purchase of books & equipment *59*
Scholarships *63*
Travel & maintenance *70*

■ Academic subjects, sciences & research *17*

Architectural research *20*
Engineering *40*
Law *51*
Medicine *53*
Physics *58*
Religions *60*
Research institutes *61*
Science & technology *64*
Social science *65*
Specialist research *66*

Conservation & environment

■ Conservation *33*

Church buildings *30*
Fauna *42*
Flora *42*
Historic buildings *46*
Lakes *51*
Landscapes *51*
Memorials & monuments *53*
Nature reserves *55*
Waterways *73*
Woodlands *74*

■ Animal facilities & services *20*

Animal homes *20*
Animal welfare *20*
Bird sanctuaries *25*
Cats – catteries & other facilities for cats *28*
Dogs – kennels & other facilities for dogs *39*
Horses – stables & other facilities for horses *48*
Wildlife parks *74*
Wildlife sanctuaries *74*
Zoos *75*

■ Environmental & animal sciences *40*

Agriculture *19*
Botany *25*
Ecology *39*
Horticulture *48*
Natural history *55*
Organic food production *56*

■ Conservation & campaigning *34*

Endangered species *40*
Environmental issues *40*
Heritage *46*
Nuclear energy, nuclear power *55*
Renewable energy, renewable power *61*
Transport & alternative transport *70*

Health

■ Health care 44

Acute health care 17
Aftercare 19
Alternative health care 19
Counselling (health) 34
First aid 42
Hospice at home 48
Nursing service 55
Prenatal care 58
Primary health care 59
Respite care, care for carers 62
Support, self help groups 67
Well woman clinics 73

■ Health facilities & buildings 45

Ambulances & mobile units 19
Convalescent homes 34
Hospices 48
Hospitals 48
Medical centres 52
Nursing homes 55
Rehabilitation centres 60

■ Medical studies & research 52

Cancer research 26
MS research 54
Neurological research 55
Ophthalmology 56
Prenatal research 59

■ Campaigning (health) 26

Health education 45
Health issues 46
Health promotion 46

■ Advocacy (health) 18

Health related volunteer schemes 46

Religion

■ Advancement of religion 18

Christian education 29
Christian outreach 29
Jewish 50
Missionaries, evangelicals 53

■ Religious buildings 60

Cemeteries & burial grounds 28
Churches 30
Mosques 54
Religious ancillary buildings 60
Synagogues 68
Temples, gurdwaras 69

■ Religious umbrella bodies 61

Anglican bodies 19
Catholic bodies 27
Diocesan boards 36
Free church 42
Jewish bodies 50

Infrastructure support & development

■ Infrastructure & technical support 49

Building services 26
Financial services 42
Information technology & computers 49
Legal services 51
Management services 52
Personnel & human resource services 57
Publishing & printing 59
Recruitment services 60

■ Infrastructure development 49

Civil society development 30
Community businesses 31
Community development 31
Economic regeneration schemes 39
Job creation 50
Small enterprises 65
Support to voluntary & community organisations 68
Support to volunteers 68
Tourism 69

■ Professional bodies 59

Health professional bodies 46
Social care professional bodies 65

■ Charity or voluntary umbrella bodies 28

Council for Voluntary Service (CVS) 34
Rural Community Council (RCC) 63
Volunteer bureaux 73

General charitable purposes *43*

The trusts listed under this heading have indicated that they are willing to consider funding from charities and good causes of all sorts. No preferences have been expressed for any specific type of project or work, nor for a specific area of activity. However, users should check whether any beneficiary or geographical area priorities have been identified.

Beneficiaries

■ Beneficiaries of all ages *22*

Children *28*
Young adults *74*
Older people *55*

■ Beneficiaries from all professional & economic groups *22*

Academics *17*
Actors & entertainment professionals *17*
Artists *21*
Chemists *28*
Clergy *30*
Employees & ex-employees *40*
Ex-service & service people *41*
Legal professionals *51*
Masons *52*
Medical professionals, nurses & doctors *52*
Musicians *55*
Research workers *61*
Retired *62*
Scientists *64*
Seafarers & fishermen *64*
Sportsmen & women *66*
Students *67*
Teachers and governesses *68*
Textile workers & designers *69*
Unemployed *70*
Volunteers *73*
Writers & poets *74*

■ Beneficiaries of all family situations *23*

In care, fostered & adopted *49*
Parents & children *57*
One parent families *56*
Widows & widowers *74*

■ Beneficiaries of all religions & cultures *24*

Baptists *22*
Buddhists & Jainists *26*
Christians *29*
Church of England *30*
Ethnic minority groups *41*
Evangelists *41*
Hindus *46*
Jews *50*
Methodists *53*
Muslims *55*
Quakers *60*
Roman Catholics *62*
Unitarians *71*

■ Beneficiaries suffering from any disease or medical condition *24*

Alzheimer's disease *19*
Arthritis & rheumatism *20*
Asthma *21*
Autism *22*
Blood disorders & haemophilia *25*
Cancers *26*
Cerebral palsy *28*
Crohn's disease *35*
Cystic fibrosis *35*
Diabetes *36*
Dietary – special dietary needs *36*
Epilepsy *40*
Friedrichs Ataxia *42*
Head & other injuries *44*
Hearing loss *46*
Heart disease *46*
HIV & AIDS *47*
Kidney disease *51*
Leprosy *51*
Mental illness *53*
Motor neurone disease *54*
Multiple sclerosis *54*
Muscular dystrophy *54*
Paediatric diseases *56*
Parkinson's disease *57*
Polio *58*
Prenatal *58*
Psoriasis *59*
Sight loss *65*
Spina bifida & Hydrocephalus *66*
Stroke *67*
Substance misuse *67*
Terminally ill *69*
Tropical diseases *70*
Tuberculosis *70*

■ Beneficiaries of all social circumstances *24*

At risk groups *21*
Carers *27*
Disabled people (physical, sensory, learning impairments) *37*
Disadvantaged by poverty *37*
Disaster victims *38*
Ex-offenders & those at risk of offending *41*
Gays & lesbians *42*
Homeless *47*
Immigrants *49*
Refugees *60*
Rural areas – living in *62*

contd

Beneficiaries continued

Socially isolated *65*
Travellers *70*
Urban areas – living in *71*
Victims of abuse *71*
Victims of crime *71*
Victims of domestic violence
   72
Victims of famine *72*
Victims of man-made or natural
   disasters *72*
Victims of war *72*

....
■ Beneficiaries by gender
Females *42*

Trusts by field of interest and type of beneficiary

■ Abuse

see Victims of abuse

■ Academic prizes

see Costs of study

■ Academic subjects, sciences & research

see also Architectural research, Engineering, Law, Medicine, Physics, Religions, Research institutes, Science & technology, Social science, Specialist research

Will consider

AGF Charitable Trust 87
Brabin's Educational Foundation 94
Britannia Building Society Foundation 95
Burall Charitable Trust, The 97
Charity for Change 101
Crosthwaite and Lyth Trust 108
Forster Charitable Trust, The 118
Joint Churches Community Project 129
Leverhulme's Charitable Trust, Lord 137
Localtrent Ltd 140
McMechan Memorial Fund, The Roy 142
Nantwich and Acton Grammar School Foundation 151
National Lottery Charities Board 151
North West Media Charitable Trust Limited 156
Parkhill Charitable Trust 160
Rowan Charitable Trust, The 176
Runcorn Community Action Trust 178
St Joseph's Educational Charity 180
Stockport Community Trust 187
Stockport Educational Foundation, The 187
Talbot Bridge Will Trust, The Elsie 189
Timperley Educational Foundation 189
Waterhouse Charitable Trust, Mrs 192
Winwick Educational Foundation, The 197
World Friendship 198

■ Academics

Funding priority

Broadhurst Charitable Trust, The Charles and Edna 96
Neave Trust, The Airey 154

Will consider

AGF Charitable Trust 87
Mayor of Chorley's Helping Hand Charity, The 145
Nantwich and Acton Grammar School Foundation 151
Stewart Trust, Sir Halley 185
Sykes Trust, The Charles 187

■ Actors & entertainment professionals

Funding priority

Chase Charity, The 101
North West Arts Board 155

Will consider

Eden Arts Trust 114
Evans Trust, Mabel 115
Granada Foundation, The 120
Harewood's Charitable Settlement, Lord 122
Mayor of Chorley's Helping Hand Charity, The 145
Nantwich and Acton Grammar School Foundation 151
Northern Arts 157
Rathbone Charitable Trust, The Eleanor 168
Sykes Trust, The Charles 187
Talbot Bridge Will Trust, The Elsie 189
Vaux Group Foundation, The 191
Yorkshire Bank Charitable Trust, The 198

■ Acute health care

see also Health care

Will consider

BNFL Risley Medical, Research and Charity Trust, The 89
Burden's Charitable Foundation 97
Ferguson Benevolent Fund Limited 116
Johnson Foundation, The 128
Lord Mayor of Chester Charitable Trust 141
Proven Family Trust, The 165
Wigan Town Relief in Need Charity 196

■ Addiction

see **Substance misuse**

■ Adoption & fostering services

see also **Community services**

Funding priority

Birkenhead and Wirral Moral Welfare Association *92*
Chester Diocesan Moral Aid Charity *103*

Will consider

Congleton Town Trust, The *107*
Ford of Britain Trust *118*
Hillards Charitable Trust, Gay & Peter Hartley's *124*
Lankelly Foundation, The *134*
Lord Mayor of Chester Charitable Trust *141*
MacNair Trust, The *142*
Scott Charitable Trust, The Francis C *180*
Scott Charitable Trust, The Frieda *181*
Vaux Group Foundation, The *191*

■ Advancement of religion

see also **Christian education, Christian outreach, Jewish, Missionaries, evangelicals**

Funding priority

Eddleston's Charity, John *114*

Will consider

AGF Charitable Trust *87*
Baddiley Consolidated Charity *90*
Charity for Change *101*
Community Trust for Greater Manchester, The *106*
Duchy of Lancaster Benevolent Fund, The *111*
Girl's Welfare Fund *120*
National Lottery Charities Board *151*
Patients' Aid Association Hospital and Medical Charities Trust *160*
Shaw Trust, Alfred *183*
Waterhouse Charitable Trust, Mrs *192*
Westminster Foundation, The *194*

Wigan Town Relief in Need Charity *196*
Wilson Trust, The Charles *196*

■ Advice & information (housing)

see also **Residential facilities & services**

Will consider

Ford of Britain Trust *118*
Hillards Charitable Trust, Gay & Peter Hartley's *124*
Lancaster's Trust, Bryan *132*
Pilkington Charities Fund *163*
Rope Third Charitable Settlement, The Mrs L D *171*
Scott Charitable Trust, The Francis C *180*

■ Advice & information (social issues)

see also **Advice centres, Law centres**

Will consider

AGF Charitable Trust *87*
Congleton Inclosure Trust, The *106*
Lankelly Foundation, The *134*
National Lottery Charities Board *151*
Pilkington Charities Fund *163*
Scott Trust, Sir James & Lady *182*
3i Charitable Trust, The *189*
Waterhouse Charitable Trust, Mrs *192*

■ Advice centres

see also **Advice & information (social issues)**

Funding priority

Kershaw Trust, The Peter *130*
Lane Foundation, The Allen *132*
Moores Foundation, John *149*
Scott Charitable Trust, The Frieda *181*

Will consider

Birkenhead and Wirral Moral Welfare Association *92*
Britannia Building Society Foundation *95*
Burden's Charitable Foundation *97*
Chiron Trust, The *103*

Davies Trust, The John Grant *109*
Ford of Britain Trust *118*
Lancaster's Trust, Bryan *132*
Marchon Works Employees Charity Fund, The *144*
Northern Rock Foundation, The *157*
Rope Third Charitable Settlement, The Mrs L D *171*
Scott Charitable Trust, The Francis C *180*
Sykes Trust, The Charles *187*

■ Advocacy (health)

see also **Health related volunteer schemes**

Funding priority

National Lottery Charities Board *151*
Patients' Aid Association Hospital and Medical Charities Trust *160*
Scott Trust, Sir James & Lady *182*

Will consider

AGF Charitable Trust *87*
Beauland Ltd *91*
Cozens-Hardy Trust, The Lord *107*
Crosby Charitable Trust, The *108*
Eagle Charity Trust, The *113*
Lord Mayor of Chester Charitable Trust *141*
Marchon Works Employees Charity Fund, The *144*
Merseyside Development Foundation *148*
Pilkington Charities Fund *163*
Waterhouse Charitable Trust, Mrs *192*

■ Advocacy (social issues)

see also **Equal opportunities**

Funding priority

Kroch Foundation, The Heinz & Anna *131*

Will consider

AGF Charitable Trust *87*
Lane Foundation, The Allen *132*
Lankelly Foundation, The *134*
National Lottery Charities Board *151*

Scott Trust, Sir James & Lady
182
Waterhouse Charitable Trust,
Mrs *192*

■ After school care

see **Community services**

■ Aftercare

see also **Health care**
Funding priority
Rowbotham Charitable Trust,
The Christopher *177*

Will consider
Aquinas Trust *88*
BNFL Risley Medical, Research
and Charity Trust, The *89*
Brotherton Trust, The Charles
96
Burden's Charitable Foundation
97
Hillards Charitable Trust, Gay &
Peter Hartley's *124*
Johnson Foundation, The *128*
Lord Mayor of Chester
Charitable Trust *141*
Moore Foundation, The George
A *148*
Rowan Charitable Trust, The
176
Scott Trust, Sir James & Lady
182

■ Agriculture

see also **Environmental &
animal sciences**
Will consider
Brotherton Trust, The Charles
96
Rowan Charitable Trust, The
176
Westminster Foundation, The
194

■ AIDS

see **HIV & AIDS**

■ Alcohol dependency

see **Substance misuse**

■ Almshouses

see also **Residential
facilities & services**
Funding priority
Booth Charities, The *93*
Chase Charity, The *101*

Will consider
Burden's Charitable Foundation
97
Congleton Town Trust, The
107
Derbyshire Trust, The Nancy
111
Rayner Charitable Trust, The
John *169*

■ Alternative health care

see also **Health care**
Will consider
Johnson Foundation, The *128*
Lancaster's Trust, Bryan *132*
Lankelly Foundation, The *134*
Rainford Trust, The *167*
Scott Trust, Sir James & Lady
182

■ Alzheimer's disease

Funding priority
Baynes Charitable Trust, James
91
Chase Charity, The *101*
Pilkington Charities Fund *163*
Rowbotham Charitable Trust,
The Christopher *177*
Stewart Trust, Sir Halley *185*

Will consider
BNFL Risley Medical, Research
and Charity Trust, The *89*
Brotherton Trust, The Charles
96
Ferguson Benevolent Fund
Limited *116*
Ford of Britain Trust *118*
Hillards Charitable Trust, Gay &
Peter Hartley's *124*
Holt Trust, The Edward *126*
Johnson Foundation, The *128*
Lankelly Foundation, The *134*
Leboff Charitable Trust, The
Paul & Evelyn *137*
Marchon Works Employees
Charity Fund, The *144*
Moore Foundation, The George
A *148*
North West Media Charitable
Trust Limited *156*
Northern Rock Foundation, The
157

Rainford Trust, The *167*
Ravensdale Trust, The *169*
Rayner Charitable Trust, The
John *169*
Scott Charitable Trust, The
Frieda *181*
Scott Trust, Sir James & Lady
182
Ward Blenkinsop Trust, The
192
Wethered Bequest, The *195*

■ Ambulances & mobile units

see also **Health facilities &
buildings**
Will consider
Blankstone Charitable Trust,
The Solomon & Isabel *93*
Burden's Charitable Foundation
97
Ford of Britain Trust *118*
Hillards Charitable Trust, Gay &
Peter Hartley's *124*
Johnson Foundation, The *128*
Marchon Works Employees
Charity Fund, The *144*
Moore Foundation, The George
A *148*
Rainford Trust, The *167*
Scott Trust, Sir James & Lady
182
Vaux Group Foundation, The
191

■ Anglican bodies

see also **Religious umbrella
bodies**
Funding priority
Chase Charity, The *101*

Will consider
Broadhurst Charitable Trust,
The Charles and Edna *96*
Hillards Charitable Trust, Gay &
Peter Hartley's *124*
Ravensdale Trust, The *169*

■ Animal breeding

see **Environmental & animal
sciences**

■ Animal conservation

see **Endangered species**

■ Animal facilities & services

see also Animal homes,
Animal welfare, Bird
sanctuaries, Cats –
catteries & other facilities
for cats, Dogs – kennels &
other facilities for dogs,
Horses – stables & other
facilities for horses, Wildlife
parks, Wildlife sanctuaries,
Zoos

Funding priority
Leach Charitable Trust, The Eric
and Dorothy *137*

Will consider
Brotherton Trust, The Charles
96
Clutterbuck Charitable Trust,
Robert *105*
Community Trust for Greater
Manchester, The *106*
National Lottery Charities Board
151
Waterhouse Charitable Trust,
Mrs *192*
Wyre Animal Welfare *198*

■ Animal homes

see also Animal facilities &
services

Funding priority
Green Memorial Fund, The Barry
121
Sykes Trust, The Charles *187*

Will consider
Hillards Charitable Trust, Gay &
Peter Hartley's *124*
Oldham Foundation *159*
Rotary Club of Wallasey, The
Charitable Fund of the *175*
Warrington Animal Welfare *192*
Wigan Town Relief in Need
Charity *196*

■ Animal sciences

see Environmental & animal
sciences

■ Animal services

see Animal facilities &
services

■ Animal welfare

see also Animal facilities &
services

Funding priority
Green Memorial Fund, The Barry
121
Rawdon-Smith Trust, The *169*
Sykes Trust, The Charles *187*

Will consider
Chiron Trust, The *103*
Hamitzvos, Keren *122*
Hillards Charitable Trust, Gay &
Peter Hartley's *124*
Lord Mayor of Chester
Charitable Trust *141*
Oldham Foundation *159*
Rotary Club of Wallasey, The
Charitable Fund of the *175*
Sainsbury Charitable Fund Ltd,
The *179*
Scott Charitable Trust, The
Frieda *181*
Scott Trust, Sir James & Lady
182
Vaux Group Foundation, The
191
Warrington Animal Welfare *192*
Wigan Town Relief in Need
Charity *196*

■ Annual meetings

see Community services

■ Anti-racism

see Cultural & religious
teaching

■ Archaeology

see Academic subjects,
sciences & research

■ Architectural research

see also Academic
subjects, sciences &
research

Will consider
Granada Foundation, The *120*
Manchester Society of
Architects, The *144*

■ Architecture

see also Arts & arts
facilities

Funding priority
Chase Charity, The *101*

Will consider
Manchester Society of
Architects, The *144*
North West Arts Board *155*
Oldham Foundation *159*
Vaux Group Foundation, The
191
Wethered Bequest, The *195*

■ Art galleries & cultural centres

see also Community
facilities

Funding priority
Chase Charity, The *101*
North West Arts Board *155*
Talbot Bridge Will Trust, The
Elsie *189*

Will consider
Blankstone Charitable Trust,
The Solomon & Isabel *93*
Northern Arts *157*
Pilkington Foundation for Arts
and Leisure, The Harry and
Mavis *163*
Vaux Group Foundation, The
191
Wethered Bequest, The *195*

■ Arthritis & rheumatism

Funding priority
Baynes Charitable Trust, James
91
Pilkington Charities Fund *163*
Rowbotham Charitable Trust,
The Christopher *177*
Stewart Trust, Sir Halley *185*

Will consider
BNFL Risley Medical, Research
and Charity Trust, The *89*
Brotherton Trust, The Charles
96
Chrimes Family Charitable
Trust, The *104*
Ford of Britain Trust *118*
Hamitzvos, Keren *122*
Hillards Charitable Trust, Gay &
Peter Hartley's *124*
Johnson Foundation, The *128*
Marchon Works Employees
Charity Fund, The *144*

■Ballet

***see* Dance & ballet**

■Baptists

Funding priority

■Beneficiaries from all professional & economic groups

Will consider

■Autism

Funding priority

■Beneficiaries of all ages

Funding priority

■ Beneficiaries of all family situations

....
■Beneficiaries of all religions & cultures
Funding priority

....
■Beneficiaries of all social circumstances
Funding priority

....
■Beneficiaries suffering from any disease or medical condition
Funding priority

Assair Charitable Trust, The *89*
BNFL Springfields Medical
 Research and Charity Trust
 Fund, The *89*
Beauland Ltd *91*
Behrend Fund, The David and
 Ruth *91*
Bibby Fund, Edward *92*
Booth Charities, The *93*
Bridges Foundation, The Harold
 95
Broadhurst Charitable Trust,
 The Charles and Edna *96*
Burden's Charitable Foundation
 97
Busby Charities Fund, Sir Matt
 98
Chadwick Trust, The Amelia
 100
Charity for Change *101*
Cheshire Provincial Fund of
 Benevolence, The *102*
Community Trust for Greater
 Manchester, The *106*
Congleton Inclosure Trust, The
 106
Cozens-Hardy Trust, The Lord
 107
Crag House Charitable Trust,
 The *108*
Duchy of Lancaster Benevolent
 Fund, The *111*
East Lancashire Masonic
 Benevolent Institution
 (Incorporated), The *113*
Eventhall Family Charitable
 Trust, The *115*
Fisher Foundation, The Sir John
 117
France's Charity *119*
Freeman Charitable Trust, A J
 119
Hadfield Charitable Trust, The
 122
Hartley Memorial Trust, The N
 and P *123*
Hemby Trust, The *124*
Holland and St Joseph's
 Charity, Maria *126*
Holt Charitable Trust, P H *126*
Hoover Foundation, The *127*
Howarth Charity Trust, Clifford
 127
Joint Churches Community
 Project *129*
Keyes Trust, The Ursula *131*
Kroch Foundation, The Heinz &
 Anna *131*
Liverpool Queen Victoria District
 Nursing Association, The
 139
Lloyd Charity Trust, The W M
 and B W *140*
Lord Mayor of Chester
 Charitable Trust *141*

Lord Mayor of Manchester's
 Charity Appeal Trust *141*
Manchester and Salford
 Saturday and Convalescent
 Homes' Fund, The *143*
Manchester Guardian Society
 Charitable Trust, The *143*
Mayor of Chorley's Helping
 Hand Charity, The *145*
Mayor of Knowsley Charity
 Fund, The *145*
Mayor of Sefton's Charity Fund,
 The *146*
Mayoress of Trafford's Charity
 Fund, The *146*
Merseyside Development
 Foundation *148*
Morgan Crucible Company plc
 Charitable Trust, The *151*
Newstead Charity, The *155*
Overton Community Trust *160*
Peel Trust, The Dowager
 Countess Eleanor *161*
Penny in the Pound Fund
 Charitable Trust *162*
Pennycress Trust, The *162*
Phelps Charitable Trust,
 Brigadier and Mrs D V *163*
Proctor Charitable Trust, The
 Albert Edward *164*
Ramsden Hall Trust, The *167*
Rapaport Charitable Trust,
 Fanny *167*
Riverside Charitable Trust
 Limited *171*
Rochdale Fund for Relief in
 Sickness, The *171*
Rose Charitable Foundation, Ian
 174
Rowley Trust, The *177*
Runcorn Community Action
 Trust *178*
Scott Charitable Will Trust, The
 Storrow *181*
Sefton Community Foundation
 182
Shepherd Charitable Trust, The
 Patricia and Donald *183*
Slater Foundation, The John
 184
Talbot Bridge Will Trust, The
 Elsie *189*
3i Charitable Trust, The *189*
United Merseyside Trust *190*
United Trusts *190*
Waterhouse Charitable Trust,
 Mrs *192*

···
■Bird sanctuaries

see also **Animal facilities &
services**

Funding priority
Sykes Trust, The Charles *187*

Will consider
Oldham Foundation *159*
Vaux Group Foundation, The
 191
Warrington Animal Welfare *192*

···
■Blindness

see **Sight loss**

···
■Blood disorders &
haemophilia

Funding priority
Baynes Charitable Trust, James
 91

Will consider
BNFL Risley Medical, Research
 and Charity Trust, The *89*
Brotherton Trust, The Charles
 96
Chronicle Cinderella Fund, The
 104
Ford of Britain Trust *118*
Hillards Charitable Trust, Gay &
 Peter Hartley's *124*
Johnson Foundation, The *128*
North West Media Charitable
 Trust Limited *156*
Pilkington Charities Fund *163*
Rainford Trust, The *167*
Ravensdale Trust, The *169*
Rayner Charitable Trust, The
 John *169*
Rowbotham Charitable Trust,
 The Christopher *177*
Scott Charitable Trust, The
 Frieda *181*
Scott Trust, Sir James & Lady
 182
Ward Blenkinsop Trust, The
 192

···
■Botany

see also **Environmental &
animal sciences**
Will consider
Brotherton Trust, The Charles
 96
Royal Botanical & Horticultural
 Society of Manchester and
 the Northern Counties, The
 178

···
■Broadcasting

see **Film, video, multimedia
broadcasting**

■ Care for carers

see **Respite care, care for carers**

■ Care in the community

see also **Community services**

Funding priority

Will consider

■ Care services

see **Community services**

■ Carers

Funding priority

Will consider

■ Catholic bodies

see also **Religious umbrella bodies**

Funding priority

Will consider

■ Catholics

see **Roman Catholics**

■ Children's illnesses

see **Paediatric diseases**

■ Christian education

see also **Advancement of
religion**

Funding priority

■ Christian outreach

see also **Advancement of
religion**

Funding priority

■ Christians

Funding priority

Marchon Works Employees
Charity Fund, The *144*
Pilkington Foundation for Arts
and Leisure, The Harry and
Mavis *163*
Police Training Centre, Bruche,
Charity, The *164*
St Helens United Voluntary
Organisations Community
Trust *179*
Scott Charitable Trust, The
Francis C *180*
Slater Trust Limited, The *184*
West Cumbria Charitable Trust,
The *193*
Wigan Town Relief in Need
Charity *196*
Youth and the Community Trust
198

■Colleges

***see** Schools & colleges*

■Combined arts

***see also** Arts & arts
facilities*
Funding priority
Chase Charity, The *101*
North West Arts Board *155*

Will consider
Rayner Charitable Trust, The
John *169*
Vaux Group Foundation, The
191

■Community arts &
recreation

***see also** Arts activities,
Arts education, Dance
groups, Opera companies,
opera groups, Orchestras,
Theatrical companies,
theatre groups*
Funding priority
Eden Arts Trust *114*
North West Arts Board *155*
Northern Arts *157*
Scott Charitable Trust, The
Frieda *181*

Will consider
Bridges Foundation, The Harold
95
Brotherton Trust, The Charles
96
Cheshire Constabulary
Community Involvement
Fund of Northwich Division
102

Clutterbuck Charitable Trust,
Robert *105*
Congleton Inclosure Trust, The
106
Crosthwaite and Lyth Trust
108
de Avenley Foundation, The
110
Dwek Family Charitable Trust,
The *113*
Ford of Britain Trust *118*
Granada Foundation, The *120*
Hadfield Charitable Trust, The
122
Harewood's Charitable
Settlement, Lord *122*
Hemby Trust, The *124*
Hutchinson Educational Charity,
The Joseph *127*
Lankelly Foundation, The *134*
Mersey Basin Trust – ICI Green
Action Grants *147*
Nantwich and Acton Grammar
School Foundation *151*
National Lottery Charities Board
151
Northern Rock Foundation, The
157
Rathbone Charitable Trust, The
Eleanor *168*
Rotary Club of New Mills Marple
and District Benevolent
Fund, The *174*
Scott Trust, Sir James & Lady
182
Slater Trust Limited, The *184*
Talbot Bridge Will Trust, The
Elsie *189*
Waterhouse Charitable Trust,
Mrs *192*
Yorkshire Bank Charitable
Trust, The *198*

■Community
businesses

***see also** Infrastructure
development*
Funding priority
Davies Trust, The John Grant
109

Will consider
Britannia Building Society
Foundation *95*
Congleton Inclosure Trust, The
106
Dwek Family Charitable Trust,
The *113*
Ferguson Benevolent Fund
Limited *116*
Ford of Britain Trust *118*

Marchon Works Employees
Charity Fund, The *144*
Wing Yip and Brothers
Charitable Trust, W *197*

■Community centres
& village halls

***see also** Community
facilities*
Funding priority
Chase Charity, The *101*
Greater Manchester Police
Community Charity *120*
Lancaster's Trust, Bryan *132*
Rawstone Trust Fund, The
Robert *169*
Wing Yip and Brothers
Charitable Trust, W *197*

Will consider
Barker Charlty, Philip *90*
Booth Charities, The *93*
Burden's Charitable Foundation
97
Cheshire Constabulary
Community Involvement
Fund of Northwich Division
102
Ford of Britain Trust *118*
Kennington (Deceased), Charity
of Mrs Hannah *130*
MacNair Trust, The *142*
Marchon Works Employees
Charity Fund, The *144*
Pilkington Foundation for Arts
and Leisure, The Harry and
Mavis *163*
Proven Family Trust, The *165*
Slater Trust Limited, The *184*
West Cumbria Charitable Trust,
The *193*
Wethered Bequest, The *195*

■Community
development

***see also** Infrastructure
development, Training for
community development*
Funding priority
Brotherton Trust, The Charles
96
Chase Charity, The *101*
Davies Trust, The John Grant
109
Lane Foundation, The Allen
132
Moores Foundation, John *149*
Scott Trust, Sir James & Lady
182

South Lakeland Communities
  Charitable Trust *185*
Westminster Foundation, The
  194

Will consider
Britannia Building Society
  Foundation *95*
Chrimes Family Charitable
  Trust, The *104*
Congleton Inclosure Trust, The
  106
Dwek Family Charitable Trust,
  The *113*
Ferguson Benevolent Fund
  Limited *116*
Ford of Britain Trust *118*
Hillards Charitable Trust, Gay &
  Peter Hartley's *124*
Lankelly Foundation, The *134*
Marchon Works Employees
  Charity Fund, The *144*
Moore Foundation, The George
  A *148*
National Lottery Charities Board
  151
Northern Rock Foundation, The
  157
Pilkington Foundation for Arts
  and Leisure, The Harry and
  Mavis *163*
Ravensdale Trust, The *169*
Rowan Charitable Trust, The
  176
Scott Charitable Trust, The
  Francis C *180*
Vaux Group Foundation, The
  191
Wigan Town Relief in Need
  Charity *196*
Wing Yip and Brothers
  Charitable Trust, W *197*

···
■ **Community facilities**

see also **Art galleries &
cultural centres,
Community centres &
village halls, Libraries &
museums, Parks,
Playgrounds, Recreation
grounds, Sports centres,
Theatres & opera houses**

Funding priority
Lloyd Charity Trust, The W M
  and B W *140*
Newstead Charity, The *155*
Pilkington Charities Fund *163*
Scott Charitable Trust, The
  Frieda *181*
Scott Trust, Sir James & Lady
  182

Will consider
AGF Charitable Trust *87*
Adlington Women's Institute
  87
Angler's Inn Trust *88*
Aquinas Trust *88*
Baddiley Consolidated Charity
  90
Baynes Charitable Trust, James
  91
Brotherton Trust, The Charles
  96
C & A Charitable Trust, The *99*
Carlisle Sick Poor Fund *99*
Clutterbuck Charitable Trust,
  Robert *105*
Community Trust for Greater
  Manchester, The *106*
Congleton Inclosure Trust, The
  106
Cozens-Hardy Trust, The Lord
  107
Dwek Family Charitable Trust,
  The *113*
Eagle Charity Trust, The *113*
East Lancashire Masonic
  Benevolent Institution
  (Incorporated), The *113*
Hadfield Charitable Trust, The
  122
Hemby Trust, The *124*
Hilmarnan Charitable Trust
  125
Hoover Foundation, The *127*
Hurst Charitable Trust, Richard
  Threlfall *127*
Hutchinson Educational Charity,
  The Joseph *127*
Integreat *128*
Lathoms Charity, Peter *136*
Leverhulme's Charitable Trust,
  Lord *137*
Llay Estate, The *140*
Merseyside Development
  Foundation *148*
National Lottery Charities Board
  151
North West Media Charitable
  Trust Limited *156*
Oldham United Charity *159*
Plimpton Foundation, The
  Charles *164*
Proctor Charitable Trust, The
  Albert Edward *164*
Rayner Charitable Trust, The
  John *169*
Rotary Club of Alderley Edge
  and Bollin Valley Trust Fund
  174
Rotary Club of New Mills Marple
  and District Benevolent
  Fund, The *174*
St Helens United Voluntary
  Organisations Community
  Trust *179*

Sefton Community Foundation
  182
3i Charitable Trust, The *189*
Waterhouse Charitable Trust,
  Mrs *192*

···
■ **Community issues**

see also **Campaigning
(social issues)**

Funding priority
Davies Trust, The John Grant
  109
Lane Foundation, The Allen
  132

Will consider
France's Charity *119*
Hamitzvos, Keren *122*
Scott Charitable Trust, The
  Francis C *180*
Vaux Group Foundation, The
  191
West Cumbria Charitable Trust,
  The *193*

···
■ **Community services**

see also **Adoption &
fostering services, Care in
the community, Clubs,
Community transport,
Counselling (social issues),
Crime prevention schemes,
Day centres, Emergency
care, refugees, famine,
Holidays & outings, Income
support & maintenance,
Meals provision,
Playschemes**

Funding priority
Pilkington Charities Fund *163*
Scott Trust, Sir James & Lady
  182

Will consider
AGF Charitable Trust *87*
Adlington Women's Institute
  87
Angler's Inn Trust *88*
Aquinas Trust *88*
Baddiley Consolidated Charity
  90
Baynes Charitable Trust, James
  91
Bowness and Windermere
  Community Care Trust *94*
Brentwood Charity, The *95*
Britannia Building Society
  Foundation *95*
Broadhurst Charitable Trust,
  The Charles and Edna *96*
Burall Charitable Trust, The *97*
C & A Charitable Trust, The *99*

■ Community transport

see also **Community
services**

Funding priority

Will consider

■ Computers

see **Information technology
& computers**

■ Conservation

see also **Church buildings,
Fauna, Flora, Historic
buildings, Lakes,
Landscapes, Memorials &
monuments, Nature
reserves, Waterways,
Woodlands**

Funding priority

Will consider

Conservation & campaigning

see also **Endangered species, Environmental issues, Heritage, Nuclear energy, nuclear power, Renewable energy, renewable power, Transport & alternative transport**

Funding priority

Mersey Basin Trust – Greenlink Awards, The *147*
South Lakeland Communities Charitable Trust *185*

Will consider

Community Trust for Greater Manchester, The *106*
Johnson Foundation, The *128*
Leach Charitable Trust, The Eric and Dorothy *137*
Mersey Basin Trust *146*
Waterhouse Charitable Trust, Mrs *192*

Conservation education & training

see **Education & training**

Convalescent homes

see also **Health facilities & buildings**

Will consider

Booth Charities, The *93*
Marchon Works Employees Charity Fund, The *144*
Moore Foundation, The George A *148*
Scott Trust, Sir James & Lady *182*

Costs of study

see also **Bursaries & fees, Fellowships, Purchase of books & equipment, Scholarships, Travel & maintenance**

Funding priority

Nantwich and Acton Grammar School Foundation *151*

Will consider

Brabin's Educational Foundation *94*
Burall Charitable Trust, The *97*
Cartmel Old Grammar School Foundation *100*
Charity for Change *101*

Community Trust for Greater Manchester, The *106*
Crosthwaite and Lyth Trust *108*
Eskdale (Cumbria) Trust, The *115*
Forster Charitable Trust, The *118*
Joint Churches Community Project *129*
Lathoms Charity, Peter *136*
Leverhulme's Charitable Trust, Lord *137*
Localtrent Ltd *140*
McMechan Memorial Fund, The Roy *142*
Merseyside Development Foundation *148*
Parkhill Charitable Trust *160*
Rowan Charitable Trust, The *176*
Runcorn Community Action Trust *178*
St Joseph's Educational Charity *180*
Stockport Community Trust *187*
Stockport Educational Foundation, The *187*
Talbot Bridge Will Trust, The Elsie *189*
Timperley Educational Foundation *189*
World Friendship *198*
Yorkshire Bank Charitable Trust, The *198*

Council for Voluntary Service (CVS)

see also **Charity or voluntary umbrella bodies**

Funding priority

Patients' Aid Association Hospital and Medical Charities Trust *160*
Pilkington Charities Fund *163*
Sainsbury Charitable Fund Ltd, The *179*
Scott Trust, Sir James & Lady *182*
Westminster Foundation, The *194*

Will consider

BNFL Risley Medical, Research and Charity Trust, The *89*
Barker Charity, Philip *90*
Congleton Inclosure Trust, The *106*
Davies Trust, The John Grant *109*
Girl's Welfare Fund *120*

Hillards Charitable Trust, Gay & Peter Hartley's *124*
Holford's Charity, John *125*
Johnson Group Cleaners Charity *129*
Lancaster's Trust, Bryan *132*
Mersey Basin Trust – ICI Green Action Grants *147*
Moores Foundation, John *149*
Rainford Trust, The *167*
Scott Charitable Trust, The Francis C *180*
Vaux Group Foundation, The *191*

Counselling (health)

see also **Health care**

Will consider

BNFL Risley Medical, Research and Charity Trust, The *89*
Birkenhead and Wirral Moral Welfare Association *92*
Davies Trust, The John Grant *109*
Drugwatch Trust *111*
Hamitzvos, Keren *122*
Hillards Charitable Trust, Gay & Peter Hartley's *124*
Lancaster's Trust, Bryan *132*
Proven Family Trust, The *165*
Scott Trust, Sir James & Lady *182*

Counselling (social issues)

see also **Community services**

Funding priority

Kershaw Trust, The Peter *130*
Scott Charitable Trust, The Frieda *181*
Sykes Trust, The Charles *187*
Yorkshire Bank Charitable Trust, The *198*

Will consider

Barnabas Charitable Trust *90*
Birkenhead and Wirral Moral Welfare Association *92*
Brotherton Trust, The Charles *96*
Chiron Trust, The *103*
Congleton Town Trust, The *107*
Davies Trust, The John Grant *109*
France's Charity *119*
Lankelly Foundation, The *134*
Lord Mayor of Chester Charitable Trust *141*
Northern Rock Foundation, The *157*

Rayner Charitable Trust, The
John *169*
Rowbotham Charitable Trust,
The Christopher *177*
Sainsbury Charitable Fund Ltd,
The *179*
Scott Charitable Trust, The
Frieda *181*
Scott Trust, Sir James & Lady
182
Ward Blenkinsop Trust, The
192

■ Dance & ballet

see also **Arts & arts
facilities**
Funding priority
Chase Charity, The *101*
North West Arts Board *155*

Will consider
Ravensdale Trust, The *169*
Rayner Charitable Trust, The
John *169*
Wethered Bequest, The *195*

■ Dance groups

see also **Community arts &
recreation**
Funding priority
Chase Charity, The *101*

Will consider
Davies Trust, The John Grant
109
Lord Mayor of Chester
Charitable Trust *141*

■ Day centres

see also **Community
services**
Funding priority
Chase Charity, The *101*
Kershaw Trust, The Peter *130*
Lankelly Foundation, The *134*
Littleborough Nursing
Association Fund *139*
Patients' Aid Association
Hospital and Medical
Charities Trust *160*
Sainsbury Charitable Fund Ltd,
The *179*
Scott Charitable Trust, The
Frieda *181*

Will consider
BNFL Risley Medical, Research
and Charity Trust, The *89*
Barnabas Charitable Trust *90*

Barnes Fund, The Norman *91*
Birkenhead and Wirral Moral
Welfare Association *92*
Booth Charities, The *93*
Brotherton Trust, The Charles
96
Cheshire Constabulary
Community Involvement
Fund of Northwich Division
102
Chiron Trust, The *103*
Crosthwaite and Lyth Trust
108
Ferguson Benevolent Fund
Limited *116*
Ford of Britain Trust *118*
Hillards Charitable Trust, Gay &
Peter Hartley's *124*
Kennington (Deceased), Charity
of Mrs Hannah *130*
Lancaster's Trust, Bryan *132*
Lord Mayor of Chester
Charitable Trust *141*
MacNair Trust, The *142*
Marchon Works Employees
Charity Fund, The *144*
Moore Foundation, The George
A *148*
Oldham Foundation *159*
Pilkington Foundation for Arts
and Leisure, The Harry and
Mavis *163*
Rainford Trust, The *167*
Scott Charitable Trust, The
Francis C *180*
Vaux Group Foundation, The
191
West Cumbria Charitable Trust,
The *193*
Wing Yip and Brothers
Charitable Trust, W *197*
Youth and the Community Trust
198

■ Day nurseries

see **Playschemes**

■ Deafness

see **Hearing loss**

■ Dentistry

see **Health care**

■ Development
activities

see **Infrastructure
development**

■ Development
proposals

see also **Campaigning
(social issues)**
Will consider
Davies Trust, The John Grant
109

■ Diabetes

Will consider
BNFL Risley Medical, Research
and Charity Trust, The *89*
Brotherton Trust, The Charles
96
Coward Trust, The *107*
Ferguson Benevolent Fund
Limited *116*
Ford of Britain Trust *118*
Hamitzvos, Keren *122*
Hillards Charitable Trust, Gay &
Peter Hartley's *124*
North West Media Charitable
Trust Limited *156*
Pilkington Charities Fund *163*
Ravensdale Trust, The *169*
Rayner Charitable Trust, The
John *169*
Rowbotham Charitable Trust,
The Christopher *177*
Sainsbury Charitable Fund Ltd,
The *179*
Scott Charitable Trust, The
Frieda *181*
Scott Trust, Sir James & Lady
182
Ward Blenkinsop Trust, The
192

■ Dietary – special
dietary needs

Will consider
BNFL Risley Medical, Research
and Charity Trust, The *89*
North West Media Charitable
Trust Limited *156*
Pilkington Charities Fund *163*
Scott Charitable Trust, The
Frieda *181*
Scott Trust, Sir James & Lady
182
Ward Blenkinsop Trust, The
192

■ Diocesan boards

see also **Religious umbrella
bodies**
Funding priority
Chase Charity, The *101*

Will consider

Broadhurst Charitable Trust,
   The Charles and Edna *96*
Hillards Charitable Trust, Gay &
   Peter Hartley's *124*
Pye Christian Trust, The *165*

■ Disabilities

see **Disabled people
(physical, sensory, learning
impairments)**

■ Disabled people (physical, sensory, learning impairments)

Funding priority

Ainsworth and Family
   Benevolent Fund, Green and
   Lilian F M *87*
BNFL Springfields Medical
   Research and Charity Trust
   Fund, The *89*
Baynes Charitable Trust, James
   91
Bowness and Windermere
   Community Care Trust *94*
Brotherton Trust, The Charles
   96
Chase Charity, The *101*
Community Trust for Greater
   Manchester, The *106*
Duchy of Lancaster Benevolent
   Fund, The *111*
East Lancashire Masonic
   Benevolent Institution
   (Incorporated), The *113*
Hartley Memorial Trust, The N
   and P *123*
Hawe Settlement, The M A
   124
Holland and St Joseph's
   Charity, Maria *126*
Integreat *128*
Kroch Foundation, The Heinz &
   Anna *131*
Lankelly Foundation, The *134*
Leboff Charitable Trust, The
   Paul & Evelyn *137*
Littleborough Nursing
   Association Fund *139*
Liverpool Queen Victoria District
   Nursing Association, The
   139
Manchester and Salford
   Saturday and Convalescent
   Homes' Fund, The *143*
Moores Foundation, John *149*
Morgan Crucible Company plc
   Charitable Trust, The *151*
Newstead Charity, The *155*

Northern Rock Foundation, The
   157
Patients' Aid Association
   Hospital and Medical
   Charities Trust *160*
Pilkington Charities Fund *163*
Queendeans Association *166*
Rayner Charitable Trust, The
   John *169*
Rochdale Fund for Relief in
   Sickness, The *171*
Rowbotham Charitable Trust,
   The Christopher *177*
Sainsbury Charitable Fund Ltd,
   The *179*
Scott Charitable Trust, The
   Francis C *180*
Scott Charitable Trust, The
   Frieda *181*
Scott Trust, Sir James & Lady
   182
Sykes Trust, The Charles *187*
West Lancashire Masonic
   Educational Trust *194*
Yorkshire Bank Charitable
   Trust, The *198*

Will consider

AGF Charitable Trust *87*
BNFL Risley Medical, Research
   and Charity Trust, The *89*
Baddiley Consolidated Charity
   90
Barker Charity, Philip *90*
Barnabas Charitable Trust *90*
Burall Charitable Trust, The *97*
Charity for Change *101*
Cheadle Royal Industries
   Charitable Trust *102*
Chorley Relief Fund, The *104*
Chrimes Family Charitable
   Trust, The *104*
Chronicle Cinderella Fund, The
   104
Congleton Inclosure Trust, The
   106
Congleton Town Trust, The
   107
Davies Trust, The John Grant
   109
Denton Relief in Sickness
   Charity *110*
Ford of Britain Trust *118*
France's Charity *119*
Girl's Welfare Fund *120*
Hadfield Charitable Trust, The
   122
Hamitzvos, Keren *122*
Hemby Trust, The *124*
Hillards Charitable Trust, Gay &
   Peter Hartley's *124*
Johnson Foundation, The *128*
Lancaster's Trust, Bryan *132*
Lathoms Charity, Peter *136*
Leverhulme's Charitable Trust,
   Lord *137*

Llay Estate, The *140*
Marchon Works Employees
   Charity Fund, The *144*
Mayor's Relief Fund, The *146*
Moore Foundation, The George
   A *148*
North West Media Charitable
   Trust Limited *156*
Northern Arts *157*
Plimpton Foundation, The
   Charles *164*
Proven Family Trust, The *165*
Rainford Trust, The *167*
Ravensdale Trust, The *169*
Rope Third Charitable
   Settlement, The Mrs L D
   171
Rotary Club of Wallasey, The
   Charitable Fund of the *175*
Rowan Charitable Trust, The
   176
St Helens United Voluntary
   Organisations Community
   Trust *179*
Sefton and West Lancashire
   Deaf Children's Society
   182
Sefton Community Foundation
   182
Stewart Trust, Sir Halley *185*
Vaux Group Foundation, The
   191

■ Disadvantaged by poverty

Funding priority

Baynes Charitable Trust, James
   91
Birkenhead and Wirral Moral
   Welfare Association *92*
Bowness and Windermere
   Community Care Trust *94*
Burall Charitable Trust, The *97*
C & A Charitable Trust, The *99*
Charity for Change *101*
Chase Charity, The *101*
Chiron Trust, The *103*
Clover Trust, The Emily *105*
Community Trust for Greater
   Manchester, The *106*
Cozens-Hardy Trust, The Lord
   107
Davies Trust, The John Grant
   109
Derbyshire Trust, The Nancy
   111
East Lancashire Masonic
   Benevolent Institution
   (Incorporated), The *113*
Florence's Charitable Trust
   118
Greater Manchester Police
   Community Charity *120*
Gurunanak *121*

Hillards Charitable Trust, Gay & Peter Hartley's *124*
Hilmarnan Charitable Trust *125*
Joint Churches Community Project *129*
Kershaw Trust, The Peter *130*
Kroch Foundation, The Heinz & Anna *131*
Lancaster's Trust, Bryan *132*
Lankelly Foundation, The *134*
Lathoms Charity, Peter *136*
Littleborough Nursing Association Fund *139*
Localtrent Ltd *140*
McKenna Charity, The Simon and Suzanne *142*
Merseyside Development Foundation *148*
Mole Charitable Trust *148*
Moores Foundation, John *149*
Moorwoods Charitable Trust, The *150*
Parkhill Charitable Trust *160*
Parkinson (Deceased) Trust, Thomas *160*
Patients' Aid Association Hospital and Medical Charities Trust *160*
Pilkington Charities Fund *163*
Preston Relief in Need Charity *164*
Proctor Charitable Trust, The Albert Edward *164*
Rochdale Fund for Relief in Sickness, The *171*
Rope Third Charitable Settlement, The Mrs L D *171*
Rowbotham Charitable Trust, The Christopher *177*
Runcorn Community Action Trust *178*
Scott Charitable Trust, The Francis C *180*
Scott Charitable Trust, The Frieda *181*
Scott Trust, Sir James & Lady *182*
Severn Trent Water Charitable Trust Fund, The *183*
West Lancashire Masonic Educational Trust *194*
Wing Yip and Brothers Charitable Trust, W *197*
Yorkshire Bank Charitable Trust, The *198*

Will consider

AGF Charitable Trust *87*
Adlington Women's Institute *87*
BNFL Risley Medical, Research and Charity Trust, The *89*
Baddiley Consolidated Charity *90*

Brentwood Charity, The *95*
Broadhurst Charitable Trust, The Charles and Edna *96*
Cheadle Royal Industries Charitable Trust *102*
Chorley Relief Fund, The *104*
Chronicle Cinderella Fund, The *104*
Congleton Inclosure Trust, The *106*
Congleton Town Trust, The *107*
Denton Relief in Sickness Charity *110*
Duchy of Lancaster Benevolent Fund, The *111*
Eddleston's Charity, John *114*
Ferguson Benevolent Fund Limited *116*
Ford of Britain Trust *118*
France's Charity *119*
Girl's Welfare Fund *120*
Hadfield Charitable Trust, The *122*
Hamitzvos, Keren *122*
Hawe Settlement, The M A *124*
Hemby Trust, The *124*
Highland Society of London *124*
Holford's Charity, John *125*
Johnson Foundation, The *128*
Johnson Group Cleaners Charity *129*
Keyes Trust, The Ursula *131*
Knights House Charity *131*
Leverhulme's Charitable Trust, Lord *137*
Llay Estate, The *140*
Manchester and Salford Saturday and Convalescent Homes' Fund, The *143*
Marchon Works Employees Charity Fund, The *144*
Northern Rock Foundation, The *157*
Oldham Foundation *159*
Oldham United Charity *159*
Proven Family Trust, The *165*
Pye Christian Trust, The *165*
Rainford Trust, The *167*
Rathbone Charitable Trust, The Eleanor *168*
Rathbone Charity, The Elizabeth *168*
Ravensdale Trust, The *169*
Rawdon-Smith Trust, The *169*
Rayner Charitable Trust, The John *169*
Riverside Charitable Trust Limited *171*
Rotary Club of Wallasey, The Charitable Fund of the *175*
Sefton Community Foundation *182*
Stewart Trust, Sir Halley *185*

Stockport Community Trust *187*
Vaux Group Foundation, The *191*
World Friendship *198*

■ Disaster victims

Funding priority

Littleborough Nursing Association Fund *139*
Patients' Aid Association Hospital and Medical Charities Trust *160*
Pilkington Charities Fund *163*
Scott Trust, Sir James & Lady *182*

Will consider

AGF Charitable Trust *87*
BNFL Risley Medical, Research and Charity Trust, The *89*
Charity for Change *101*
Congleton Inclosure Trust, The *106*
Congleton Town Trust, The *107*
Duchy of Lancaster Benevolent Fund, The *111*
Eddleston's Charity, John *114*
France's Charity *119*
Hadfield Charitable Trust, The *122*
Hamitzvos, Keren *122*
Hemby Trust, The *124*
Holford's Charity, John *125*
Lancaster's Trust, Bryan *132*
Lathoms Charity, Peter *136*
Leverhulme's Charitable Trust, Lord *137*
Lloyd Charity Trust, The W M and B W *140*
Rainford Trust, The *167*
Rotary Club of Wallasey, The Charitable Fund of the *175*
Sainsbury Charitable Fund Ltd, The *179*
Scott Charitable Trust, The Frieda *181*

■ Doctors

see **Medical professionals, nurses & doctors**

■ Dogs – kennels & other facilities for dogs

see also **Animal facilities & services**

Funding priority
Green Memorial Fund, The Barry 121

Will consider
Oldham Foundation 159
Sykes Trust, The Charles 187
Vaux Group Foundation, The 191
Warrington Animal Welfare 192

■ Domestic Violence

see **Victims of domestic violence**

■ Drug abuse

see **Substance misuse**

■ Ecology

see also **Environmental & animal sciences**

Funding priority
Mersey Basin Trust – ICI Green Action Grants 147

Will consider
Brotherton Trust, The Charles 96
Rowan Charitable Trust, The 176
Westminster Foundation, The 194

■ Economic regeneration schemes

see also **Infrastructure development**

Funding priority
Westminster Foundation, The 194

Will consider
Britannia Building Society Foundation 95
Davies Trust, The John Grant 109
Ferguson Benevolent Fund Limited 116
Ford of Britain Trust 118

Northern Rock Foundation, The 157
Scott Charitable Trust, The Francis C 180
Scott Trust, Sir James & Lady 182
Vaux Group Foundation, The 191
Wing Yip and Brothers Charitable Trust, W 197

■ Economics

see **Academic subjects, sciences & research**

■ Education & training

see also **Cultural & religious teaching, English as a second or foreign language – TESL & TEFL, IT training, Literacy, Professional, specialist training, Special needs education, Speech therapy, Textiles & upholstery, Training for community development, Training for personal development, Training for work, Vocational training**

Funding priority
Brotherton Trust, The Charles 96
Nantwich and Acton Grammar School Foundation 151

Will consider
AGF Charitable Trust 87
Baddiley Consolidated Charity 90
Baynes Charitable Trust, James 91
Booth Charities, The 93
Brabin's Educational Foundation 94
Brentwood Charity, The 95
Britannia Building Society Foundation 95
Burall Charitable Trust, The 97
Charity for Change 101
Clover Trust, The Emily 105
Community Trust for Greater Manchester, The 106
Crosthwaite and Lyth Trust 108
DAG Charitable Trust 109
Duchy of Lancaster Benevolent Fund, The 111
Eddleston's Charity, John 114
Florence's Charitable Trust 118
Forster Charitable Trust, The 118

Fort Foundation 119
Hadfield Charitable Trust, The 122
Hawe Settlement, The M A 124
Hemby Trust, The 124
Hoover Foundation, The 127
Joint Churches Community Project 129
Lathoms Charity, Peter 136
Leverhulme's Charitable Trust, Lord 137
Liverpool R C Archdiocesan Trustees Incorporated Special Trusts 139
Lloyd Charity Trust, The W M and B W 140
Localtrent Ltd 140
McKenna Charity, The Simon and Suzanne 142
McMechan Memorial Fund, The Roy 142
Merseyside Development Foundation 148
Mole Charitable Trust 148
National Lottery Charities Board 151
Neave Trust, The Airey 154
North West Media Charitable Trust Limited 156
Parkhill Charitable Trust 160
Rathbone Charitable Trust, The Eleanor 168
Rawdon-Smith Trust, The 169
Riverside Charitable Trust Limited 171
Rotary Club of New Mills Marple and District Benevolent Fund, The 174
Rowan Charitable Trust, The 176
Runcorn Community Action Trust 178
St Joseph's Educational Charity 180
Sefton and West Lancashire Deaf Children's Society 182
Sefton Community Foundation 182
Stewart Trust, Sir Halley 185
Stockport Community Trust 187
Stockport Educational Foundation, The 187
Talbot Bridge Will Trust, The Elsie 189
Timperley Educational Foundation 189
Waterhouse Charitable Trust, Mrs 192
Winwick Educational Foundation, The 197
World Friendship 198
Yorkshire Bank Charitable Trust, The 198

■ Education hardship funds

see Costs of study

■ Emergency & short-term housing

see also Residential facilities & services

Funding priority
Chase Charity, The *101*
Littleborough Nursing Association Fund *139*

Will consider
BNFL Risley Medical, Research and Charity Trust, The *89*
Britannia Building Society Foundation *95*
Congleton Inclosure Trust, The *106*
Ford of Britain Trust *118*
Girl's Welfare Fund *120*
Hillards Charitable Trust, Gay & Peter Hartley's *124*
Pilkington Charities Fund *163*
Ravensdale Trust, The *169*
Rope Third Charitable Settlement, The Mrs L D *171*
Scott Charitable Trust, The Francis C *180*

■ Emergency appeals

see Victims of man-made or natural disasters

■ Emergency care, refugees, famine

see also Community services

Will consider
Burden's Charitable Foundation *97*
Chiron Trust, The *103*
Congleton Town Trust, The *107*
Lancaster's Trust, Bryan *132*
Rainford Trust, The *167*

■ Employees & ex-employees

Funding priority
AGF Charitable Trust *87*
Florence's Charitable Trust *118*

■ Endangered habitats

see Animal facilities & services

■ Endangered species

see also Conservation & campaigning

Will consider
Hamitzvos, Keren *122*
National Lottery Charities Board *151*
Oldham Foundation *159*

■ Engineering

see also Academic subjects, sciences & research

Will consider
Ford of Britain Trust *118*
Hoover Foundation, The *127*
Manchester Society of Architects, The *144*

■ English as a second or foreign language – TESL & TEFL

see also Education & training

Will consider
Neave Trust, The Airey *154*
Rayner Charitable Trust, The John *169*
Wing Yip and Brothers Charitable Trust, W *197*

■ English literature

see Cultural heritage (of national & historical importance)

Funding priority
Chase Charity, The *101*

Will consider
Oldham Foundation *159*

■ Entertainment professionals

see Actors & entertainment professionals

■ Environmental & animal sciences

see also Agriculture, Botany, Ecology, Horticulture, Natural history, Organic food production

Funding priority
Mersey Basin Trust – Greenlink Awards, The *147*

Will consider
Community Trust for Greater Manchester, The *106*
Hemby Trust, The *124*
Johnson Foundation, The *128*
National Lottery Charities Board *151*
South Lakeland Communities Charitable Trust *185*
Waterhouse Charitable Trust, Mrs *192*

■ Environmental issues

see also Conservation & campaigning

Funding priority
Mersey Basin Trust – ICI Green Action Grants *147*

Will consider
Davies Trust, The John Grant *109*
Hamitzvos, Keren *122*
Hemby Trust, The *124*
Johnson Foundation, The *128*
National Lottery Charities Board *151*
Oldham Foundation *159*
Rainford Trust, The *167*
Rowan Charitable Trust, The *176*
Scott Trust, Sir James & Lady *182*

■ Epilepsy

Funding priority
Rowbotham Charitable Trust, The Christopher *177*

Will consider
BNFL Risley Medical, Research and Charity Trust, The *89*
Brotherton Trust, The Charles *96*
Chronicle Cinderella Fund, The *104*
Ford of Britain Trust *118*
Hillards Charitable Trust, Gay & Peter Hartley's *124*

■ Equal opportunities

see also **Advocacy (social issues)**

Will consider

■ Equipment for study

see **Purchase of books & equipment**

■ Equipment (health)

see **Health facilities & buildings**

■ Ethnic minority groups

Funding priority

Will consider

■ Evangelists

Funding priority

Will consider

■ Ex-offenders & those at risk of offending

Funding priority

Will consider

■ Ex-service & service people

Funding priority

Will consider

■ Family planning clinic

see **Health care**

■ Famine

see **Victims of famine**

■ Fauna

see also Conservation

Funding priority
Mersey Basin Trust – ICI Green
Action Grants *147*

Will consider
Eskdale (Cumbria) Trust, The
115
Hamitzvos, Keren *122*
Royal Botanical & Horticultural
Society of Manchester and
the Northern Counties, The
178

■ Fees

see Bursaries & fees

■ Fellowships

see also Costs of study

Funding priority
Fetal Medicine Foundation, The
117
Neave Trust, The Airey *154*

Will consider
Wing Yip and Brothers
Charitable Trust, W *197*

■ Females

Funding priority
Hawe Settlement, The M A
124
Moores Foundation, John *149*
Rathbone Charitable Trust, The
Eleanor *168*

■ Festivals

see Arts activities

■ Film, video, multimedia broadcasting

see also Arts & arts
facilities
Funding priority
Chase Charity, The *101*
North West Arts Board *155*

Will consider
Granada Foundation, The *120*

■ Financial services

see also Infrastructure &
technical support
Will consider
Pilkington Foundation for Arts
and Leisure, The Harry and
Mavis *163*

■ Fine art

see also Arts & arts
facilities

Funding priority
Blankstone Charitable Trust,
The Solomon & Isabel *93*
Chase Charity, The *101*
Granada Foundation, The *120*
North West Arts Board *155*

Will consider
Oldham Foundation *159*
Rayner Charitable Trust, The
John *169*
Wethered Bequest, The *195*

■ First aid

see also Health care
Will consider
BNFL Risley Medical, Research
and Charity Trust, The *89*
Barker Charity, Philip *90*
Brotherton Trust, The Charles
96
Scott Trust, Sir James & Lady
182

■ Fishermen

see Seafarers & fishermen

■ Flora

see also Conservation
Funding priority
Mersey Basin Trust – ICI Green
Action Grants *147*

Will consider
Eskdale (Cumbria) Trust, The
115
Hamitzvos, Keren *122*
Royal Botanical & Horticultural
Society of Manchester and
the Northern Counties, The
178

■ Fostering

see Adoption & fostering
services, In care, fostered &
adopted

■ Free church

see also Religious umbrella
bodies
Funding priority
Chase Charity, The *101*

Will consider
Broadhurst Charitable Trust,
The Charles and Edna *96*
Hillards Charitable Trust, Gay &
Peter Hartley's *124*
Pye Christian Trust, The *165*
Ravensdale Trust, The *169*

■ Friedrichs Ataxia

Will consider
BNFL Risley Medical, Research
and Charity Trust, The *89*
Brotherton Trust, The Charles
96
Ford of Britain Trust *118*
North West Media Charitable
Trust Limited *156*
Scott Charitable Trust, The
Frieda *181*
Scott Trust, Sir James & Lady
182
Ward Blenkinsop Trust, The
192

■ Further education

see Schools & colleges

■ Gay & lesbian rights (campaigning)

see also Campaigning
(social issues)
Will consider
Davies Trust, The John Grant
109
Lane Foundation, The Allen
132

■ Gays & lesbians

Funding priority
Scott Charitable Trust, The
Frieda *181*
Scott Trust, Sir James & Lady
182

Will consider

Charity for Change *101*
Davies Trust, The John Grant *109*
Duchy of Lancaster Benevolent Fund, The *111*
Hamitzvos, Keren *122*
Lane Foundation, The Allen *132*
Lankelly Foundation, The *134*
Northern Rock Foundation, The *157*
Patients' Aid Association Hospital and Medical Charities Trust *160*
Vaux Group Foundation, The *191*

....

■ General charitable purposes

Funding priority

Ainsworth and Family Benevolent Fund, Green and Lilian F M *87*
Amelan Charitable Trust, The Harold *88*
Behrend Fund, The David and Ruth *91*
Bridges Foundation, The Harold *95*
Busby Charities Fund, Sir Matt *98*
Chadwick Trust, The Amelia *100*
Cumberland and Westmorland Provincial Grand Lodge Benevolent Fund, The *108*
Duchy of Lancaster Benevolent Fund, The *111*
Eventhall Family Charitable Trust, The *115*
Fisher Foundation, The Sir John *117*
Holt Charitable Trust, P H *126*
Howarth Charity Trust, Clifford *127*
Johnson Charitable Settlement, The N B *128*
Lord Mayor of Manchester's Charity Appeal Trust *141*
Manchester Guardian Society Charitable Trust, The *143*
Mayor of Chorley's Helping Hand Charity, The *145*
Mayor of Knowsley Charity Fund, The *145*
Mayor of Sefton's Charity Fund, The *146*
Mayoress of Trafford's Charity Fund, The *146*
Overton Community Trust *160*
Phelps Charitable Trust, Brigadier and Mrs D V *163*
Queendeans Association *166*

Rainford Trust, The *167*
Ramsden Hall Trust, The *167*
Rapaport Charitable Trust, Fanny *167*
Rose Charitable Foundation, Ian *174*
Scott Charitable Trust, The Frieda *181*
Scott Charitable Will Trust, The Storrow *181*
Shepherd Charitable Trust, The Patricia and Donald *183*
Stokes Memorial Trust, The Alan Jenkin *187*
United Merseyside Trust *190*
Ward Blenkinsop Trust, The *192*
Waterhouse Charitable Trust, Mrs *192*
Westmorland Charity Concerts Society *195*

Will consider

Assair Charitable Trust, The *89*
Bibby Fund, Edward *92*
Bicket Charitable Trust, H B *92*
Birkenhead and Wirral Moral Welfare Association *92*
Borough of Blackburn Common Good Trust *94*
Bowness and Windermere Community Care Trust *94*
C & A Charitable Trust, The *99*
Charity for Change *101*
Cheadle Royal Industries Charitable Trust *102*
Cheshire Constabulary Community Involvement Fund of Northwich Division *102*
Cheshire Constabulary Involvement Fund for the Northern Divisions, The *102*
Cheshire Provincial Fund of Benevolence, The *102*
Cheshire Provincial Grand Lodge of Mark Master Mason's Fund of Benevolence, The *103*
City of Manchester Common Good Trust *104*
Claremont Association, The *105*
Collins Charitable Trust, The C D *105*
Community Trust for Greater Manchester, The *106*
Crag House Charitable Trust, The *108*
Crosby Charitable Trust, The *108*
DAG Charitable Trust *109*
Davies Welfare Trust, The Thomas Pearce *110*

Dixon Memorial Fund, Edward *111*
Eden's Foundation, James *114*
Egton Parish Lands Charity *115*
Ellison Marsden Charitable Trust, The *115*
Evans Trust, Mabel *115*
Famos Foundation Trust *116*
Fetal Medicine Foundation, The *117*
Fidler Charitable Trust, The J S and L R *117*
Forster Charitable Trust, The *118*
Fort Foundation *119*
Freeman Charitable Trust, A J *119*
Grosberg Foundation, The Esther and Harry *121*
Gurunanak *121*
Hale and Hale Barns Charitable Trust *122*
Hamitzvos, Keren *122*
Harewood's Charitable Settlement, Lord *122*
Harris Charity, The *123*
Hartley Memorial Trust, The N and P *123*
Haslingden Local Charities Account *123*
Hawe Settlement, The M A *124*
Hillards Charitable Trust, Gay & Peter Hartley's *124*
Hilmarnan Charitable Trust *125*
Hoover Foundation, The *127*
Hurst Charitable Trust, Richard Threlfall *127*
Kennington (Deceased), Charity of Mrs Hannah *130*
Knights House Charity *131*
Leasgill Quarry *137*
Leverhulme's Charitable Trust, Lord *137*
Linen and Woollen Stock Charity, The *138*
Lions Club, Lancaster and Morecambe, Charity Trust *139*
Liverpool Sailors' Home Trust *140*
McAllister Memorial Trust, R P *142*
McKenna Charity, The Simon and Suzanne *142*
Manackerman Charitable Trust *142*
Marchon Works Employees Charity Fund, The *144*
Marks Foundation, The Ann and David *145*
Mayor of Hyde's Trust Fund *145*

■ Governesses

see Teachers and governesses

■ Gurdwaras

see Temples, gurdwaras

■ Haemophilia

see Blood disorders & haemophilia

■ Handicapped

see Disabled people (physical, sensory, learning impairments)

■ Head & other injuries

Funding priority

Will consider

■ Health care

see also Acute health care, Aftercare, Alternative health care, Counselling (health), First aid, Hospice at home, Nursing service, Prenatal care, Primary health care, Respite care, care for carers, Support, self help groups, Well woman clinics

Funding priority

Will consider

■ Health economics

see **Medical studies & research**

■ Health education

see also **Campaigning (health)**

Will consider

■ Health facilities & buildings

see also **Ambulances & mobile units, Convalescent homes, Hospices, Hospitals, Medical centres, Nursing homes, Rehabilitation centres**

Funding priority

Will consider

Stockport Community Trust
187
Talbot Bridge Will Trust, The
Elsie *189*
Waterhouse Charitable Trust,
Mrs *192*
Wigan Town Relief in Need
Charity *196*
Woolf Charitable Trust, The
Leslie and Renee *197*

■ Health issues

see also Campaigning
(health)
Will consider
Hamitzvos, Keren *122*
Marchon Works Employees
Charity Fund, The *144*

■ Health professional bodies

see also Professional
bodies
Funding priority
Feryal Rajah Educational Trust
117
Fetal Medicine Foundation, The
117
Patients' Aid Association
Hospital and Medical
Charities Trust *160*

Will consider
Congleton Inclosure Trust, The
106
Johnson Foundation, The *128*

■ Health promotion

see also Campaigning
(health)
Will consider
Hamitzvos, Keren *122*

■ Health related volunteer schemes

see also Advocacy (health)
Will consider
BNFL Risley Medical, Research
and Charity Trust, The *89*
Birkenhead and Wirral Moral
Welfare Association *92*
Brotherton Trust, The Charles
96
Hillards Charitable Trust, Gay &
Peter Hartley's *124*
Proven Family Trust, The *165*

■ Hearing loss

Funding priority
Baynes Charitable Trust, James
91
Chase Charity, The *101*
Lankelly Foundation, The *134*
Leboff Charitable Trust, The
Paul & Evelyn *137*
Queendeans Association *166*
Rowbotham Charitable Trust,
The Christopher *177*
Sykes Trust, The Charles *187*

Will consider
BNFL Risley Medical, Research
and Charity Trust, The *89*
Brotherton Trust, The Charles
96
Chrimes Family Charitable
Trust, The *104*
Chronicle Cinderella Fund, The
104
Ferguson Benevolent Fund
Limited *116*
Ford of Britain Trust *118*
Hillards Charitable Trust, Gay &
Peter Hartley's *124*
Johnson Foundation, The *128*
Moore Foundation, The George
A *148*
North West Media Charitable
Trust Limited *156*
Northern Rock Foundation, The
157
Pilkington Charities Fund *163*
Rainford Trust, The *167*
Ravensdale Trust, The *169*
Rayner Charitable Trust, The
John *169*
Scott Charitable Trust, The
Frieda *181*
Scott Trust, Sir James & Lady
182
Sefton and West Lancashire
Deaf Children's Society
182
Ward Blenkinsop Trust, The
192

■ Heart disease

Funding priority
Baynes Charitable Trust, James
91
Rowbotham Charitable Trust,
The Christopher *177*

Will consider
BNFL Risley Medical, Research
and Charity Trust, The *89*
Brotherton Trust, The Charles
96
Ferguson Benevolent Fund
Limited *116*
Ford of Britain Trust *118*

Hillards Charitable Trust, Gay &
Peter Hartley's *124*
Johnson Foundation, The *128*
Marchon Works Employees
Charity Fund, The *144*
Moore Foundation, The George
A *148*
North West Media Charitable
Trust Limited *156*
Pilkington Charities Fund *163*
Rainford Trust, The *167*
Ravensdale Trust, The *169*
Rayner Charitable Trust, The
John *169*
Scott Charitable Trust, The
Frieda *181*
Scott Trust, Sir James & Lady
182
Ward Blenkinsop Trust, The
192

■ Heritage

see also Conservation &
campaigning
Funding priority
Sykes Trust, The Charles *187*

Will consider
Hamitzvos, Keren *122*
National Lottery Charities Board
151
Oldham Foundation *159*
Scott Charitable Trust, The
Frieda *181*
Scott Trust, Sir James & Lady
182

■ Higher education

see Tertiary & higher
education

■ Hindus

Funding priority
Chase Charity, The *101*

Will consider
Barnabas Charitable Trust *90*
Lord Mayor of Manchester's
Charity Appeal Trust *141*
Ramsden Hall Trust, The *167*

■ Historic buildings

see also Conservation
Funding priority
Chase Charity, The *101*

■ Immigrants

Funding priority

Lane Foundation, The Allen *132*

Scott Charitable Trust, The Frieda *181*

Scott Trust, Sir James & Lady *182*

Will consider

Charity for Change *101*

Davies Trust, The John Grant *109*

Duchy of Lancaster Benevolent Fund, The *111*

France's Charity *119*

Lancaster's Trust, Bryan *132*

Lankelly Foundation, The *134*

Northern Rock Foundation, The *157*

Proctor Charitable Trust, The Albert Edward *164*

■ Immunology

see **Medical studies & research**

■ In care, fostered & adopted

Funding priority

Birkenhead and Wirral Moral Welfare Association *92*

Chester Diocesan Moral Aid Charity *103*

Patients' Aid Association Hospital and Medical Charities Trust *160*

Will consider

Adlington Women's Institute *87*

BNFL Risley Medical, Research and Charity Trust, The *89*

C & A Charitable Trust, The *99*

Chorley Relief Fund, The *104*

Ferguson Benevolent Fund Limited *116*

Girl's Welfare Fund *120*

Hutchinson Educational Charity, The Joseph *127*

Littleborough Nursing Association Fund *139*

Marks Foundation, The Ann and David *145*

Proven Family Trust, The *165*

Pye Christian Trust, The *165*

Rayner Charitable Trust, The John *169*

Wigan Town Relief in Need Charity *196*

■ Income support & maintenance

see also **Community services**

Will consider

Booth Charities, The *93*

Brotherton Trust, The Charles *96*

Lankelly Foundation, The *134*

MacNair Trust, The *142*

Marchon Works Employees Charity Fund, The *144*

Wigan Town Relief in Need Charity *196*

■ Independent schools

see also **Schools & colleges**

Funding priority

Kershaw Trust, The Peter *130*

Will consider

Hillards Charitable Trust, Gay & Peter Hartley's *124*

Pilkington Foundation for Arts and Leisure, The Harry and Mavis *163*

Vaux Group Foundation, The *191*

■ Individual rights

Funding priority

Chase Charity, The *101*

Will consider

Hamitzvos, Keren *122*

Northern Rock Foundation, The *157*

Scott Charitable Trust, The Francis C *180*

Scott Charitable Trust, The Frieda *181*

■ Individual rights (advocacy)

see **Advocacy (social issues)**

■ Information technology & computers

see also **Infrastructure & technical support**

Funding priority

Pilkington Charities Fund *163*

Will consider

Ferguson Benevolent Fund Limited *116*

Ford of Britain Trust *118*

Lancaster's Trust, Bryan *132*

Lankelly Foundation, The *134*

Marchon Works Employees Charity Fund, The *144*

Pilkington Foundation for Arts and Leisure, The Harry and Mavis *163*

Rope Third Charitable Settlement, The Mrs L D *171*

Vaux Group Foundation, The *191*

■ Infrastructure & technical support

see also **Building services, Financial services, Information technology & computers, Legal services, Management services, Personnel & human resource services, Publishing & printing, Recruitment services**

Funding priority

Scott Charitable Trust, The Frieda *181*

Will consider

AGF Charitable Trust *87*

Hadfield Charitable Trust, The *122*

National Lottery Charities Board *151*

Scott Charitable Trust, The Francis C *180*

Waterhouse Charitable Trust, Mrs *192*

■ Infrastructure development

see also **Civil society development, Community businesses, Community development, Economic regeneration schemes, Job creation, Small enterprises, Support to voluntary & community organisations, Support to volunteers, Tourism**

Funding priority

Moorwoods Charitable Trust, The *150*

Scott Charitable Trust, The Frieda *181*

Pilkington Foundation for Arts and Leisure, The Harry and Mavis *163*
Police Training Centre, Bruche, Charity, The *164*

Kennels

see Dogs – kennels & other facilities for dogs

Kidney disease

Funding priority
Baynes Charitable Trust, James *91*

Will consider
BNFL Risley Medical, Research and Charity Trust, The *89*
Brotherton Trust, The Charles *96*
Chronicle Cinderella Fund, The *104*
Ford of Britain Trust *118*
Hillards Charitable Trust, Gay & Peter Hartley's *124*
Marchon Works Employees Charity Fund, The *144*
Moore Foundation, The George A *148*
North West Media Charitable Trust Limited *156*
Pilkington Charities Fund *163*
Pye Christian Trust, The *165*
Rainford Trust, The *167*
Ravensdale Trust, The *169*
Rayner Charitable Trust, The John *169*
Rowbotham Charitable Trust, The Christopher *177*
Scott Charitable Trust, The Frieda *181*
Scott Trust, Sir James & Lady *182*
Ward Blenkinsop Trust, The *192*

Lakes

see also Conservation
Funding priority
Mersey Basin Trust – ICI Green Action Grants *147*

Landscapes

see also Conservation
Funding priority
Mersey Basin Trust – ICI Green Action Grants *147*

Will consider
Royal Botanical & Horticultural Society of Manchester and the Northern Counties, The *178*

Language schools

see Schools & colleges

Law

see also Academic subjects, sciences & research
Funding priority
Neave Trust, The Airey *154*

Law centres

see also Advice & information (social issues)
Funding priority
Moores Foundation, John *149*

Will consider
Davies Trust, The John Grant *109*
Lancaster's Trust, Bryan *132*
Scott Charitable Trust, The Francis C *180*
Scott Charitable Trust, The Frieda *181*

Leadership training

see Training for personal development

Learning difficulties

see Disabled people (physical, sensory, learning impairments)

Legal professionals

Funding priority
Neave Trust, The Airey *154*

Will consider
Mayor of Chorley's Helping Hand Charity, The *145*
Nantwich and Acton Grammar School Foundation *151*
Sykes Trust, The Charles *187*

Legal services

see also Infrastructure & technical support
Will consider
Lankelly Foundation, The *134*

Leprosy

Funding priority
Pilkington Charities Fund *163*

Will consider
Brotherton Trust, The Charles *96*
Ferguson Benevolent Fund Limited *116*
North West Media Charitable Trust Limited *156*
Northern Rock Foundation, The *157*
Rainford Trust, The *167*
Rayner Charitable Trust, The John *169*
Scott Charitable Trust, The Frieda *181*
Scott Trust, Sir James & Lady *182*
Ward Blenkinsop Trust, The *192*

Libraries & museums

see also Community facilities
Funding priority
Chase Charity, The *101*
Talbot Bridge Will Trust, The Elsie *189*

Will consider
Eskdale (Cumbria) Trust, The *115*
Ford of Britain Trust *118*
Hamitzvos, Keren *122*
Oldham Foundation *159*
Vaux Group Foundation, The *191*

Literacy

see also Education & training
Funding priority
Britannia Building Society Foundation *95*
Chase Charity, The *101*

Will consider
Davies Trust, The John Grant *109*
Ford of Britain Trust *118*

East Lancashire Masonic
Benevolent Institution
(Incorporated), The *113*
Hadfield Charitable Trust, The
122
Hemby Trust, The *124*
Holt Trust, The Edward *126*
Hoover Foundation, The *127*
Leach Charitable Trust, The Eric
and Dorothy *137*
Lloyd Charity Trust, The W M
and B W *140*
Manchester Local Medical
Committee Compassionate
Fund *144*
Merseyside Development
Foundation *148*
Morgan Crucible Company plc
Charitable Trust, The *151*
Peel Trust, The Dowager
Countess Eleanor *161*
Proven Family Trust, The *165*
Ravensdale Trust, The *169*
Rayner Charitable Trust, The
John *169*
Rochdale Fund for Relief in
Sickness, The *171*
Rotary Club of Alderley Edge
and Bollin Valley Trust Fund
174
Rotary Club of New Mills Marple
and District Benevolent
Fund, The *174*
Stewart Trust, Sir Halley *185*
Ward Blenkinsop Trust, The
192
Waterhouse Charitable Trust,
Mrs *192*
Westminster Foundation, The
194
Woolton Charitable Trust, The
197

■ Medicine

***see also* Academic
subjects, sciences &
research**

Funding priority
Feryal Rajah Educational Trust
117
Fetal Medicine Foundation, The
117
Kershaw Trust, The Peter *130*
Patients' Aid Association
Hospital and Medical
Charities Trust *160*

Will consider
BNFL Risley Medical, Research
and Charity Trust, The *89*
Hamitzvos, Keren *122*
Lloyd Charity Trust, The W M
and B W *140*
Pilkington Charities Fund *163*

Rayner Charitable Trust, The
John *169*
Stewart Trust, Sir Halley *185*

■ Memorials &
monuments

***see also* Conservation**

Will consider
Eskdale (Cumbria) Trust, The
115
Hamitzvos, Keren *122*
Moore Foundation, The George
A *148*
Vaux Group Foundation, The
191
Wigan Town Relief in Need
Charity *196*

■ Mental health

***see* Mental illness**

■ Mental illness

Funding priority
Baynes Charitable Trust, James
91
Chase Charity, The *101*
Lane Foundation, The Allen
132
Lankelly Foundation, The *134*
Leboff Charitable Trust, The
Paul & Evelyn *137*
North West Media Charitable
Trust Limited *156*
Pilkington Charities Fund *163*
Rowbotham Charitable Trust,
The Christopher *177*
Sykes Trust, The Charles *187*

Will consider
BNFL Risley Medical, Research
and Charity Trust, The *89*
Brotherton Trust, The Charles
96
Chronicle Cinderella Fund, The
104
Ford of Britain Trust *118*
Hamitzvos, Keren *122*
Hillards Charitable Trust, Gay &
Peter Hartley's *124*
Holt Trust, The Edward *126*
Moore Foundation, The George
A *148*
Northern Rock Foundation, The
157
Oldham Foundation *159*
Rainford Trust, The *167*
Ravensdale Trust, The *169*
Rayner Charitable Trust, The
John *169*

Scott Charitable Trust, The
Frieda *181*
Scott Trust, Sir James & Lady
182
Ward Blenkinsop Trust, The
192

■ Mentally
handicapped

***see* Disabled people
(physical, sensory, learning
impairments)**

■ Methodists

Funding priority
Chase Charity, The *101*

Will consider
Barnabas Charitable Trust *90*
Birkenhead and Wirral Moral
Welfare Association *92*
Ferguson Benevolent Fund
Limited *116*
Hillards Charitable Trust, Gay &
Peter Hartley's *124*
Lord Mayor of Manchester's
Charity Appeal Trust *141*
Moore Foundation, The George
A *148*
Pye Christian Trust, The *165*
Ramsden Hall Trust, The *167*
Rayner Trust Fund, The
Nathaniel *170*
Scott Charitable Trust, The
Frieda *181*
Wilson Trust, The Charles *196*

■ Missionaries,
evangelicals

***see also* Advancement of
religion**

Funding priority
Bryn Christian Fellowship, The
97
Moorwoods Charitable Trust,
The *150*
Pye Christian Trust, The *165*
Rayner Trust Fund, The
Nathaniel *170*
Whiteley Trust, Norman *196*

Will consider
Bible Preaching Trust, The *92*
Broadhurst Charitable Trust,
The Charles and Edna *96*
North and East Lancashire
Unitarian Mission *155*

Will consider
Evans Trust, Mabel *115*
Granada Foundation, The *120*
Marchon Works Employees
　Charity Fund, The *144*
Oldham Foundation *159*
Rainford Trust, The *167*
Ravensdale Trust, The *169*
Rayner Charitable Trust, The
　John *169*
Wethered Bequest, The *195*

■ Music education

see Education & training

■ Musicians

Funding priority
Chase Charity, The *101*
de Avenley Foundation, The
　110
North West Arts Board *155*

Will consider
Blankstone Charitable Trust,
　The Solomon & Isabel *93*
Eden Arts Trust *114*
Evans Trust, Mabel *115*
Granada Foundation, The *120*
Harewood's Charitable
　Settlement, Lord *122*
Mayor of Chorley's Helping
　Hand Charity, The *145*
Nantwich and Acton Grammar
　School Foundation *151*
Northern Arts *157*
Rathbone Charitable Trust, The
　Eleanor *168*
Rayner Charitable Trust, The
　John *169*
Sykes Trust, The Charles *187*
Talbot Bridge Will Trust, The
　Elsie *189*
Yorkshire Bank Charitable
　Trust, The *198*

■ Muslims

Funding priority
Chase Charity, The *101*

Will consider
Barnabas Charitable Trust *90*
Lord Mayor of Manchester's
　Charity Appeal Trust *141*
Ramsden Hall Trust, The *167*
Scott Charitable Trust, The
　Frieda *181*

■ Natural history

see also Environmental &
animal sciences
Funding priority
Mersey Basin Trust – ICI Green
　Action Grants *147*

Will consider
Brotherton Trust, The Charles
　96
Clutterbuck Charitable Trust,
　Robert *105*

■ Nature reserves

see also Conservation
Funding priority
Chase Charity, The *101*
Mersey Basin Trust – ICI Green
　Action Grants *147*

Will consider
Chiron Trust, The *103*
Hamitzvos, Keren *122*
Vaux Group Foundation, The
　191

■ Needy

see Disadvantaged by
poverty

■ Neurological research

see also Medical studies &
research
Funding priority
Holt Trust, The Edward *126*

Will consider
Johnson Foundation, The *128*
Rainford Trust, The *167*

■ Nuclear energy, nuclear power

see also Conservation &
campaigning
Will consider
Hamitzvos, Keren *122*

■ Nurses

see Medical professionals,
nurses & doctors

■ Nursing homes

see also Health facilities &
buildings
Will consider
Barnes Fund, The Norman *91*
Booth Charities, The *93*
Marchon Works Employees
　Charity Fund, The *144*
Scott Trust, Sir James & Lady
　182

■ Nursing service

see also Health care
Funding priority
Kershaw Trust, The Peter *130*

Will consider
BNFL Risley Medical, Research
　and Charity Trust, The *89*
Brotherton Trust, The Charles
　96
Hillards Charitable Trust, Gay &
　Peter Hartley's *124*
Johnson Foundation, The *128*
Oldham Foundation *159*
Proven Family Trust, The *165*
Scott Trust, Sir James & Lady
　182

■ Older people

Funding priority
Barnes Fund, The Norman *91*
Baynes Charitable Trust, James
　91
Booth Charities, The *93*
Bowness and Windermere
　Community Care Trust *94*
Eden Arts Trust *114*
Florence's Charitable Trust
　118
France's Charity *119*
Hartley Memorial Trust, The N
　and P *123*
Hawe Settlement, The M A
　124
Hilmarnan Charitable Trust
　125
Holt Trust, The Edward *126*
Kershaw Trust, The Peter *130*
Littleborough Nursing
　Association Fund *139*
Peel Trust, The Dowager
　Countess Eleanor *161*
Rotary Club of New Mills Marple
　and District Benevolent
　Fund, The *174*
Sainsbury Charitable Fund Ltd,
　The *179*
Shaw Trust, Alfred *183*

Hillards Charitable Trust, Gay &
Peter Hartley's *124*
Marchon Works Employees
Charity Fund, The *144*
Moore Foundation, The George
A *148*
North West Media Charitable
Trust Limited *156*
Northern Rock Foundation, The
157
Pilkington Charities Fund *163*
Police Training Centre, Bruche,
Charity, The *164*
Rainford Trust, The *167*
Ravensdale Trust, The *169*
Scott Charitable Trust, The
Frieda *181*
Scott Trust, Sir James & Lady
182
Ward Blenkinsop Trust, The
192

■ Parents & children

Funding priority
Baynes Charitable Trust, James
91
Birkenhead and Wirral Moral
Welfare Association *92*
C & A Charitable Trust, The *99*
Littleborough Nursing
Association Fund *139*
Sainsbury Charitable Fund Ltd,
The *179*

Will consider
Adlington Women's Institute
87
Barnabas Charitable Trust *90*
Cheadle Royal Industries
Charitable Trust *102*
Cheshire Provincial Fund of
Benevolence, The *102*
Chorley Relief Fund, The *104*
Davies Trust, The John Grant
109
Girl's Welfare Fund *120*
Hadfield Charitable Trust, The
122
Hutchinson Educational Charity,
The Joseph *127*
Marks Foundation, The Ann and
David *145*
Moore Foundation, The George
A *148*
Northern Rock Foundation, The
157
Preston Relief in Need Charity
164
Rayner Charitable Trust, The
John *169*
Wigan Town Relief in Need
Charity *196*

■ Parkinson's disease

Funding priority
Baynes Charitable Trust, James
91

Will consider
BNFL Risley Medical, Research
and Charity Trust, The *89*
Brotherton Trust, The Charles
96
Ford of Britain Trust *118*
Hillards Charitable Trust, Gay &
Peter Hartley's *124*
Lankelly Foundation, The *134*
Marchon Works Employees
Charity Fund, The *144*
Moore Foundation, The George
A *148*
North West Media Charitable
Trust Limited *156*
Northern Rock Foundation, The
157
Pilkington Charities Fund *163*
Ravensdale Trust, The *169*
Rayner Charitable Trust, The
John *169*
Rowbotham Charitable Trust,
The Christopher *177*
Scott Charitable Trust, The
Frieda *181*
Scott Trust, Sir James & Lady
182
Ward Blenkinsop Trust, The
192

■ Parks

see also **Community
facilities**
Will consider
Cheshire Constabulary
Community Involvement
Fund of Northwich Division
102
Crosthwaite and Lyth Trust
108
Hamitzvos, Keren *122*
Joint Churches Community
Project *129*
MacNair Trust, The *142*
Mersey Basin Trust – ICI Green
Action Grants *147*
Proven Family Trust, The *165*
Vaux Group Foundation, The
191

■ Pastoral care

see **Community services**

■ Peace

see also **Campaigning
(social issues)**
Funding priority
Lancaster's Trust, Bryan *132*

■ Peace studies

see **Academic subjects,
sciences & research,
Campaigning (social
issues)**

■ Penal reform

see also **Campaigning
(social issues)**
Funding priority
Lane Foundation, The Allen
132

Will consider
Davies Trust, The John Grant
109
Rope Third Charitable
Settlement, The Mrs L D
171

■ Pensions

see **Community services**

■ Personal
development

see **Training for personal
development**

■ Personnel & human
resource services

see also **Infrastructure &
technical support**
Funding priority
Pilkington Charities Fund *163*

Will consider
Lancaster's Trust, Bryan *132*
Lankelly Foundation, The *134*
Marks Foundation, The Ann and
David *145*
Pilkington Foundation for Arts
and Leisure, The Harry and
Mavis *163*
Vaux Group Foundation, The
191

■ Prenatal research

see also **Medical studies & research**

Funding priority
Fetal Medicine Foundation, The *117*
Stewart Trust, Sir Halley *185*

■ Pre-school education

see also **Schools & colleges**

Funding priority
Greater Manchester Police Community Charity *120*
Moores Foundation, John *149*

Will consider
Barnabas Charitable Trust *90*
Congleton Inclosure Trust, The *106*
Ford of Britain Trust *118*
Hillards Charitable Trust, Gay & Peter Hartley's *124*
Littleborough Nursing Association Fund *139*
Pilkington Foundation for Arts and Leisure, The Harry and Mavis *163*

■ Prevention of disease

see **Health education**

■ Primary health care

see also **Health care**

Will consider
BNFL Risley Medical, Research and Charity Trust, The *89*
Johnson Foundation, The *128*

■ Primary schools

see also **Schools & colleges**

Funding priority
Chadwick Educational Foundation, The *100*

Will consider
Congleton Inclosure Trust, The *106*
Darnhill Exhibition Foundation, The *109*
Ford of Britain Trust *118*
Marchon Works Employees Charity Fund, The *144*
Marks Foundation, The Ann and David *145*

Pilkington Foundation for Arts and Leisure, The Harry and Mavis *163*
Police Training Centre, Bruche, Charity, The *164*
Vaux Group Foundation, The *191*
Verdin Trust Fund, The *191*

■ Printing

see **Publishing & printing**

■ Prison reform

see **Penal reform**

■ Professional bodies

see also **Health professional bodies, Social care professional bodies**

Funding priority
Pilkington Charities Fund *163*

Will consider
AGF Charitable Trust *87*
Congleton Town Trust, The *107*
Ford of Britain Trust *118*
Hadfield Charitable Trust, The *122*
Hemby Trust, The *124*
Marchon Works Employees Charity Fund, The *144*
Waterhouse Charitable Trust, Mrs *192*

■ Professional, specialist training

see also **Education & training**

Funding priority
Feryal Rajah Educational Trust *117*
Fetal Medicine Foundation, The *117*

Will consider
Girl's Welfare Fund *120*
Lancaster's Trust, Bryan *132*
Manchester Society of Architects, The *144*
North West Arts Board *155*
Rowbotham Charitable Trust, The Christopher *177*

■ Psoriasis

Will consider
BNFL Risley Medical, Research and Charity Trust, The *89*
Brotherton Trust, The Charles *96*
Hillards Charitable Trust, Gay & Peter Hartley's *124*
North West Media Charitable Trust Limited *156*
Pilkington Charities Fund *163*
Rainford Trust, The *167*
Rayner Charitable Trust, The John *169*
Scott Charitable Trust, The Frieda *181*
Scott Trust, Sir James & Lady *182*
Ward Blenkinsop Trust, The *192*

■ Publishing & printing

see also **Infrastructure & technical support**

Funding priority
North West Arts Board *155*
Pilkington Foundation for Arts and Leisure, The Harry and Mavis *163*

Will consider
Lancaster's Trust, Bryan *132*
Marchon Works Employees Charity Fund, The *144*
Rope Third Charitable Settlement, The Mrs L D *171*

■ Purchase of books & equipment

Funding priority
Chadwick Educational Foundation, The *100*

Will consider
Brotherton Trust, The Charles *96*
Holford's Charity, John *125*
Lancaster's Trust, Bryan *132*

■ Quaker

see **Advancement of religion**

■ Quakers

Funding priority
Chase Charity, The *101*

Will consider
Barnabas Charitable Trust *90*
Hillards Charitable Trust, Gay &
  Peter Hartley's *124*
Lancaster's Trust, Bryan *132*
Lord Mayor of Manchester's
  Charity Appeal Trust *141*
Ramsden Hall Trust, The *167*
Scott Charitable Trust, The
  Frieda *181*
Wilson Trust, The Charles *196*

■ Racial equality, discrimination, relations

see also **Campaigning (social issues)**
Funding priority
Integreat *128*
Lane Foundation, The Allen
  132

Will consider
Davies Trust, The John Grant
  109
Hamitzvos, Keren *122*

■ Recreation

see **Community arts & recreation**

■ Recreation grounds

see also **Community facilities**
Funding priority
Greater Manchester Police
  Community Charity *120*

Will consider
Burall Charitable Trust, The *97*
Cheshire Constabulary
  Community Involvement
  Fund of Northwich Division
  102
Crosthwaite and Lyth Trust
  108
Davies Trust, The John Grant
  109
Hamitzvos, Keren *122*
Joint Churches Community
  Project *129*
Lancaster's Trust, Bryan *132*
MacNair Trust, The *142*
Marchon Works Employees
  Charity Fund, The *144*

Proven Family Trust, The *165*
Rycroft Children's Fund *178*
Slater Trust Limited, The *184*
West Cumbria Charitable Trust,
  The *193*

■ Recruitment services

see also **Infrastructure & technical support**
Will consider
Lankelly Foundation, The *134*

■ Refugees

Funding priority
Chase Charity, The *101*
Lane Foundation, The Allen
  132
Lankelly Foundation, The *134*
Neave Trust, The Airey *154*
Scott Charitable Trust, The
  Frieda *181*
Scott Trust, Sir James & Lady
  182

Will consider
Charity for Change *101*
Davies Trust, The John Grant
  109
Duchy of Lancaster Benevolent
  Fund, The *111*
France's Charity *119*
Hamitzvos, Keren *122*
Lancaster's Trust, Bryan *132*
Moores Foundation, John *149*
Northern Rock Foundation, The
  157
Proctor Charitable Trust, The
  Albert Edward *164*
Rope Third Charitable
  Settlement, The Mrs L D
  171

■ Rehabilitation centres

see also **Health facilities & buildings**
Will consider
Drugwatch Trust *111*
Parkinson (Deceased) Trust,
  Thomas *160*
Rainford Trust, The *167*

■ Religion

see **Advancement of religion**

■ Religions

see also **Academic subjects, sciences & research**
Funding priority
Famos Foundation Trust *116*

Will consider
Rope Third Charitable
  Settlement, The Mrs L D
  171

■ Religious ancillary buildings

see also **Religious buildings**
Will consider
Angler's Inn Trust *88*
Brotherton Trust, The Charles
  96
Bryn Christian Fellowship, The
  97
Hillards Charitable Trust, Gay &
  Peter Hartley's *124*
Proven Family Trust, The *165*
Rayner Trust Fund, The
  Nathaniel *170*

■ Religious buildings

see also **Cemeteries & burial grounds, Churches, Mosques, Religious ancillary buildings, Synagogues, Temples, gurdwaras**
Funding priority
Scott Charitable Trust, The
  Frieda *181*

Will consider
Community Trust for Greater
  Manchester, The *106*
Duchy of Lancaster Benevolent
  Fund, The *111*
Fearn Trust, George *116*
National Lottery Charities Board
  151
Scott Trust, Sir James & Lady
  182
Waterhouse Charitable Trust,
  Mrs *192*
Westminster Foundation, The
  194

■ Religious teaching

see **Cultural & religious teaching**

■ Religious umbrella bodies

see also **Anglican bodies, Catholic bodies, Diocesan boards, Free church, Jewish bodies**

Funding priority

Proctor Charitable Trust, The Albert Edward *164*
Scott Charitable Trust, The Frieda *181*

Will consider

AGF Charitable Trust *87*
Bryn Christian Fellowship, The *97*
Burden's Charitable Foundation *97*
C & A Charitable Trust, The *99*
Community Trust for Greater Manchester, The *106*
Congleton Inclosure Trust, The *106*
Ferguson Benevolent Fund Limited *116*
Girl's Welfare Fund *120*
Lancaster's Trust, Bryan *132*
National Lottery Charities Board *151*
Scott Trust, Sir James & Lady *182*
Slater Trust Limited, The *184*
Waterhouse Charitable Trust, Mrs *192*

■ Renewable energy, renewable power

see also **Conservation & campaigning**

Will consider

Hamitzvos, Keren *122*

■ Research

see **Academic subjects, sciences & research, Medical studies & research, Specialist research**

■ Research institutes

see also **Academic subjects, sciences & research**

Funding priority

Fetal Medicine Foundation, The *117*

Will consider

Brotherton Trust, The Charles *96*

■ Research workers

Funding priority

Broadhurst Charitable Trust, The Charles and Edna *96*
Capenhurst Medical and Research Charity Trust Fund, The *99*
Chase Charity, The *101*
Cozens-Hardy Trust, The Lord *107*
Neave Trust, The Airey *154*
Patients' Aid Association Hospital and Medical Charities Trust *160*
Pilkington Charities Fund *163*
Woolton Charitable Trust, The *197*

Will consider

Brotherton Trust, The Charles *96*
Mayor of Chorley's Helping Hand Charity, The *145*
Morgan Crucible Company plc Charitable Trust, The *151*
Nantwich and Acton Grammar School Foundation *151*
North West Media Charitable Trust Limited *156*
Rayner Charitable Trust, The John *169*
Stewart Trust, Sir Halley *185*
Sykes Trust, The Charles *187*

■ Residences

see also **Arts & arts facilities**

Funding priority

Chase Charity, The *101*
North West Arts Board *155*

■ Residential facilities

see also **Residential facilities & services**

Funding priority

Chase Charity, The *101*
Pilkington Charities Fund *163*

Will consider

Britannia Building Society Foundation *95*
Ferguson Benevolent Fund Limited *116*
Ford of Britain Trust *118*
Holt Trust, The Edward *126*
Johnson Foundation, The *128*
Lancaster's Trust, Bryan *132*
Marchon Works Employees Charity Fund, The *144*

Parkinson (Deceased) Trust, Thomas *160*
Rainford Trust, The *167*
Scott Charitable Trust, The Francis C *180*

■ Residential facilities & services

see also **Advice & information (housing), Almshouses, Emergency & short-term housing, Holiday accommodation, Hostels, Housing associations, Residential facilities, Respite, Sheltered accommodation**

Funding priority

Lankelly Foundation, The *134*
National Lottery Charities Board *151*
Scott Charitable Trust, The Frieda *181*

Will consider

AGF Charitable Trust *87*
Adlington Women's Institute *87*
Baddiley Consolidated Charity *90*
Baynes Charitable Trust, James *91*
Bowness and Windermere Community Care Trust *94*
Brentwood Charity, The *95*
Britannia Building Society Foundation *95*
Broadhurst Charitable Trust, The Charles and Edna *96*
Brotherton Trust, The Charles *96*
C & A Charitable Trust, The *99*
Chorley Relief Fund, The *104*
Clover Trust, The Emily *105*
Cozens-Hardy Trust, The Lord *107*
Denton Relief in Sickness Charity *110*
Eddleston's Charity, John *114*
Hadfield Charitable Trust, The *122*
Hawe Settlement, The M A *124*
Hemby Trust, The *124*
Keyes Trust, The Ursula *131*
Leverhulme's Charitable Trust, Lord *137*
Manchester and Salford Saturday and Convalescent Homes' Fund, The *143*
Merseyside Development Foundation *148*
North West Media Charitable Trust Limited *156*

■ Rural arts

see **Community arts & recreation**

■ Rural Community Council (RCC)

see also **Charity or voluntary umbrella bodies**

Funding priority

■ Sail training

see **Education & training**

■ Scholarships

see also **Costs of study**

Funding priority

■ School nature reserves & schemes

see **Conservation**

■ Schools & colleges

see also **Business schools, Church schools, Independent schools, Junior schools, Postgraduate education, Pre-school education, Primary schools, Secondary schools, Special schools, Tertiary & higher education**

Funding priority

■ Science & technology

see also Academic
subjects, sciences &
research

Funding priority

Will consider

■ Sciences

see Academic subjects,
sciences & research

■ Scientists

Funding priority

Will consider

■ Seafarers & fishermen

Funding priority

Will consider

■ Secondary schools

see also Schools & colleges

Funding priority

Will consider

■ Self help projects

see Community services

■ Sensory impairment

see Disabled people
(physical, sensory, learning
impairments), Hearing loss,
Sight loss

■ Service people

see Ex-service & service
people

■ Sheltered accommodation

see also Residential
facilities & services

Funding priority

Will consider

■ Short-term housing

see Emergency & short-
term housing

■ Special needs education

see also **Education & training**

Funding priority
Patients' Aid Association Hospital and Medical Charities Trust *160*

Will consider
BNFL Risley Medical, Research and Charity Trust, The *89*
Barker Charity, Philip *90*
Bryn Christian Fellowship, The *97*
Burden's Charitable Foundation *97*
Congleton Town Trust, The *107*
Ford of Britain Trust *118*
Girl's Welfare Fund *120*
Hillards Charitable Trust, Gay & Peter Hartley's *124*
Johnson Foundation, The *128*
Lankelly Foundation, The *134*
Lord Mayor of Chester Charitable Trust *141*
Parkinson (Deceased) Trust, Thomas *160*
Rowbotham Charitable Trust, The Christopher *177*

■ Special schools

see also **Schools & colleges**
Funding priority
Chadwick Educational Foundation, The *100*
Chase Charity, The *101*
Patients' Aid Association Hospital and Medical Charities Trust *160*
West Lancashire Masonic Educational Trust *194*

Will consider
BNFL Risley Medical, Research and Charity Trust, The *89*
Congleton Inclosure Trust, The *106*
Ferguson Benevolent Fund Limited *116*
Ford of Britain Trust *118*
Hillards Charitable Trust, Gay & Peter Hartley's *124*
Johnson Foundation, The *128*
Leboff Charitable Trust, The Paul & Evelyn *137*
Marchon Works Employees Charity Fund, The *144*
Marks Foundation, The Ann and David *145*
Moore Foundation, The George A *148*

Parkinson (Deceased) Trust, Thomas *160*
Pilkington Foundation for Arts and Leisure, The Harry and Mavis *163*
Police Training Centre, Bruche, Charity, The *164*
Rainford Trust, The *167*
Rayner Charitable Trust, The John *169*
Vaux Group Foundation, The *191*

■ Specialist research

see also **Academic subjects, sciences & research**
Funding priority
Neave Trust, The Airey *154*
Patients' Aid Association Hospital and Medical Charities Trust *160*

Will consider
Hamitzvos, Keren *122*
Swales Scholarship Fund, The *187*

■ Specialist training

see **Professional, specialist training**

■ Speech therapy

see also **Education & training**
Funding priority
Patients' Aid Association Hospital and Medical Charities Trust *160*
Sykes Trust, The Charles *187*

Will consider
BNFL Risley Medical, Research and Charity Trust, The *89*
Hillards Charitable Trust, Gay & Peter Hartley's *124*
Johnson Foundation, The *128*
Lankelly Foundation, The *134*
Rowbotham Charitable Trust, The Christopher *177*

■ Spina bifida & Hydrocephalus

Funding priority
Pilkington Charities Fund *163*
Rowbotham Charitable Trust, The Christopher *177*

Will consider
BNFL Risley Medical, Research and Charity Trust, The *89*
Brotherton Trust, The Charles *96*
Ford of Britain Trust *118*
Hillards Charitable Trust, Gay & Peter Hartley's *124*
Lankelly Foundation, The *134*
North West Media Charitable Trust Limited *156*
Northern Rock Foundation, The *157*
Rainford Trust, The *167*
Rayner Charitable Trust, The John *169*
Scott Charitable Trust, The Frieda *181*
Scott Trust, Sir James & Lady *182*
Ward Blenkinsop Trust, The *192*

■ Sports centres

see also **Community facilities**
Funding priority
Greater Manchester Police Community Charity *120*

Will consider
Burall Charitable Trust, The *97*
Cheshire Constabulary Community Involvement Fund of Northwich Division *102*
Crosthwaite and Lyth Trust *108*
Joint Churches Community Project *129*
Kennington (Deceased), Charity of Mrs Hannah *130*
MacNair Trust, The *142*
Proven Family Trust, The *165*

■ Sportsmen & women

Funding priority
Clutterbuck Charitable Trust, Robert *105*

Will consider
Angler's Inn Trust *88*
Mayor of Chorley's Helping Hand Charity, The *145*
Nantwich and Acton Grammar School Foundation *151*
Rowbotham Charitable Trust, The Christopher *177*
Sykes Trust, The Charles *187*

▪ Street children

see **Homeless**

▪ Street events

see **Community arts & recreation**

▪ Stroke

Funding priority
Baynes Charitable Trust, James *91*
Pilkington Charities Fund *163*
Rowbotham Charitable Trust, The Christopher *177*

Will consider
BNFL Risley Medical, Research and Charity Trust, The *89*
Brotherton Trust, The Charles *96*
Ford of Britain Trust *118*
Hillards Charitable Trust, Gay & Peter Hartley's *124*
Lankelly Foundation, The *134*
Marchon Works Employees Charity Fund, The *144*
North West Media Charitable Trust Limited *156*
Northern Rock Foundation, The *157*
Rainford Trust, The *167*
Ravensdale Trust, The *169*
Rayner Charitable Trust, The John *169*
Scott Charitable Trust, The Frieda *181*
Scott Trust, Sir James & Lady *182*
Ward Blenkinsop Trust, The *192*

▪ Students

Funding priority
Chadwick Educational Foundation, The *100*
Eden's Foundation, James *114*
Mayor of Chorley's Helping Hand Charity, The *145*
Mole Charitable Trust *148*
Nantwich and Acton Grammar School Foundation *151*
Runcorn Community Action Trust *178*
Wing Yip and Brothers Charitable Trust, W *197*

Will consider
AGF Charitable Trust *87*
Bible Preaching Trust, The *92*
Brabin's Educational Foundation *94*
Brotherton Trust, The Charles *96*
Cartmel Old Grammar School Foundation *100*
Eddleston's Charity, John *114*
Eskdale (Cumbria) Trust, The *115*
Forster Charitable Trust, The *118*
Hamitzvos, Keren *122*
Hawe Settlement, The M A *124*
Hillards Charitable Trust, Gay & Peter Hartley's *124*
Hoover Foundation, The *127*
Leverhulme's Charitable Trust, Lord *137*
Lloyd Charity Trust, The W M and B W *140*
McMechan Memorial Fund, The Roy *142*
Marchon Works Employees Charity Fund, The *144*
Mersey Basin Trust – ICI Green Action Grants *147*
North West Media Charitable Trust Limited *156*
Rathbone Charitable Trust, The Eleanor *168*
Rawdon-Smith Trust, The *169*
Rowan Charitable Trust, The *176*
Stockport Educational Foundation, The *187*
Swales Scholarship Fund, The *187*
Sykes Trust, The Charles *187*
Talbot Bridge Will Trust, The Elsie *189*
Timperley Educational Foundation *189*
Wethered Bequest, The *195*
Wigan Town Relief in Need Charity *196*
Winwick Educational Foundation, The *197*
World Friendship *198*

▪ Substance misuse

Funding priority
Pilkington Charities Fund *163*
Rayner Charitable Trust, The John *169*

Will consider
Drugwatch Trust *111*
Ford of Britain Trust *118*
Hillards Charitable Trust, Gay & Peter Hartley's *124*

Johnson Group Cleaners Charity *129*
Lankelly Foundation, The *134*
North West Media Charitable Trust Limited *156*
Rainford Trust, The *167*
Ravensdale Trust, The *169*
Rowbotham Charitable Trust, The Christopher *177*
Scott Charitable Trust, The Frieda *181*
Scott Trust, Sir James & Lady *182*
Ward Blenkinsop Trust, The *192*

▪ Support, self help groups

see also **Health care**
Funding priority
Kershaw Trust, The Peter *130*
Rowbotham Charitable Trust, The Christopher *177*
Scott Trust, Sir James & Lady *182*

Will consider
BNFL Risley Medical, Research and Charity Trust, The *89*
Birkenhead and Wirral Moral Welfare Association *92*
Brotherton Trust, The Charles *96*
Davies Trust, The John Grant *109*
Ferguson Benevolent Fund Limited *116*
Ford of Britain Trust *118*
Hamitzvos, Keren *122*
Hillards Charitable Trust, Gay & Peter Hartley's *124*
Lancaster's Trust, Bryan *132*
Lord Mayor of Chester Charitable Trust *141*
Marchon Works Employees Charity Fund, The *144*
Moores Foundation, John *149*
Northern Rock Foundation, The *157*
Parkinson (Deceased) Trust, Thomas *160*
Proven Family Trust, The *165*
Wigan Town Relief in Need Charity *196*

■ Temples, gurdwaras

see also **Religious buildings**

Will consider

Proven Family Trust, The *165*

■ Terminally ill

Funding priority

Chiron Trust, The *103*

North West Media Charitable Trust Limited *156*

Pilkington Charities Fund *163*

Will consider

BNFL Risley Medical, Research and Charity Trust, The *89*

Brotherton Trust, The Charles *96*

Chrimes Family Charitable Trust, The *104*

Hillards Charitable Trust, Gay & Peter Hartley's *124*

Leboff Charitable Trust, The Paul & Evelyn *137*

Moore Foundation, The George A *148*

Pye Christian Trust, The *165*

Rainford Trust, The *167*

Ravensdale Trust, The *169*

Rayner Charitable Trust, The John *169*

Rowbotham Charitable Trust, The Christopher *177*

Scott Charitable Trust, The Frieda *181*

Scott Trust, Sir James & Lady *182*

Stewart Trust, Sir Halley *185*

Ward Blenkinsop Trust, The *192*

■ Tertiary & higher education

see also **Schools & colleges**

Funding priority

Eden's Foundation, James *114*

Will consider

Pilkington Foundation for Arts and Leisure, The Harry and Mavis *163*

■ Textile workers & designers

Funding priority

North West Arts Board *155*

Will consider

de Avenley Foundation, The *110*

Eden Arts Trust *114*

Granada Foundation, The *120*

Harewood's Charitable Settlement, Lord *122*

Mayor of Chorley's Helping Hand Charity, The *145*

Nantwich and Acton Grammar School Foundation *151*

Northern Arts *157*

Rathbone Charitable Trust, The Eleanor *168*

Sykes Trust, The Charles *187*

Talbot Bridge Will Trust, The Elsie *189*

Yorkshire Bank Charitable Trust, The *198*

■ Textiles & upholstery

see also **Education & training**

Will consider

Girl's Welfare Fund *120*

■ Theatre

see also **Arts & arts facilities**

Funding priority

Chase Charity, The *101*

North West Arts Board *155*

Will consider

Evans Trust, Mabel *115*

Ravensdale Trust, The *169*

Rayner Charitable Trust, The John *169*

■ Theatres & opera houses

see also **Community facilities**

Funding priority

Chase Charity, The *101*

Will consider

Northern Arts *157*

Pilkington Foundation for Arts and Leisure, The Harry and Mavis *163*

■ Theatrical companies, theatre groups

see also **Community arts & recreation**

Funding priority

Chase Charity, The *101*

Will consider

Davies Trust, The John Grant *109*

Lord Mayor of Chester Charitable Trust *141*

Oldham Foundation *159*

Ravensdale Trust, The *169*

Vaux Group Foundation, The *191*

■ Tourism

see also **Infrastructure development**

Will consider

McMechan Memorial Fund, The Roy *142*

Vaux Group Foundation, The *191*

■ Training

see **Education & training**

■ Training for community development

see also **Education & training**

Funding priority

Kershaw Trust, The Peter *130*

Lane Foundation, The Allen *132*

Moores Foundation, John *149*

Will consider

Congleton Inclosure Trust, The *106*

Davies Trust, The John Grant *109*

Ferguson Benevolent Fund Limited *116*

Girl's Welfare Fund *120*

Lankelly Foundation, The *134*

North West Arts Board *155*

Scott Charitable Trust, The Francis C *180*

Scott Charitable Trust, The Frieda *181*

Scott Trust, Sir James & Lady *182*

Wing Yip and Brothers
Charitable Trust, W *197*
Youth and the Community Trust
198

■ Training for personal development

see also Education & training

Funding priority
Britannia Building Society
Foundation *95*
Chase Charity, The *101*
Kershaw Trust, The Peter *130*

Will consider
Girl's Welfare Fund *120*
North West Arts Board *155*
Scott Charitable Trust, The
Francis C *180*
Scott Trust, Sir James & Lady
182
Verdin Trust Fund, The *191*

■ Training for work

see also Education & training

Funding priority
Britannia Building Society
Foundation *95*
Girl's Welfare Fund *120*
Kershaw Trust, The Peter *130*
Rowbotham Charitable Trust,
The Christopher *177*

Will consider
Congleton Town Trust, The
107
Ferguson Benevolent Fund
Limited *116*
Ford of Britain Trust *118*
Lane Foundation, The Allen
132
North West Arts Board *155*
Scott Charitable Trust, The
Francis C *180*
Scott Charitable Trust, The
Frieda *181*
Scott Trust, Sir James & Lady
182

■ Transport & alternative transport

see also Conservation & campaigning

Will consider
Davies Trust, The John Grant
109

Hamitzvos, Keren *122*
National Lottery Charities Board
151

■ Transport proposals

see also Campaigning
(social issues)

Will consider
Davies Trust, The John Grant
109
Hamitzvos, Keren *122*

■ Travel & maintenance

see also Costs of study

Funding priority
Mayor of Chorley's Helping
Hand Charity, The *145*

■ Travellers

Funding priority
Chase Charity, The *101*
Lane Foundation, The Allen
132
Moores Foundation, John *149*

Will consider
Charity for Change *101*
Duchy of Lancaster Benevolent
Fund, The *111*
Lancaster's Trust, Bryan *132*
Lankelly Foundation, The *134*
Northern Rock Foundation, The
157
Scott Charitable Trust, The
Francis C *180*
Scott Charitable Trust, The
Frieda *181*
Scott Trust, Sir James & Lady
182

■ Tropical diseases

Funding priority
Pilkington Charities Fund *163*
Stewart Trust, Sir Halley *185*

Will consider
Blankstone Charitable Trust,
The Solomon & Isabel *93*
Brotherton Trust, The Charles
96
North West Media Charitable
Trust Limited *156*
Rainford Trust, The *167*
Ravensdale Trust, The *169*

Rayner Charitable Trust, The
John *169*
Ward Blenkinsop Trust, The
192

■ Tuberculosis

Funding priority
Pilkington Charities Fund *163*

Will consider
BNFL Risley Medical, Research
and Charity Trust, The *89*
Brotherton Trust, The Charles
96
Hillards Charitable Trust, Gay &
Peter Hartley's *124*
North West Media Charitable
Trust Limited *156*
Ravensdale Trust, The *169*
Rayner Charitable Trust, The
John *169*
Scott Charitable Trust, The
Frieda *181*
Scott Trust, Sir James & Lady
182
Ward Blenkinsop Trust, The
192

■ Unborn children's rights (campaigning)

see also Campaigning
(social issues)

Will consider
Rope Third Charitable
Settlement, The Mrs L D
171

■ Unemployed

Funding priority
Chase Charity, The *101*
Davies Trust, The John Grant
109
Moores Foundation, John *149*
National Lottery Charities Board
151
Pilkington Charities Fund *163*
Rope Third Charitable
Settlement, The Mrs L D
171
Rowbotham Charitable Trust,
The Christopher *177*
Scott Trust, Sir James & Lady
182

Will consider
Barnabas Charitable Trust *90*
Derbyshire Trust, The Nancy
111
Ferguson Benevolent Fund
Limited *116*

Unitarians

Funding priority

Will consider

Universities

see **Tertiary & higher
education**

Upholstery

see **Textiles & upholstery**

Urban areas – living in

Funding priority

Will consider

Victims of abuse

Funding priority

Will consider

Victims of crime

Funding priority

Will consider

Brentwood Charity, The *95*
Burall Charitable Trust, The *97*
Charity for Change *101*
Chorley Relief Fund, The *104*
Congleton Inclosure Trust, The
106
Duchy of Lancaster Benevolent
Fund, The *111*
Eddleston's Charity, John *114*
Ford of Britain Trust *118*
France's Charity *119*
Girl's Welfare Fund *120*
Hadfield Charitable Trust, The
122
Hamitzvos, Keren *122*
Hemby Trust, The *124*
Hillards Charitable Trust, Gay &
Peter Hartley's *124*
Lancaster's Trust, Bryan *132*
Lankelly Foundation, The *134*
Lathoms Charity, Peter *136*
Leverhulme's Charitable Trust,
Lord *137*
Lloyd Charity Trust, The W M
and B W *140*
Moore Foundation, The George
A *148*
Northern Rock Foundation, The
157
Pilkington Charities Fund *163*
Rainford Trust, The *167*
Ravensdale Trust, The *169*
Rotary Club of Wallasey, The
Charitable Fund of the *175*
Rowbotham Charitable Trust,
The Christopher *177*
Vaux Group Foundation, The
191

■ Victims of domestic violence

Funding priority
Birkenhead and Wirral Moral
Welfare Association *92*
Chase Charity, The *101*
Johnson Group Cleaners Charity
129
Kroch Foundation, The Heinz &
Anna *131*
Lane Foundation, The Allen
132
Lankelly Foundation, The *134*
Patients' Aid Association
Hospital and Medical
Charities Trust *160*
Scott Charitable Trust, The
Francis C *180*
Scott Charitable Trust, The
Frieda *181*
Scott Trust, Sir James & Lady
182

Will consider
AGF Charitable Trust *87*
BNFL Risley Medical, Research
and Charity Trust, The *89*
Baddiley Consolidated Charity
90
Brentwood Charity, The *95*
Bryn Christian Fellowship, The
97
Burall Charitable Trust, The *97*
Charity for Change *101*
Chorley Relief Fund, The *104*
Congleton Inclosure Trust, The
106
Davies Trust, The John Grant
109
Duchy of Lancaster Benevolent
Fund, The *111*
Eddleston's Charity, John *114*
Ferguson Benevolent Fund
Limited *116*
Ford of Britain Trust *118*
France's Charity *119*
Girl's Welfare Fund *120*
Hadfield Charitable Trust, The
122
Hamitzvos, Keren *122*
Hemby Trust, The *124*
Hillards Charitable Trust, Gay &
Peter Hartley's *124*
Lancaster's Trust, Bryan *132*
Lathoms Charity, Peter *136*
Leverhulme's Charitable Trust,
Lord *137*
Lloyd Charity Trust, The W M
and B W *140*
Marchon Works Employees
Charity Fund, The *144*
Northern Rock Foundation, The
157
Pilkington Charities Fund *163*
Preston Relief in Need Charity
164
Proven Family Trust, The *165*
Ravensdale Trust, The *169*
Rayner Charitable Trust, The
John *169*
Rope Third Charitable
Settlement, The Mrs L D
171
Rotary Club of Wallasey, The
Charitable Fund of the *175*
Rowbotham Charitable Trust,
The Christopher *177*
Vaux Group Foundation, The
191

■ Victims of famine

Will consider
Baddiley Consolidated Charity
90
Bryn Christian Fellowship, The
97
Charity for Change *101*

Chiron Trust, The *103*
Congleton Inclosure Trust, The
106
Duchy of Lancaster Benevolent
Fund, The *111*
Girl's Welfare Fund *120*
Lancaster's Trust, Bryan *132*
Pilkington Charities Fund *163*
Rainford Trust, The *167*
Rotary Club of Wallasey, The
Charitable Fund of the *175*

■ Victims of manmade or natural disasters

Funding priority
Littleborough Nursing
Association Fund *139*

Will consider
BNFL Risley Medical, Research
and Charity Trust, The *89*
Charity for Change *101*
Chiron Trust, The *103*
Congleton Inclosure Trust, The
106
Duchy of Lancaster Benevolent
Fund, The *111*
Lancaster's Trust, Bryan *132*
Oldham Foundation *159*
Pilkington Charities Fund *163*
Rainford Trust, The *167*
Rotary Club of Wallasey, The
Charitable Fund of the *175*
Sainsbury Charitable Fund Ltd,
The *179*
Scott Charitable Trust, The
Frieda *181*
Scott Trust, Sir James & Lady
182

■ Victims of war

Funding priority
Kroch Foundation, The Heinz &
Anna *131*
Patients' Aid Association
Hospital and Medical
Charities Trust *160*

Will consider
BNFL Risley Medical, Research
and Charity Trust, The *89*
Bryn Christian Fellowship, The
97
Charity for Change *101*
Chiron Trust, The *103*
Duchy of Lancaster Benevolent
Fund, The *111*
Lancaster's Trust, Bryan *132*
Pilkington Charities Fund *163*
Rotary Club of Wallasey, The
Charitable Fund of the *175*

Scott Charitable Trust, The
Frieda *181*
Scott Trust, Sir James & Lady
182

■ Video

see **Film, video, multimedia
broadcasting**

■ Village halls

see **Community centres &
village halls**

■ Visual arts

see also **Arts & arts
facilities**
Funding priority
Chase Charity, The *101*
North West Arts Board *155*

Will consider
Rainford Trust, The *167*
Ravensdale Trust, The *169*
Rayner Charitable Trust, The
John *169*
Vaux Group Foundation, The
191

■ Visual impairment

see **Sight loss**

■ Vocational training

see also **Education &
training**
Funding priority
Girl's Welfare Fund *120*
Kershaw Trust, The Peter *130*

Will consider
Chiron Trust, The *103*
Evans Trust, Mabel *115*
Ferguson Benevolent Fund
Limited *116*
Ford of Britain Trust *118*
Rainford Trust, The *167*
Scott Charitable Trust, The
Frieda *181*
Scott Trust, Sir James & Lady
182

■ Voluntary umbrella bodies

see **Charity or voluntary
umbrella bodies**

■ Volunteer bureaux

see also **Charity or
voluntary umbrella bodies**
Funding priority
Sainsbury Charitable Fund Ltd,
The *179*
Scott Trust, Sir James & Lady
182

Will consider
BNFL Risley Medical, Research
and Charity Trust, The *89*
Congleton Inclosure Trust, The
106
Davies Trust, The John Grant
109
Lancaster's Trust, Bryan *132*
Mersey Basin Trust – ICI Green
Action Grants *147*
Moores Foundation, John *149*
Proven Family Trust, The *165*
Rope Third Charitable
Settlement, The Mrs L D
171
Scott Charitable Trust, The
Francis C *180*
Vaux Group Foundation, The
191
Youth and the Community Trust
198

■ Volunteers

Funding priority
Chase Charity, The *101*
Chiron Trust, The *103*
Eden Arts Trust *114*
Lord Mayor of Chester
Charitable Trust *141*
Mersey Basin Trust – ICI Green
Action Grants *147*
National Lottery Charities Board
151
Patients' Aid Association
Hospital and Medical
Charities Trust *160*
Pilkington Charities Fund *163*
Rope Third Charitable
Settlement, The Mrs L D
171
Rowbotham Charitable Trust,
The Christopher *177*
Scott Trust, Sir James & Lady
182

Will consider
Baddiley Consolidated Charity
90
Barker Charity, Philip *90*
Barnabas Charitable Trust *90*
Brotherton Trust, The Charles
96
Chrimes Family Charitable
Trust, The *104*

Davies Trust, The John Grant
109
Ford of Britain Trust *118*
Hamitzvos, Keren *122*
Hillards Charitable Trust, Gay &
Peter Hartley's *124*
Lankelly Foundation, The *134*
Mayor of Chorley's Helping
Hand Charity, The *145*
Moores Foundation, John *149*
Nantwich and Acton Grammar
School Foundation *151*
Parkinson (Deceased) Trust,
Thomas *160*
Rayner Charitable Trust, The
John *169*
Scott Charitable Trust, The
Frieda *181*
Sykes Trust, The Charles *187*
Youth and the Community Trust
198

■ War

see **Victims of war**

■ Waterways

see also **Conservation**
Funding priority
Mersey Basin Trust – ICI Green
Action Grants *147*
Mersey Basin Trust – Stream
Care Project *147*
Mersey Basin Trust – Waterside
Revival Grants *148*

Will consider
Eskdale (Cumbria) Trust, The
115
Hamitzvos, Keren *122*

■ Welfare services

see **Community facilities,
Community services**

■ Well woman clinics

see also **Health care**
Will consider
Moore Foundation, The George
A *148*
Moores Foundation, John *149*
Proven Family Trust, The *165*
Scott Trust, Sir James & Lady
182

■ Widows & widowers

Funding priority

Littleborough Nursing
 Association Fund *139*

Will consider

Adlington Women's Institute
 87
BNFL Risley Medical, Research
 and Charity Trust, The *89*
Barnes Fund, The Norman *91*
Cheshire Provincial Fund of
 Benevolence, The *102*
Chorley Relief Fund, The *104*
Hadfield Charitable Trust, The
 122
Hutchinson Educational Charity,
 The Joseph *127*
Moore Foundation, The George
 A *148*
Preston Relief in Need Charity
 164
Rayner Charitable Trust, The
 John *169*
Sainsbury Charitable Fund Ltd,
 The *179*
Wigan Town Relief in Need
 Charity *196*

■ Wildflowers

see **Flora**

■ Wildlife areas

see **Wildlife parks**

■ Wildlife parks

see also **Animal facilities &
 services**

Funding priority

Talbot Bridge Will Trust, The
 Elsie *189*

Will consider

Oldham Foundation *159*
Sykes Trust, The Charles *187*
Vaux Group Foundation, The
 191

■ Wildlife sanctuaries

see also **Animal facilities &
 services**

Funding priority

Talbot Bridge Will Trust, The
 Elsie *189*

Will consider

Hamitzvos, Keren *122*
Oldham Foundation *159*
Rainford Trust, The *167*
Sykes Trust, The Charles *187*

■ Woodlands

see also **Conservation**

Funding priority

Mersey Basin Trust – ICI Green
 Action Grants *147*

Will consider

Chiron Trust, The *103*
Rainford Trust, The *167*

■ Work

see **Training for work**

■ Writers & poets

Funding priority

Chase Charity, The *101*
North West Arts Board *155*

Will consider

de Avenley Foundation, The
 110
Eden Arts Trust *114*
Granada Foundation, The *120*
Harewood's Charitable
 Settlement, Lord *122*
Mayor of Chorley's Helping
 Hand Charity, The *145*
Nantwich and Acton Grammar
 School Foundation *151*
Northern Arts *157*
Rathbone Charitable Trust, The
 Eleanor *168*
Scott Charitable Trust, The
 Frieda *181*
Sykes Trust, The Charles *187*
Talbot Bridge Will Trust, The
 Elsie *189*
Yorkshire Bank Charitable
 Trust, The *198*

■ Young adults

Funding priority

Barker Charity, Philip *90*
Baynes Charitable Trust, James
 91
Brotherton Trust, The Charles
 96
C & A Charitable Trust, The *99*
Chadwick Educational
 Foundation, The *100*
Eden Arts Trust *114*
Eden's Foundation, James
 114

Famos Foundation Trust *116*
Fearn Trust, George *116*
Feryal Rajah Educational Trust
 117
Harris Charity, The *123*
Hutchinson Educational Charity,
 The Joseph *127*
Integreat *128*
Kershaw Trust, The Peter *130*
McMechan Memorial Fund, The
 Roy *142*
Mayor of Chorley's Helping
 Hand Charity, The *145*
Mersey Basin Trust *146*
Mersey Basin Trust – ICI Green
 Action Grants *147*
Merseyside Development
 Foundation *148*
Mole Charitable Trust *148*
Morgan Crucible Company plc
 Charitable Trust, The *151*
Nantwich and Acton Grammar
 School Foundation *151*
Neave Trust, The Airey *154*
North West Arts Board *155*
Rope Third Charitable
 Settlement, The Mrs L D
 171
Runcorn Community Action
 Trust *178*
Rycroft Children's Fund *178*
Stewart Trust, Sir Halley *185*
Stokes Memorial Trust, The
 Alan Jenkin *187*
Talbot Bridge Will Trust, The
 Elsie *189*
Wedge, The *193*
West Lancashire Masonic
 Educational Trust *194*
Wing Yip and Brothers
 Charitable Trust, W *197*
Yorkshire Bank Charitable
 Trust, The *198*

Will consider

Adlington Women's Institute
 87
Angler's Inn Trust *88*
Baddiley Consolidated Charity
 90
Blankstone Charitable Trust,
 The Solomon & Isabel *93*
Booth Charities, The *93*
Brabin's Educational
 Foundation *94*
Brentwood Charity, The *95*
Burall Charitable Trust, The *97*
Cartmel Old Grammar School
 Foundation *100*
Cheshire Constabulary
 Community Involvement
 Fund of Northwich Division
 102
Cheshire Constabulary
 Involvement Fund for the

....

■Zoos

see also **Animal facilities &
services**

Will consider

Trusts by grant type

List of grant types

Trusts by grant type

■Project only

■ Research

BNFL Risley Medical, Research and Charity Trust, The *89*
Britannia Building Society Foundation *95*
Brotherton Trust, The Charles *96*
Burden's Charitable Foundation *97*
Chase Charity, The *101*
Davies Trust, The John Grant *109*
Ferguson Benevolent Fund Limited *116*
Fetal Medicine Foundation, The *117*
Hemby Trust, The *124*
Hillards Charitable Trust, Gay & Peter Hartley's *124*
Holt Trust, The Edward *126*
Johnson Foundation, The *128*
Kershaw Trust, The Peter *130*
Kroch Foundation, The Heinz & Anna *131*
Lane Foundation, The Allen *132*
Leach Charitable Trust, The Eric and Dorothy *137*
Leboff Charitable Trust, The Paul & Evelyn *137*
Nantwich and Acton Grammar School Foundation *151*
National Lottery Charities Board *151*
Neave Trust, The Airey *154*
Newstead Charity, The *155*
North West Arts Board *155*
North West Cancer Research Fund *156*
Pilkington Charities Fund *163*
Rainford Trust, The *167*
Rayner Charitable Trust, The John *169*
Scott Charitable Trust, The Francis C *180*
Scott Charitable Trust, The Frieda *181*
Scott Trust, Sir James & Lady *182*
Stewart Trust, Sir Halley *185*

■ Recurring costs

Barker Charity, Philip *90*
Barnabas Charitable Trust *90*
Bible Preaching Trust, The *92*
Britannia Building Society Foundation *95*
Burden's Charitable Foundation *97*
Capenhurst Medical and Research Charity Trust Fund, The *99*
Chadwick Trust, The Amelia *100*

Denton Relief in Sickness Charity *110*
Derbyshire Trust, The Nancy *111*
Duchy of Lancaster Benevolent Fund, The *111*
Eden's Foundation, James *114*
Eskdale (Cumbria) Trust, The *115*
Florence's Charitable Trust *118*
Girl's Welfare Fund *120*
Green Memorial Fund, The Barry *121*
Hawe Settlement, The M A *124*
Johnson Foundation, The *128*
Lane Foundation, The Allen *132*
Lankelly Foundation, The *134*
Leboff Charitable Trust, The Paul & Evelyn *137*
Leverhulme's Charitable Trust, Lord *137*
Lions Club, Lancaster and Morecambe, Charity Trust *139*
Manchester Local Medical Committee Compassionate Fund *144*
Manchester Society of Architects, The *144*
Moores Foundation, John *149*
Morgan Crucible Company plc Charitable Trust, The *151*
National Lottery Charities Board *151*
Northern Arts *157*
Northern Rock Foundation, The *157*
Pennycress Trust, The *162*
Pilkington Charities Fund *163*
Pilkington Foundation for Arts and Leisure, The Harry and Mavis *163*
Provincial Grand Mark Lodge of Cumberland and Westmorland Benevolent Fund *165*
Provincial Insurance Company Trust for Bolton *165*
Pye Christian Trust, The *165*
Riverside Charitable Trust Limited *171*
Rotary Club of Alderley Edge and Bollin Valley Trust Fund *174*
Rotary Club of Preston South Trust Fund, The *175*
Round Table No 8, Liverpool, Charitable Trust *175*
Rowan Charitable Trust, The *176*
Rowbotham Charitable Trust, The Christopher *177*

Scott Charitable Trust, The Francis C *180*
Scott Charitable Trust, The Frieda *181*
Scott Trust, Sir James & Lady *182*
Slater Trust Limited, The *184*
Timperley Educational Foundation *189*
Verdin Trust Fund, The *191*
Waterhouse Charitable Trust, Mrs *192*
Wedge, The *193*
West Lancashire Masonic Educational Trust *194*
Westmorland Charity Concerts Society *195*
Whiteley Trust, Norman *196*
Wigan Town Relief in Need Charity *196*
Woolton Charitable Trust, The *197*
Youth and the Community Trust *198*

■ Running costs (eg post, telephone, rent, etc)

Barnabas Charitable Trust *90*
Barnes Fund, The Norman *91*
Bowness and Windermere Community Care Trust *94*
Britannia Building Society Foundation *95*
Burden's Charitable Foundation *97*
Chiron Trust, The *103*
Famos Foundation Trust *116*
Ford of Britain Trust *118*
Greater Manchester Police Community Charity *120*
Green Memorial Fund, The Barry *121*
Hillards Charitable Trust, Gay & Peter Hartley's *124*
Johnson Group Cleaners Charity *129*
Kershaw Trust, The Peter *130*
Lancaster's Trust, Bryan *132*
Lane Foundation, The Allen *132*
Lankelly Foundation, The *134*
Leach Charitable Trust, The Eric and Dorothy *137*
Moores Foundation, John *149*
National Lottery Charities Board *151*
North West Arts Board *155*
North West Cancer Research Fund *156*
Northern Rock Foundation, The *157*

··

■ Up to two years

··

■ Up to three years

··

■ More than three years

············

Alphabetical register of grant making trusts

■ AGF Charitable Trust (formerly NEM Charitable Trust)

WHAT IS FUNDED Support for past and present members of AGF staff charitable initiatives. Support for charities local to AGF branches. This includes: residential facilities and services; infrastructure, support and development; religion; health care; education and training; and social care and development

WHAT IS NOT FUNDED No grants to individuals, or to national charities

WHO CAN BENEFIT Staff and pensioners of AGF. Local charitable bodies benefiting older people; academics; retired people; and students. There are few restrictions on the social circumstances of, and no restrictions on the disease or medical condition suffered by the beneficiaries

WHERE FUNDING CAN BE GIVEN Milton Keynes, Manchester, City of London

TYPE OF GRANT Single donations

RANGE OF GRANTS £100–£2,000, typical grant £250

SAMPLE GRANTS £500 to Insurance Benevolent Fund for Insurance Charities Day August 1998
£500 to Trek China – staff personal effort for Barnardo's
£340 to Children's Safety Books for local distribution of safety information to schools
£300 to Scout Hut, Apsley Guise for local scout group
£300 to Mencap for a personal initiative to raise funds
£300 to Lord Mayor of London for annual charity appeal
£300 to Schools outreach at Oakfield School
£250 to Milton Keynes Play Association for Milton Keynes Children's Day
£250 to Rotary Club of Milton Keynes Swimathon for Milton Keynes charities

FINANCES
- Year 1996
- Income £15,187
- Grants £17,530

TRUSTEES A Dean, R Neal

HOW TO APPLY Applications received during a quarter normally accumulated and reviewed at the subsequent meeting of the Trustees

WHO TO APPLY TO Mrs A Ward, AGF Charitable Trust, AGF House, 500 Avebury Boulevard, Milton Keynes MK9 2LA *Tel* 01908 683260 *Fax* 01908 669783

CC NO 327671　　　**ESTABLISHED** 1988

■ Adlington Women's Institute

WHAT IS FUNDED To improve and develop conditions of rural life in accordance with the constitution and rules of the Women's Institute

WHO CAN BENEFIT Females

WHERE FUNDING CAN BE GIVEN Adlington, Poynton and Worth

FINANCES
- Year 1994–95
- Income £8,091
- Grants £1,424

WHO TO APPLY TO Mrs E J Bateson, Adlington Women's Institute, 13 Redbrook Way, Adlington, Macclesfield, Cheshire SK10 4NF

CC NO 515610　　　**ESTABLISHED** 1984

■ Green and Lilian F M Ainsworth and Family Benevolent Fund

WHAT IS FUNDED The Trustees have a comprehensive list of charitable objects from whom they select each year. Other applicants are made secondary to these preferred charities, including those supporting the young, elderly and the handicapped

WHAT IS NOT FUNDED Payments to registered charities only considered. The Trustees do not sponsor individuals but preference for secondary awards is given to charities whose work is in the North West of England

WHO CAN BENEFIT The young, the elderly and the handicapped preferred

WHERE FUNDING CAN BE GIVEN North West England

RANGE OF GRANTS £250–£1,400

SAMPLE GRANTS £1,400 to Benevolent Fund of Chartered Accountants
£1,400 to RSPCA
£1,400 to British Heart Foundation
£1,400 to RNLI
£1,400 to RNIB
£1,400 to NSPCC
£1,400 to Barnardo's
£1,400 to Help the Aged
£1,000 to Kirkgate Centre Trust, Cockermouth
£1,000 to Motability, North West

FINANCES
- Year 1996
- Income £31,689
- Grants £14,450

TRUSTEES The Royal Bank of Scotland plc

Does the trust you have chosen match your needs? Haphazard applications waste postage and time

87

WHO TO APPLY TO Preston Trustee Office, Green and Lilian F M Ainsworth and Family Benevolent Fund, The Royal Bank of Scotland plc, Guildhall House, Guildhall Street, Preston, Lancashire PR1 3NU

CC NO 267577   **ESTABLISHED** 1974

■The Harold Amelan Charitable Trust

WHAT IS FUNDED General charitable purposes. The Trust will support national charities, but preference will be given to local charities around the Greater Manchester area

WHAT IS NOT FUNDED No grants to individuals

WHO CAN BENEFIT There are no restrictions on the age; professional and economic group; family situation; religion and culture; and social circumstances of; or disease or medical condition suffered by, the beneficiaries

WHERE FUNDING CAN BE GIVEN UK with preference for Greater Manchester area

RANGE OF GRANTS £50–£2,500

SAMPLE GRANTS £2,500 to Hale and District Hebrew Congregation
£2,000 to JPAIME
£1,000 to JIAME
£1,000 to GRET
£1,000 to JIA
£600 to Institute of Orthopaedics, Oswestry
£500 to Well Being
£400 to Didsbury and South Manchester WIZO
£400 to Jewish Care
£400 to Sale and Altrincham District Spastics

FINANCES
- Year 1996
- Income £18,602
- Grants £14,445

TRUSTEES R E Amelan, J F Middleweek

WHO TO APPLY TO J E Avery-Gee, The Harold Amelan Charitable Trust, c/o Kay Johnson-Gee, Griffin Court, 201 Chapel Street, Salford, Manchester M3 5EQ

CC NO 263804   **ESTABLISHED** 1972

■Angler's Inn Trust

WHAT IS FUNDED To support local schools, vicarage, bowling club, playgrounds, youth clubs

WHO CAN BENEFIT Individuals and institutions benefiting children, young adults, clergy and other local facilities

WHERE FUNDING CAN BE GIVEN Kendal, Cumbria

SAMPLE GRANTS £3,098 to Burneside Organisations for computer facilities
£2,393 to Burneside School

£1,500 to Queen Katherine School
£1,500 to Kirkbie Kendal School
£1,500 to Lakes School
£1,000 to Stricklandgate Methodist Church
£700 to Burneside Bowling Club
£500 to Kendal Lads and Girls Club
£200 to Burneside Youth Club
£186 to Gowan Lea Old People's Flats for colour television rental and licence

FINANCES
- Year 1997
- Income £16,358
- Grants £14,384

TRUSTEES O G D Ackland, J A Cropper, D E Willink

WHO TO APPLY TO L Buckle, Secretary, Angler's Inn Trust, c/o James Cropper plc, Burneside Mills, Kendal, Cumbria LA9 6PZ

CC NO 234193   **ESTABLISHED** 1938

■Aquinas Trust

This trust did not respond to CAF's request to amend its entry and, by 30 June 1998, CAF's researchers did not find financial records for later than 1995 on its file at the Charity Commission. Trusts are legally required to submit annual accounts to the Charity Commission under section 42 of the Charities Act 1993

WHAT IS FUNDED Medicine and health, welfare, particularly children's needs, especially those that fall outside the mainstream charity aid

WHAT IS NOT FUNDED None

WHO CAN BENEFIT Small local projects helping children who have very rare or individual problems who cannot find any help through other charities

WHERE FUNDING CAN BE GIVEN Manchester and UK

TYPE OF GRANT One-off small grants of £1,000 or less

TRUSTEES S Mathis, S McCarthy, H F Riley, G Cosgrave, D Robson

HOW TO APPLY To the address under Who To Apply To in writing at any time

WHO TO APPLY TO S N McCarthy, Aquinas Trust, Holiday Inn, Crowne Plaza, Peter Street, Manchester M60 2DS

CC NO 1033098   **ESTABLISHED** 1993

■ The Assair Charitable Trust

This trust did not respond to CAF's request to amend its entry and, by 30 June 1998, CAF's researchers did not find financial records for later than 1995 on its file at the Charity Commission. Trusts are legally required to submit annual accounts to the Charity Commission under section 42 of the Charities Act 1993

WHAT IS FUNDED General charitable purposes

WHO CAN BENEFIT There are no restrictions on the age; professional and economic group; family situation; religion and culture; and social circumstances of; or disease or medical condition suffered by, the beneficiaries

WHERE FUNDING CAN BE GIVEN UK, with a possible preference for Manchester

HOW TO APPLY To the address under Who To Apply To in writing

WHO TO APPLY TO B Olsberg, Accountant, The Assair Charitable Trust, 1st Floor, 35 Whitworth Street West, Manchester M1 5NG

CC NO 327558   **ESTABLISHED** 1987

■ The BNFL Risley Medical, Research and Charity Trust

WHAT IS FUNDED Provision of medical equipment; health; accomodation and housing; charity or voluntary umbrella bodies; special schools; special needs education; speech therapy; medical research; care in the community; community transport; and day centres

WHAT IS NOT FUNDED Individual sponsorship and revenue expenditure

WHO CAN BENEFIT Organisations benefiting: children; young adults; older people; those in care, fostered and adopted; widows and widowers; at risk groups; disabled people; those disadvantaged by poverty; disaster victims; homeless people; those living in rural and urban areas; socially isolated people; victims of crime, abuse and domestic violence; and victims of war. There are few restrictions on the disease or medical condition suffered by the beneficiaries

WHERE FUNDING CAN BE GIVEN Cheshire, Greater Manchester, Lancashire and Merseyside

TYPE OF GRANT Building, capital and research

FINANCES
- Year 1997
- Income £52,772

TRUSTEES R J Balmer, M Howarth, M C Mackenzie

HOW TO APPLY To the address below in writing

WHO TO APPLY TO Mrs M Howarth, Secretary, The BNFL Risley Medical, Research and Charity Trust, British Nuclear Fuels plc, Risley, Warrington WA3 6AS *Tel* 01925 833211

CC NO 512584   **ESTABLISHED** 1982

■ The BNFL Springfields Medical Research and Charity Trust Fund

WHAT IS FUNDED Grants to hospitals and local medical and welfare charities for medical equipment

WHO CAN BENEFIT Organisations benefiting disabled people. There is no restriction on the disease or medical condition suffered by the beneficiaries

WHERE FUNDING CAN BE GIVEN Lancashire

RANGE OF GRANTS £8–£4,760

SAMPLE GRANTS £4,760 to Blackpool Bears
£3,020 to Highfield Nursery
£2,528 to Trinity Hospice
£2,068 to Heartbeat NW Cardia Centre
£1,981 to Lancashire Priority Services for
Harriet McAvoy Ashworth Trading
£1,785 to Health Centre, Great Eccleston
£1,704 to Scan Mobility
£1,673 to BWF Blenheim House
£1,550 to BWF Devonshire Road Hospital
£1,482 to Moorfield School, Preston

FINANCES
- Year 1997
- Income £108,602
- Grants £35,802

TRUSTEES D Singleton, D Pine, Mrs P Goodacre

HOW TO APPLY To the address under Who To
Apply To in writing

WHO TO APPLY TO The BNFL Springfields Medical
Research and Charity Trust Fund, British
Nuclear Fuels plc, Springfield Works, Salwick,
Preston, Lancashire PR4 0XJ

CC NO 518005   **ESTABLISHED** 1986

······································

■ Baddiley Consolidated Charity

WHAT IS FUNDED The advancement of welfare

WHO CAN BENEFIT Individuals and organisations

WHERE FUNDING CAN BE GIVEN The parishes of
Baddiley, Faddiley, Burland and Brindley

FINANCES
- Year 1996
- Income £10,163

HOW TO APPLY To the Correspondent in writing

WHO TO APPLY TO Peter Winward, Trustee,
Baddiley Consolidated Charity, Baddiley Farm,
Baddiley, Nantwich, Cheshire CW5 8PY

CC NO 242915   **ESTABLISHED** 1965

······································

■ Philip Barker Charity

WHAT IS FUNDED Principally: local youth
organisations; medical; health; disabled;
welfare and educational charities

WHAT IS NOT FUNDED No grants to individuals
who are not sponsored by a registered charity

WHO CAN BENEFIT Registered charities
benefiting: children and young adults; carers;
disabled people; and volunteers

WHERE FUNDING CAN BE GIVEN Cheshire

TYPE OF GRANT Principally one-off grants. Will
consider contribution towards recurring costs,
core costs and projects. Funding is available
for up to two years

RANGE OF GRANTS £200–£1,000

FINANCES
- Year 1996–97
- Income £78,693
- Grants £74,696

TRUSTEES Mrs M G Mather, H J Partington, Mrs
C Munday, E F G Burton, Mrs A V R Burton,
Capt S P Barker

NOTES The Trustees will consider applications
from individuals sponsored by registered
charities, supporting youth projects, medical,
health, welfare and educational objectives

HOW TO APPLY To the address under Who To
Apply To in writing only

WHO TO APPLY TO Mrs M G Mather,
Correspondent, Philip Barker Charity,
1a Rothesay Road, Curzon Park, Chester
CH4 8AJ

CC NO 1000227   **ESTABLISHED** 1990

······································

■ Barnabas Charitable Trust

WHAT IS FUNDED Trustees will consider a wide
range of Christian outreach including inner-city
projects. Children's education including arts
education; community services; and bursaries
and fees

WHAT IS NOT FUNDED No grants for projects or
large charities

WHO CAN BENEFIT Individuals and organisations
benefiting: unemployed people; volunteers;
parents and children; one parent families; at
risk groups; disabled people; and ex-offenders
and those at risk of offending. There is no
restriction on the age, and few on the religion
and culture of the beneficiaries

WHERE FUNDING CAN BE GIVEN West Midlands,
North West, Sheffield and Derbyshire

TYPE OF GRANT Core costs, one-off, project,
recurring costs, running costs, salaries and
start-up costs. Funding is available for up to
three years

RANGE OF GRANTS £100–£10,000

SAMPLE GRANTS £8,050 to Furnival Project,
Sheffield for community project salary
£5,000 to Bilston Care Centre for care of the
elderly
£4,000 to Urban Solidarity, Wolverhampton for
salaries
£3,050 to Bilston Congregational Church for
support to community project for elderly
£2,652 to Liverpool Metropolitan Cathedral for
bursaries for children in choir
£2,000 to Wash Nursery School, Derbyshire
for bursaries and parenting skill courses

FINANCES
- Year 1997
- Income £38,000
- Grants £38,000

TRUSTEES D Harding, Mrs R Harding, R L Harding

HOW TO APPLY Write with full information. There are no application forms. No reply will be sent if application is unsuccessful

WHO TO APPLY TO D Harding, Barnabas Charitable Trust, Gorstylow Farm, The Wash, High Peak SK23 0QL *Tel* 01663 750546

CC NO 299718 **ESTABLISHED** 1988

■The Norman Barnes Fund

WHAT IS FUNDED To advance the welfare of the elderly in the Beneficial Area

WHO CAN BENEFIT Individuals and organisations concerned with the elderly

WHERE FUNDING CAN BE GIVEN The area of the former County Borough of Rochdale

TYPE OF GRANT Buildings, capital costs, running costs, one-off

SAMPLE GRANTS £250 to a pensioner to purchase high chair following strokes which restrict his mobility
£250 to a Christian organisation for equipment for a luncheon club
£200 to a pensioner to purchase a freezer
£200 to a pensioner to replace a bed
£200 to a pensioner for redecorating
£150 to housebound luncheon club for the elderly towards outings/day trips

FINANCES
- Year 1996–97
- Income £11,345
- Grants £6,810

TRUSTEES Arnold Bagnall, Cllr Ray Colley, Cllr Jane Gartside, JP, Cllr Jean Hornby, Cllr Rodney Stott

NOTES The Trustees give maximum grants of £250

HOW TO APPLY Application forms are available from: The Clerk to the Norman Barnes Fund, PO Box 15, Town Hall, Rochdale, Lancashire OL16 1AB

WHO TO APPLY TO Chief Executive and Treasurer, The Norman Barnes Fund, Corporate Services Department, PO Box 39, Municipal Offices, Smith Street, Rochdale, Lancashire OL16 1LQ

CC NO 511646 **ESTABLISHED** 1989

■James Baynes Charitable Trust

WHAT IS FUNDED To give grants to welfare organisations on behalf of individuals

WHAT IS NOT FUNDED No ex-offenders

WHO CAN BENEFIT Individuals and organisations

WHERE FUNDING CAN BE GIVEN North West of England

TYPE OF GRANT One-off

SAMPLE GRANTS £500 to Electronic Aids for the Blind for computer equipment
£200 to Manchester Housing for starting up new home
£200 to Wigan NHS towards the cost of a special chair for a child

FINANCES
- Year 1995–96
- Income £3,968
- Grants £3,837

TRUSTEES W M Cliff, J D Maxwell, C E Rowley

HOW TO APPLY In writing to the Correspondent via a third party. (Applications not accepted from individuals personally)

WHO TO APPLY TO W M Cliff, Trustee, James Baynes Charitable Trust, Cooper Lancaster Brewers, 14 Wood Street, Bolton, Lancashire BL1 1DZ *Tel* 01204 531573

CC NO 516525 **ESTABLISHED** 1985

■Beauland Ltd

WHAT IS FUNDED Healthcare charities and exclusively Jewish projects supported

WHO CAN BENEFIT To benefit Jewish people and the sick. There is no restriction on the disease or medical condition suffered by the beneficiaries

WHERE FUNDING CAN BE GIVEN Greater Manchester

FINANCES
- Year 1997
- Income £285,567
- Grants £204,444

TRUSTEES W Neuman, F Neuman, H Neuman, M Neuman, P Neuman, E Neuman, E Henry, M Friedlander, H Roseman, J Bleirer, R Delange

WHO TO APPLY TO W Newman, Beauland Ltd, 4 Cheltenham Crescent, Salford, Manchester M7 4FE

CC NO 511374 **ESTABLISHED** 1981

■The David and Ruth Behrend Fund

WHAT IS FUNDED General charitable purposes. The Trust only gives funding to charities known to the Settlors

WHO CAN BENEFIT There are no restrictions on the age; professional and economic group; family situation; religion and culture; and social circumstances of; or disease or medical condition suffered by, the beneficiaries

WHERE FUNDING CAN BE GIVEN Merseyside

SAMPLE GRANTS £11,000 to Merseyside Development Foundation

£7,500 to Fair Play for Children
£2,000 to Barnstable Trust
£2,000 to FORME
£2,000 to Mustard Seed Ministries
£2,000 to Sheila Kay Fund
£1,000 to PSS
£1,000 to Merseyside Holiday Scheme
£1,000 to KIND

FINANCES
- Year 1997
- Income £45,000
- Grants £19,000

TRUSTEES Liverpool Council of Social Services (Inc)

PUBLICATIONS Annual Report

HOW TO APPLY **This Trust states that it does not respond to unsolicited applications**

WHO TO APPLY TO Carol Champman, Financial Services Manager, The David and Ruth Behrend Fund, Liverpool Council of Social Services (Inc), 14 Castle Street, Liverpool L2 ONJ *Tel* 0151-236 7728 *Fax* 0151-258 1153

CC NO 261567   **ESTABLISHED** 1969

■Edward Bibby Fund

WHAT IS FUNDED General charitable purposes. Preference to charities of which the Trust has special interest, knowledge or association and located on Merseyside

WHAT IS NOT FUNDED No grants to individuals

WHO CAN BENEFIT There are no restrictions on the age; professional and economic group; family situation; religion and culture; and social circumstances of; or disease or medical condition suffered by, the beneficiaries

WHERE FUNDING CAN BE GIVEN Merseyside

FINANCES
- Year 1997
- Income £16,796
- Grants £17,000

TRUSTEES Liverpool Council of Social Service (Inc), C L Bibby

WHO TO APPLY TO The Secretary, Edward Bibby Fund, Liverpool Council of Social Service (Inc), 14 Castle Street, Liverpool, Merseyside L2 ONJ

CC NO 200593   **ESTABLISHED** 1960

■The Bible Preaching Trust

WHAT IS FUNDED To advance religion by providing financial aid to support preaching of the Evangelical Calvanistic Christian faith in any part of the world

WHAT IS NOT FUNDED Only those able to sign the doctrinal statement considered

WHO CAN BENEFIT Individuals and organisations

WHERE FUNDING CAN BE GIVEN UK and overseas

TYPE OF GRANT Recurring. Single payments to ministers of £100–£500. Theological seminary £500

FINANCES
- Year 1996–97
- Income £7,739
- Grants £5,205

TRUSTEES Rev C J L Bennett, Rev G B Brady, R L Van den Broek, Rev Dr P E Golding, V Pool

HOW TO APPLY Initially in writing, followed by application form which includes a doctrinal statement. Applications are normally acknowledged

WHO TO APPLY TO Victor Pool, The Bible Preaching Trust, 38 Station Crescent, Ashford, Middlesex TW15 3HJ *Tel* 01784 253474

CC NO 262160   **ESTABLISHED** 1966

■H B Bicket Charitable Trust

WHAT IS FUNDED General charitable purposes

WHO CAN BENEFIT Individuals and organisations

WHERE FUNDING CAN BE GIVEN The former Metropolitan Area of Merseyside

TYPE OF GRANT Cash, in small amounts

FINANCES
- Year 1994–95
- Income £8,985
- Grants £2,036

TRUSTEES Mrs K M Bicket, L D Hayward

WHO TO APPLY TO The Trustees, H B Bicket Charitable Trust, 3 The Orchard, North Sudley Road, Liverpool L17 6BT

CC NO 282674   **ESTABLISHED** 1981

■Birkenhead and Wirral Moral Welfare Association

WHAT IS FUNDED To advance education in moral and social welfare, and to enlist the interest and support of church people for educational and remedial welfare work in the Deaneries. All funds are fully utilised in church social work

WHO CAN BENEFIT Individuals and institutions

WHERE FUNDING CAN BE GIVEN Birkenhead and parts of Wirral

TYPE OF GRANT One-off and core costs

FINANCES
- Year 1995–96
- Income £8,638
- Grants £5,177

92

Think carefully about every application. Is it justified?

TRUSTEES Rev C W Winton (Chairman), C Haycocks (Hon Treasurer), Mrs A Foster (Social worker), Mrs E Lane (Social worker), Mrs E J Davis, Canon D C Kelly, N Goodwin, M Iddon, Rev R Powley, Mrs A Sutton

NOTES At present funds are fully committed to previously chosen projects

WHO TO APPLY TO Colin Haycocks, Birkenhead and Wirral Moral Welfare Association, Redstone, 71 Mill Lane, Greasby, Wirral L49 3NR

CC NO 218360   **ESTABLISHED** 1963

■ The Solomon & Isabel Blankstone Charitable Trust

WHAT IS FUNDED Charities working in the fields of the advancement of the Jewish religion, synagogues, Jewish religious umbrella bodies, fine arts, music, orchestras, ambulances and mobile units, hospitals, secondary schools, and art galleries and cultural centres

WHAT IS NOT FUNDED No grants to individuals

WHO CAN BENEFIT Organisations benefiting young adults, musicians, Jews and those suffering from autism and tropical diseases

WHERE FUNDING CAN BE GIVEN North-West England

TYPE OF GRANT One-off funding for one year or less

FINANCES
- Year 1997
- Income £17,807
- Grants £9,845

TRUSTEES M D Blankstone, Mrs A Blankstone, M L Blankstone, N S Blankstone

HOW TO APPLY In writing to the address under Who To Apply To

WHO TO APPLY TO M D Blankstone, The Solomon & Isabel Blankstone Charitable Trust, 71 Woolton Hill Road, Liverpool L25 4RD *Tel* 0151-707 1707 (daytime only)

CC NO 282244   **ESTABLISHED** 1980

■ The Booth Charities (194)

This trust failed to supply a copy of its annual report and accounts to CAF as required under section 47(2) of the Charities Act 1993. The information given here was obtained independently by CAF's researchers at the Charity Commission

---

WHAT IS FUNDED Benefit of inhabitants of the City of Salford. (a) Relief of aged, impotent and poor inhabitants, including payments of pensions to them and provision of almshouses for them. Preference given to those over 60 years of age. (b) Relief of the distress and sickness of inhabitants. (c) Provision and support of facilities for recreation and other leisure-time occupation (with the aim of improving the conditions of life for inhabitants, in the interest of social welfare). (d) Provision and support of education facilities for inhabitants. (e) Any other charitable purpose for the benefit of inhabitants

WHAT IS NOT FUNDED Grants are not made outside the City of Salford

WHO CAN BENEFIT Inhabitants of the City of Salford, especially those over 60 years of age. There are no restrictions on the age; professional and economic group; family situation; religion and culture; and social circumstances of; or disease or medical condition suffered by, the beneficiaries

WHERE FUNDING CAN BE GIVEN City of Salford, in Greater Manchester

TYPE OF GRANT Capital, salaries

FINANCES
- Year 1996
- Income £542,196
- Grants £892,420

TRUSTEES Mrs J Bryans, JP, Mrs V Hart, JP, E W Hunt, W Jones, OBE, MA (Chairman), P Knowles, Rt Worshipful Mayor of the City of Salford, Cllr K Murray, E S Tudor-Evans, MA, FCA, Cllr S Turner

WHO TO APPLY TO R Spence, Administrator, The Booth Charities, Midwood Hall, 1 Eccles Old Road, Salford, Manchester M6 7AE

CC NO 221800   **ESTABLISHED** 1963

Commentary

The Booth Charities were established in the 1960s and consisted of the Charity of Henry Booth the Elder and the Charity of Henry Booth the Grandson. These charities were registered with the Charity Commission in 1963, but their governing document is a Scheme of 1985. The main aim of the Trust is to benefit the inhabitants of the City of Salford.

The Trust has at least ten subsidiary charities and administers several other trusts. It administers the Charity of Thomas Dickanson, the Kirkdale Holiday House and the Humphrey Booth Housing Charity.

The other subsidiaries of the Trust are: the Charity of Charles Haworth for the Poor; Charity of George Beurdsell; Charity of Robert Cuthbertson; Charity of Charles Broster; Charity of Elkanah Armitage; Samuel Haward Educational Foundation; Charity of Alexander Davies; Charity of Henry Booth the Elder; and Charity of Henry Booth the Grandson.

The Trust was established to support the inhabitants of the City of Salford, and will make grants in the following areas: (a) the relief of the aged, impotent and poor, which includes the payment of pensions to and the provision and maintenance of almshouses for the poor, with preference given to those over 60 years of age; (b) the relief of distress and sickness of inhabitants; (c) the provision and support of facilities for recreation and other leisure-time occupation (with the aim of improving conditions of life for inhabitants in the interests of social welfare); (d) the provision and support of educational facilities for inhabitants; and (e) any other charitable purpose for the benefit of inhabitants. Grants are made by the Trust in three main categories: elderly, youth and general. The category benefiting the elderly received the largest amount of grants in 1996 with £596,597 and remains the principle focus of attention. Youth received £141,005 and general causes received £44,274.

The funding policies of the Trust were set out in the governing documents from the 1960s, but it is not known whether they have changed significantly since.

The Trust has supported statutory bodies in the past, for example, it made a grant to Salford Social Services in 1996 for the provision of a therapist to work with sexually abused children. Although the objectives of the Charities indicate that pensions are paid to poor inhabitants of Salford, it is not known whether the Trust is prepared to replace statutory funding. The Trust's attitude to co-funding projects is not known.

Grants are made for a wide variety of purposes within these categories. Grants are made to elderly individuals for lighting and heating costs. Capital grants are frequently made for projects by organisations for the elderly, such as for building conversions and extensions to improve facilities. A grant was made for the conversion of a room of Manchester Cathedral into a drop-in/activities centre for the homeless. The salaries and costs of support workers are often supported, for example a grant was made to Dr Barnardo's for a part-time voluntary worker organiser, and another grant was made to National Children's Homes for a support worker who finds accommodation for 'at risk' young people in the Salford area. It is not known whether loans are made or if infrastructure costs are supported.

The preferred application and the assessment procedures are not known

SAMPLE GRANTS
The top ten grants made in 1996 were:
£301,724 to New Day Care Centre
£192,157 to Kirkdale Holiday House
£25,000 to Manchester Cathedral Development Trust
£24,400 to Ladywell Reminiscence
£24,305 to City of Salford Social Services
£21,016 to Humphrey Booth Clinical Fellowship
£20,000 to NCH Action for Children

£18,974 to Humphrey Booth Clinical Research Fellowship
£18,000 to Sacred Trinity Centre
£15,000 to Salford Children's Holiday Camp

■ Borough of Blackburn Common Good Trust

WHAT IS FUNDED General charitable purposes

WHO CAN BENEFIT Charitable organisations

WHERE FUNDING CAN BE GIVEN The Borough of Blackburn with Darwen

FINANCES
- Year 1995–96
- Income £1,400
- Grants £1,500

HOW TO APPLY To the Correspondent in writing

WHO TO APPLY TO The Director of Legal and Admin Services, Borough of Blackburn Common Good Trust, Town Hall, Blackburn, Lancashire BB1 7DY *Tel* 01254 583550

CC NO 501168   **ESTABLISHED** 1961

■ Bowness and Windermere Community Care Trust

WHAT IS FUNDED The relief of those in need who are poor, aged or disabled in Windermere and the surrounding area; other general charitable purposes

WHO CAN BENEFIT Organisations benefiting older people, those disadvantaged by poverty and disabled people

WHERE FUNDING CAN BE GIVEN Windermere and the surrounding area

TYPE OF GRANT Running costs and salaries are considered

FINANCES
- Year 1997
- Income £20,730
- Grants £301

WHO TO APPLY TO Clive W Langley, Bowness and Windermere Community Care Trust, Oak Ridge, Meadowcroft Lane, Bowness on Windermere LA23 3JJ

CC NO 1056802   **ESTABLISHED** 1996

■ Brabin's Educational Foundation

WHAT IS FUNDED Grants for educational purposes in the Beneficial Area

WHERE FUNDING CAN BE GIVEN Bowland with Leagram, Thornton with Wheatley, Chipping

FINANCES
- Year 1996–97
- Income £11,630

HOW TO APPLY To the Correspondent in writing

WHO TO APPLY TO P E Turver, Secretary, Brabin's Educational Foundation, Overwater House, 5 Prospect Court, Longridge, Preston, Lancashire PR3 2XJ

CC NO 526292   **ESTABLISHED** 1976

■ The Brentwood Charity

WHAT IS FUNDED Grants are given to help individuals in need or to organisations working to help individuals in need who live in Lancashire

WHAT IS NOT FUNDED No debts or rent bonds considered

WHO CAN BENEFIT Individuals and organisations

WHERE FUNDING CAN BE GIVEN Lancashire (pre-1974)

TYPE OF GRANT One-off

SAMPLE GRANTS £100 to Fleetwood Family Day Centre
£100 to Fylde Coast Women's Aid
£100 to Barnardos
£100 to Preston Single Homeless
£100 to Preston Community Mental Health Team
£100 to Lancashire Diabetes Foundation
£90 to Team for Children and Young People with Disabilities
£89 to Burnley Community Advice Centre
£50 to Lancaster District Women's Aid
£40 to Clayton Brook Clinic

FINANCES
- Year 1995–96
- Income £6,600
- Grants £6,906

NOTES Individuals have priority over groups

HOW TO APPLY On an application form from the Correspondent, which has been completed only by the referral agency. No response without an sae

WHO TO APPLY TO The Secretary, The Brentwood Charity, Community Council of Lancashire, 15 Victoria Road, Fulwood, Preston, Lancashire PR2 8PS *Tel* 01772 718710/717461
Fax 01772 718710
E-mail cclancashire@mcmail.com

CC NO 225249   **ESTABLISHED** 1964

■ The Harold Bridges Foundation

WHAT IS FUNDED General charitable purposes, particularly the young, the elderly and supporting village activities

WHAT IS NOT FUNDED No grants to individuals

WHO CAN BENEFIT There are no restrictions on the age; professional and economic group; family situation; religion and culture; and social circumstances of; or disease or medical condition suffered by, the beneficiaries. However, particular favour is given to children young adults, the elderly and village activities

WHERE FUNDING CAN BE GIVEN Preference to the North West of England (as far south as Preston)

RANGE OF GRANTS £500–£5,000

SAMPLE GRANTS £5,000 to St Martin's College, Lancaster
£5,000 to The Airborne Forces Security Fund
£5,000 to Kirby Lonsdale Rugby Club
£2,000 to St John's Churchyard Fund, Tunstall
£2,000 to Cowan Bridge Youth Centre
£1,000 to The Army Benevolent Fund
£1,000 to Quermore Recreation Club
£1,000 to Lonsdale and District Scout Council
£1,000 to Vernon Carus Cricket Club, Penwortham
£1,000 to Kirby Lonsdale Brass Band

FINANCES
- Year 1997
- Income £87,792
- Grants £33,000

TRUSTEES The Royal Bank of Scotland plc, R N Hardy, J W Greenwood

NOTES The Trustees have a comprehensive list of charitable objects whom they benefit each year. Other applicants are secondary to these preferred charities

HOW TO APPLY In writing

WHO TO APPLY TO The Trust Manager, The Harold Bridges Foundation, Royal Bank of Scotland plc, Private Trust and Taxation, PO Box 356, 45 Moseley Street, Manchester M60 2BE

CC NO 236654   **ESTABLISHED** 1963

■ Britannia Building Society Foundation

WHAT IS FUNDED Initiatives and projects that will make a difference to local communities. Priorities are: homelessness, including helping people to stay in their homes; educational achievement and aspirations; community safety, including crime prevention schemes; encouraging prudent money management, by improving financial literacy and money advice services. Infrastructure development is also considered

WHAT IS NOT FUNDED No grants to: individuals, including expeditions and overseas travel; hospitals; medical centres; medical treatment or medical research

WHO CAN BENEFIT Organisations benefiting: homeless people; and those in need of training, especially in financial matters

WHERE FUNDING CAN BE GIVEN Within 25 miles of Leek, in the counties of Staffordshire, Cheshire and Derbyshire

TYPE OF GRANT Any, but preferably special items, and not general contributions towards large appeals. Funding for core costs normally restricted to maximum of three years. Buildings, capital, feasibility studies, one-off, project, research, recurring costs, running costs, salaries and start-up costs are all considered for funding

RANGE OF GRANTS £250–£25,000

FINANCES
- Year 1998
- Income £225,000

TRUSTEES G Brown, J Bullock, C Connolly, E Filkin (Chairman), J Gifford, G Gregory, G H Stow

PUBLICATIONS Grants and Donations Policy leaflet

HOW TO APPLY Copy of Grants and Donations Policy and application form on request from the Secretary. We welcome initial telephone calls

WHO TO APPLY TO L Mullinger, Secretary, Britannia Building Society Foundation, Britannia House, Leek, Staffordshire ST13 5RG *Tel* 01538 391460 *Fax* 01538 399261

CC NO 1069081   **ESTABLISHED** 1998

···································

■The Charles and Edna Broadhurst Charitable Trust

WHAT IS FUNDED Grants are mainly given to social welfare, medical, academic research and Christian causes

WHAT IS NOT FUNDED No grants to individuals

WHO CAN BENEFIT Academics; research workers; Christians; at risk groups; those disadvantaged by poverty; and socially isolated people. There are no restrictions on the disease or medical condition suffered by the beneficiaries

WHERE FUNDING CAN BE GIVEN Southport

RANGE OF GRANTS £250–£6,000

SAMPLE GRANTS £6,000 to Wesley Southbank Road Methodist Church
£2,000 to Winged Fellowship
£2,000 to Birkdale School for Hearing Impaired Children
£2,000 to Light for Life
£2,000 to Ellerslie Court
£2,000 to KGV College
£1,250 to Southport Music Festival
£1,000 to Merseyside Drugs Council

£1,000 to Ainsdale Community Care
£1,000 to NSPCC

FINANCES
- Year 1997
- Grants £25,000
- Income £31,566

TRUSTEES H G Highton (Chairman), D H Hobley, Mrs J Carver, Mrs M P Smith, Mrs G Edmundson

HOW TO APPLY To the address under Who To Apply To in writing. Applications are considered twice a year, usually in June and November

WHO TO APPLY TO D H Hobley, The Charles and Edna Broadhurst Charitable Trust, 399 Lord Street, Southport PR9 0AS

CC NO 702543   **ESTABLISHED** 1988

···································

■The Charles Brotherton Trust

WHAT IS FUNDED Advancement of education including the establishment and maintenance of scholarships and the recreational training and education of young persons – furtherance of medical and surgical research – support of medical or surgical charities. Charities working in the fields of: housing and accommodation; arts; culture and recreation; conservation and environment; and community facilities and services will be considered. Support may also go to community development, volunteers and voluntary organisations, churches and religious ancillary buildings

WHAT IS NOT FUNDED No grants to individuals – only to registered charities and recognised bodies

WHO CAN BENEFIT Organisations benefiting: chemists; ex-service and service people; research workers; scientists; students; volunteers; carers and disabled people. There may be a few restrictions on the disease or medical condition of the beneficiaries

WHERE FUNDING CAN BE GIVEN Birmingham, Liverpool, Wakefield, York, Leeds, Borough of Bebington (Cheshire)

TYPE OF GRANT Buildings, capital, core costs, one-off and research will be considered. Funding may be given for up to three years

RANGE OF GRANTS £100–£350

FINANCES
- Year 1996
- Grants £80,000
- Income £88,000

TRUSTEES D R Brotherton (Custodian), S B Turner, C M Brotherton-Ratcliffe, J S Riches, Management: D R Brotherton, Mrs A Henson, Mrs P L M H Seeley, C M Brotherton-Ratcliffe, S B Turner

HOW TO APPLY Applicants annual accounts required. Applications not acknowledged. Distribution made annually in June for successful applications received by 31 January. Applications for student grants and scholarships should be made to the Bursar at the Universities of Leeds and Liverpool, the Registrar at York University and the Students Welfare Adviser at Birmingham University

WHO TO APPLY TO C Brotherton-Ratcliffe, Secretary, The Charles Brotherton Trust, PO Box 374, Harrogate, North Yorkshire HG1 4YW

CC NO 227067　　　**ESTABLISHED** 1940

■The Bryn Christian Fellowship

WHAT IS FUNDED To advance the Christian Faith in the Beneficial Area by any means, including the provision and upkeep of a place of religious worship and the carrying on of religious services. Other charitable purposes as determined by the Trustees

WHO CAN BENEFIT Christian individuals and organisations

WHERE FUNDING CAN BE GIVEN Parish of Bryn, Ashton in Makerfield

SAMPLE GRANTS £500 for gifts to Russian Jews
£200 for gifts to Prison Ministries
£27 to Bibles for Youth

FINANCES
- Year 1996–97
- Income £10,500
- Grants £2,000

WHO TO APPLY TO Carol L Wood, The Bryn Christian Fellowship, 28 Bowland Avenue, Ashton in Makerfield, Wigan, Lancashire WN4 8BD

CC NO 519624　　　**ESTABLISHED** 1987

■The Burall Charitable Trust

WHAT IS FUNDED To benefit communities where the Burall Company operates, with an interest in education, health relief, hardship or purposes for that benefit of the community. In particular they are interested in charitable activity that benefits youth, sporting or cultural projects where they are also of an educational nature

WHO CAN BENEFIT Children, young adults and students, those disadvantaged by poverty, at risk groups, disabled people, socially isolated people, and victims of abuse, crime and domestic violence

WHERE FUNDING CAN BE GIVEN UK and overseas, although the Trustees have been asked to give preference to communities where Burall Business operates: Cambridgeshire, Merseyside and Leeds

HOW TO APPLY Please send a letter outlining your work and interests before writing a letter of application

WHO TO APPLY TO Colin Arnold, The Burall Charitable Trust, Frasers, 29 Old Market, Wisbech, Cambridgeshire PE13 1ND *Tel* 01945 468700 *Fax* 01945 468709

CC NO 1069455　　　**ESTABLISHED** 1998

■Burden's Charitable Foundation (379)

WHAT IS FUNDED To support local charities which are of special interest to the Trustees including charities working in the fields of: almshouses and sheltered accommodation; acute health care and after care; ambulances and mobile units; hospitals; cancer and MS research. Also religious umbrella bodies; cultural and religious teaching; special needs education; community centres; village halls; care in the community; emergency care and advice centres may also be funded

WHAT IS NOT FUNDED No support is given for the London area, humanities, sport, environmental projects, political activities, archaeology, psychology, animal charities or individuals

WHO CAN BENEFIT Registered charities only. There are no restrictions on the age; social circumstances of; or disease or medical condition suffered by, the beneficiaries

WHERE FUNDING CAN BE GIVEN UK, Ireland and developing countries overseas

TYPE OF GRANT Generally one-off grants, exceptionally more than one-year. Capital, project, research, running and recurring costs, salaries and start-up costs will also be considered. No loans are made

RANGE OF GRANTS £25–£15,000; typical grant £1,000

FINANCES
- Year 1997
- Income £466,767
- Grants £376,758

TRUSTEES Arthur J Burden, FCA, Godfrey W Burden, DipArch(Manc), FRIBA, Roland D W Evans, MC, LLM, Mrs Hilary M Perkins, MCSP, SRP, Mrs Sally Anne Schofield, DipCOT, SROT

NOTES Applications will not be considered without audited accounts

HOW TO APPLY In writing, enclosing proposal, budget and audited accounts

WHO TO APPLY TO A J Burden, Trustee, Burden's Charitable Foundation, St George's House, 215–219 Chester Road, Manchester M15 4JE

CC NO 273535   **ESTABLISHED** 1977

Commentary

Burden's Charitable Foundation was established on 6 April 1977 by Wilfred Thomas Burden and Mrs Ann Elizabeth Burden for general charitable purposes.

Although the Trust Deed gives the Trustees very wide discretionary powers, they are substantially guided by the following tenets – most of which were clarified during the lifetime of the Settlors: (i) Emphasis is on the relief of human suffering and impairment, and on economic deprivation. (ii) Preference is given to small/local groups rather than to large or national and publicly well funded groups. (iii) Emphasis is given to needs in the communities in which the Trustees are themselves active. (iv) Relief and development in the world's most impoverished countries is being targeted with a growing number of agencies providing a helpful and reliable conduit for such funding. (v) Applications are not encouraged from otherwise qualifying charities which are perceived by the Trustees as being located in areas of comparatively substantial wealth. (vi) The social outreach projects of local churches are very much favoured, but not so church buildings designed exclusively or chiefly for worship purposes. This emphasis also largely holds good in the case of the arts generally and historic buildings. It is not known if there are any scales of preference within these policies; however, there are no restrictions on the use of the funds available.

It is not known if the Foundation will replace statutory funding or fund statutory bodies. The Foundation's attitude to co-funding is not known. The Foundation generally makes one-off grants, although funding may exceptionally be for more the one year. Loans are not made.

Applications should be in writing, enclosing a proposal, budget and set of audited accounts. The decision-making processes for dealing with applications, and whether the Foundation has an assessment process for grant recipients, are not known

SAMPLE GRANTS
The top ten grants made in 1997 were:
£45,000 to Frenchay Healthcare Trust for a breast scanner
£22,000 to Citizens Advice Bureau Open Door Project, Moss Side, Manchester
£17,500 to Homefield Project, Prestatyn
£14,000 to Easton Christian Family Centre, Bristol for work with parent groups
£10,000 to Action Partners for a library in Khartoum
£6,000 to William Hulme Grammar School for an educational project

£5,000 to After Adoption for advice and counselling following adoption
£5,000 to Disabled Persons Housing Association for housing and community care
£5,000 to Emmaus, Greater Manchester for a homeless project
£5,000 to Family Welfare Association, Manchester for a bereavement counsellor

■ Sir Matt Busby Charities Fund

WHAT IS FUNDED General charitable purposes to support local charities

WHO CAN BENEFIT Registered charities. There are no restrictions on the age; professional and economic group; family situation; religion and culture; and social circumstances of; or disease or medical condition suffered by, the beneficiaries

WHERE FUNDING CAN BE GIVEN Greater Manchester

SAMPLE GRANTS £1,000 to Rainbow Trust
£1,000 to Dehon House
£1,000 to Henshaws Society for the Blind
£1,000 to Sense
£500 to Childline
£500 to Our Lady and St John
£500 to Autistic Society
£250 to Bishop of Manchester

FINANCES
- Year 1995
- Income £24,414
- Grants £5,750

TRUSTEES D McMorrow (Treasurer), M W Sweeney (Secretary)

HOW TO APPLY To the address under Who To Apply To in writing

WHO TO APPLY TO John Doherty, Secretary, Sir Matt Busby Charities Fund, 4 Beaulieu, Leicester Road, Hale, Altruncham, Cheshire WA15 9QA

CC NO 1008119   **ESTABLISHED** 1991

■The C & A Charitable Trust

WHAT IS FUNDED The C&A Charitable Trust operates primarily through the local C&A stores. Staff take the initiative both in selecting the small number of registered charities to benefit in their area and in helping to raise funds for them. Preferred charities directly benefit children, the elderly or the disadvantaged within the UK. Brochure appeals are not supported. The Trust is therefore unable to respond to unsolicited appeals

WHO CAN BENEFIT Registered charities including religious organisations, hospitals and other medical bodies, schools, community projects, child welfare organisations and homes for the aged. Organisations benfiting: children; young adults; those in care, fostered and adopted; parents and children; one parent families; and those disadvantaged by poverty

WHERE FUNDING CAN BE GIVEN UK with preference to areas where C&A stores operate

RANGE OF GRANTS £50–£7,000; typical £1,000

SAMPLE GRANTS £39,249 to Childline
£30,744 Cot Death Society
£17,396 to Whizz Kids
£8,000 to Institute of Child Health
£6,011 to British Kidney Patient Association

FINANCES
- Year 1996–97
- Income £344,323
- Grants £279,270

TRUSTEES C&A Charitable Trustees

HOW TO APPLY Through stores and London charity committees. **This Trust states that it does not respond to unsolicited applications**

WHO TO APPLY TO The Secretary, C & A Charitable Trust, 20 Old Bailey, London EC4M 7BH

CC NO 269881   **ESTABLISHED** 1975

■The Capenhurst Medical and Research Charity Trust Fund

WHAT IS FUNDED Medical equipment for medical research establishments, hospitals, nursing homes, doctors' surgeries or other medical establishments

WHAT IS NOT FUNDED Preference for actually purchasing needed equipment rather than making cash donations as contributions,

although this is possible exceptionally. Expeditions and scholarships are not funded

WHO CAN BENEFIT Organisations benefiting medical professionals and research workers

WHERE FUNDING CAN BE GIVEN Cheshire, Denbyshire, Flintshire and Wrexham

TYPE OF GRANT One-off, capital and recurrent grants will be considered

RANGE OF GRANTS £5,000–£10,000. Grants in excess of £10,000 unlikely

SAMPLE GRANTS £2,000 to Manor Hospital, Wrexham, the Special Baby Care Unit towards a ventilator
£1,541 to an individual (relative of former employee) for electric wheelchair
£1,000 to Roy Castle Cause for Hope Foundation
£1,000 to the Royal School for the Blind
£850 to an individual (ex-employee) for a second-hand electric scooter
£729 to British Red Cross, Merseyside Branch for two Resusci junior dolls
£664 to The Cot Death Society for two apnoea/respiration monitors
£500 to LUPUS (UK) for assistance with purchase of a computer
£500 to West Cheshire Project for assistance with purchase of a computer
£366 to an individual (wife of employee) for a portable air conditioning unit

FINANCES
- Year 1997
- Income £26,300
- Grants £9,807

TRUSTEES P T Farrington, D Kilfoyle, D Upton, J Edwards, D Bond, L Taylor, D Knight, J G Williams

HOW TO APPLY To the address under Who To Apply To in writing, stating the purpose of the equipment wanted and what the medical benefits are. The committee meets quarterly

WHO TO APPLY TO P T Farrington, The Capenhurst Medical and Research Charity, Urenco (Capehurst) Limited, Capenhurst Works, Chester CH1 6ER *Tel* 0151-347 3618

CC NO 513722   **ESTABLISHED** 1983

■Carlisle Sick Poor Fund

WHAT IS FUNDED The advancement of health and welfare

WHO CAN BENEFIT Individuals and institutions

WHERE FUNDING CAN BE GIVEN Carlisle

FINANCES
- Year 1994
- Income £6,000
- Grants £6,025

HOW TO APPLY To the Correspondent in writing

WHO TO APPLY TO Carlisle Sick Poor Fund, 15 Fisher Street, Carlisle, Cumbria CA3 8RW

CC NO 223124 **ESTABLISHED** 1964

■ Cartmel Old Grammar School Foundation

WHAT IS FUNDED Students and schools within the Beneficial Area. Prime calls upon some of the income are the Brow Edge and Cartmel General Charities

WHAT IS NOT FUNDED The beneficiaries cannot be under 18 or over 25 at 30 September of grant year

WHO CAN BENEFIT Individual scholars, local schools, named charities

WHERE FUNDING CAN BE GIVEN The parishes of Cartmel Fell, Broughton East, Grange-over-Sands, Lower Halker, Staveley, Upper Allithwaite and the part of Haverthwaite to the east of the River Leven

TYPE OF GRANT Individual scholarships to students for up to three years, annual grants to local schools, mandatory grant to named charities above

SAMPLE GRANTS £1,300 to a secondary school
£280 to Brow Edge and Cartmel General Charities
£260 to primary schools
£105 to individual scholars

FINANCES
- Year 1996–97
- Income £7,545
- Grants £7,142

TRUSTEES F B Hampson, A Baxter, J Johnson, K Watkins, J Ball, B E Berry, Rev C Atkinson, Mrs E Mortimer, Mrs M Cannon, Dr Phizacklea

HOW TO APPLY On application form available from the address below

WHO TO APPLY TO A W Coles, Clerk, Cartmel Old Grammar School Foundation, 2 Rowan Side, Grange over Sands, Cumbria LA11 7EQ

CC NO 526467 **ESTABLISHED** 1979

■ The Chadwick Educational Foundation

WHAT IS FUNDED Educational purposes in the Beneficial Area

WHAT IS NOT FUNDED Maximum age of beneficiary 25

WHO CAN BENEFIT Schools and school children/ students

WHERE FUNDING CAN BE GIVEN Bolton and the district of Turton

TYPE OF GRANT Cash for text books and equipment

SAMPLE GRANTS Average size of grant £100

FINANCES
- Year 1996
- Income £1,900
- Grants £1,800

HOW TO APPLY To the Correspondent in writing on an application form

WHO TO APPLY TO Diane Abbott, Secretary, The Chadwick Educational Foundation, Wolfenden and Naylor, 1 Chorley New Road, Bolton, Lancashire BL1 4QR *Tel* 01204 534421

CC NO 526373 **ESTABLISHED** 1977

■ The Amelia Chadwick Trust

WHAT IS FUNDED The Trust has a preference for Merseyside with a wide range of charities supported

WHO CAN BENEFIT Neighbourhood-based community projects, some national organisations. There are no restrictions on the age; professional and economic group; family situation; religion and culture; and social circumstances of; or disease or medical condition suffered by, the beneficiaries

WHERE FUNDING CAN BE GIVEN UK, especially Merseyside

TYPE OF GRANT Recurring

RANGE OF GRANTS £200–£29,750

SAMPLE GRANTS £29,750 to Merseyside Development Foundation
£7,500 to Fair Play for Children
£6,500 to St Helens Women's Aid
£6,500 to Liverpool PSS
£2,700 to European Playworkers
£2,000 to Centrepoint
£2,000 to Garston Adventure Playground
£2,000 to Rotunda Community College
£1,500 to Merseyside Holiday Service
£1,000 to Neston Nomads Junior Football Club

FINANCES
- Year 1997
- Income £94,716
- Grants £86,251

TRUSTEES J R McGibbon, J C H Bibby

NOTES The Trust's funds are fully committed

HOW TO APPLY To the address under Who To Apply To in writing. The Trust does not welcome telephone calls. There is no application form or guidelines, and no deadlines for applications. No sae is required

WHO TO APPLY TO J R M McGibbon, Partner, The Amelia Chadwick Trust, Layton & Co, Victoria House, 20 Hoghton Street, Southport PR9 0NX *Tel* 01704 547117

CC NO 213795   **ESTABLISHED** 1960

··

■ Charity for Change

This trust did not respond to CAF's request to amend its entry and, by 30 June 1998, CAF's researchers did not find financial records for later than 1995 on its file at the Charity Commission. Trusts are legally required to submit annual accounts to the Charity Commission under section 42 of the Charities Act 1993

WHAT IS FUNDED The relief of poverty, advancement of education, advancement of religion and other charitable purposes at the discretion of the Trustees

WHO CAN BENEFIT At the discretion of the Trustees. There are no restrictions on the age; professional and economic group; family situation; religion and culture; and social circumstances of; or disease or medical condition suffered by, the beneficiaries

WHERE FUNDING CAN BE GIVEN Lancashire, UK and overseas

TYPE OF GRANT At the discretion of the Trustees

TRUSTEES F C Collins, A T Eastham, D R Watkinson

WHO TO APPLY TO A Eastham, Charity for Change, Eastham Solicitors, Continental House, 292–302 Church Street, Blackpool, Lancashire FY1 3QA

CC NO 1050388   **ESTABLISHED** 1994

··

■ The Chase Charity

WHAT IS FUNDED The Trustees do not contribute to large general appeals, nor to annual running costs. They work over a wide field but projects in rural areas of particular interest together with strengthening vulnerable groups. They try to make an impact with each grant. Starter finance, unforeseen capital or other expenditure, even help over a bad patch are considered. Small charities and projects are preferred. This Trust considers funding: accommodation and housing; infrastructure development; churches; religious umbrella bodies; arts, culture and recreation; respite care for carers; church buildings; historical buildings; nature reserves; literacy; training for personal development; community facilities; care in the community; day centres; and individual rights

WHAT IS NOT FUNDED No grants are made for projects abroad or in Greater London; individuals; travel; expeditions; sport; endowment funds; hospices; the advancement of religion; animal welfare; medical research; formal education; festivals; individual youth clubs and uniformed youth groups; holidays; projects in receipt of Millennium Lottery Board funding; and other grant making bodies

WHO CAN BENEFIT Mostly small organisations often in rural areas. This includes: actors and entertainment professionals; musicians; research workers; scientists; retired and unemployed people; volunteers; and writers and poets. There is no restriction on the age or family situation, and some restrictions on the religion or culture and social circumstances of, and the disease or medical condition suffered by the beneficiaries

WHERE FUNDING CAN BE GIVEN Great Britain, except London

TYPE OF GRANT Buildings, capital, core costs, one-off, project, research, salaries and start-up costs. Funding is available for up to three years

RANGE OF GRANTS £1,000–£10,000

SAMPLE GRANTS £5,000 to the Griffin Almshouse, Alphington, Devon towards the cost of replacing windows
£5,000 to Deckham Community Centre, Gateshead for replacing roof
£4,000 to St Mark's Church Community Centre, Bedford for purchasing Portakabin as base for local autistic society
£4,000 to South Leeds Team Ministry Charity Ltd, Belle Isle, Leeds to refurbish and extend Belle Isle Day Centre for elderly people
£4,000 to Bridge Accommodation Project, Rushden, Northamptonshire to expand service for homeless people into rural areas, an 18 month pilot scheme
£4,000 to Voluntary Hostels Group, Norwich to establish a register of hostel workers as a one year pilot scheme
£3,500 to Lochaber Community Care Forum, Fort William, Scotland to help establish a 20 week pilot scheme involving visually impaired people
£3,120 to Community Campus '87, Middlesbrough to run evening tenant participation sessions for young people
£3,000 to Art Discovery, The Orkneys towards the cost of Ancient Minds – Modern Art Project with school children
£2,200 to the Crumbs Project, Bournemouth to open the kitchen for a third day to involve more people with mental health problems

FINANCES
* Year 1996–97   * Income £289,476
* Grants £207,770

TRUSTEES The Council of Management: A Ramsay Hack (Chairman), Gordon Halcrow, Richard Mills, Elizabeth Moore, Ninian Perry, Ann Stannard

PUBLICATIONS Annual Report; *How to Apply for a Grant*

HOW TO APPLY At any time. The Trustees meet quarterly, but there is a waiting list so projects are not often considered within three months of applying

WHO TO APPLY TO Ailsa Hornsby, The Chase Charity, 2 The Court, High Street, Harwell, Didcot, Oxfordshire OX11 0EY *Tel* 01235 820044

CC NO 207108   **ESTABLISHED** 1962

■Cheadle Royal Industries Charitable Trust

WHAT IS FUNDED To relieve employees and their dependants who are in need. To support the work of the hospital and to relieve the poor and infirm as the Trustees direct

WHO CAN BENEFIT Individuals and institutions

WHERE FUNDING CAN BE GIVEN UK, Cheadle

FINANCES
• Year 1995–96   • Income £8,876

WHO TO APPLY TO Mrs M J Barry, Cheadle Royal Industries Charitable Trust, 100 Wilmslow Road, Cheadle, Cheshire SK8 3DG

CC NO 509813   **ESTABLISHED** 1980

■Cheshire Constabulary Community Involvement Fund of Northwich Division

WHAT IS FUNDED To develop the physical, mental and spiritual well being of young people, mainly through leisure activities, or any other charitable purposes

WHO CAN BENEFIT Young people

WHERE FUNDING CAN BE GIVEN Cheshire

FINANCES
• Year 1995–96   • Income £9,196
• Grants £2,540

WHO TO APPLY TO PC Raymond M Pond, Cheshire Constabulary Community Involvement Fund Collingham Way, Winsford, Cheshire CW7 2WA

CC NO 510795   **ESTABLISHED** 1981

■The Cheshire Constabulary Involvement Fund for the Northern Divisions

WHAT IS FUNDED Young people and other charitable purposes

WHO CAN BENEFIT Individuals and institutions

WHERE FUNDING CAN BE GIVEN North Cheshire

FINANCES
• Year 1995   • Income £11,900
• Grants £2,362

NOTES The Trust has its income divided between two funds: the CCC Involvement Fund being the largest, and the Elderly Fund

HOW TO APPLY To the Correspondent in writing

WHO TO APPLY TO Superintendent, Chairperson, The Cheshire Constabulary Involvement Fund for the Northern Divisions, County Police Office, Arpley Street, Warrington, Cheshire WA1 1LQ

CC NO 1013348   **ESTABLISHED** 1992

■The Cheshire Provincial Fund of Benevolence

WHAT IS FUNDED The relief of masons and their dependants, masonic charities and other charities, especially medical

WHO CAN BENEFIT Individuals and organisations benefiting masons and their families. There is no restriction on the disease or medical condition suffered by the beneficiaries

WHERE FUNDING CAN BE GIVEN Cheshire

SAMPLE GRANTS £7,000 to PGM Charity Account
£1,500 to St Luke's Hospice
£1,500 to St Ann's Hospice
£1,500 to East Cheshire Hospice
£1,500 to St John's Hospice
£1,500 to Hospice of the Good Shepherd
£1,500 to Rainbow Family Trust
£1,500 to Hope House Children's Respite Hospice
£1,500 to Beechwood Cancer Care Centre
£1,500 to Tameside and Glossop Hospice

FINANCES
• Year 1997   • Income £322,663
• Grants £237,501

TRUSTEES J A T Collins, A E Cross, G Glover, G R Humphries, P W Wellings, J Williams

NOTES In 1997, payments of £26,251 were made to individuals, £177,500 were made to masonic charities, and £33,750 were made to non-masonic charities

HOW TO APPLY To the address under Who To Apply To in writing

WHO TO APPLY TO J A T Collins, Provincial Grand Secretary, The Cheshire Provincial Fund of Benevolence, Ashcroft House, 36 Clay Lane, Timperley, Altrincham WA15 7AB

CC NO 219177 **ESTABLISHED** 1963

....

■ The Cheshire Provincial Grand Lodge of Mark Master Mason's Fund of Benevolence

WHAT IS FUNDED Masonic charities, the relief of poor masons and their families and other charitable purposes

WHO CAN BENEFIT Charities and other organisations benefiting masons, individual masons and their families

WHERE FUNDING CAN BE GIVEN Cheshire, Merseyside and Greater Manchester

RANGE OF GRANTS £100–£1,500

SAMPLE GRANTS £1,500 to Masonic Dorset Festival 1997
£1,182 to Cheshire Scouts and Guides
£1,000 to Masonic West Lancashire Festival 2005
£1,000 to Masonic Cheshire Festival 2000
£500 to Hospice of the Good Shepherd
£500 to Children's Heart Foundation
£400 to Distressed Brethren as three grants
£100 to St Johns Hospice

FINANCES
- Year 1997
- Income £33,453
- Grants £6,182

TRUSTEES H Statter (Chairman), J T Crompton, C J MacDonald

HOW TO APPLY To the address under Who To Apply To in writing. Applications from non-Masonic charities are considered once a year at the AGM

WHO TO APPLY TO J A T Collins, Provincial Grand Secretary, The Cheshire Provincial Grand Lodge of Mark Master Mason's Fund of Benevolence, Ashcroft House, 36 Clay Lane, Timperley, Altrincham WA15 7AB

CC NO 512541 **ESTABLISHED** 1982

....

■ Chester Diocesan Moral Aid Charity (St Bridget's Trust)

WHAT IS FUNDED Societies supporting women in moral danger and their children

WHAT IS NOT FUNDED No grants to individuals

WHO CAN BENEFIT Women (and their children), particularly those in care, fostered and adopted, and victims of abuse

WHERE FUNDING CAN BE GIVEN Cheshire

TYPE OF GRANT Core costs

RANGE OF GRANTS £1,100pa–£11,000pa; typical £1,800pa

SAMPLE GRANTS £11,400 to Chester Diocese Adoption Services for core costs
£9,100 to Chester Diocese Committee for Social Responsibility for family services
£1,800 to Chester Womens Aid for abused women and children
£1,800 to Macclesfield Cradle Concern to support their care for unmarried mothers and babies
£1,600 to Save the Family for work with unmarried mothers and their children
£1,100 to YWCA Winsford to support their care for unmarried mothers and babies

FINANCES
- Year 1997–98
- Income £28,092
- Grants £26,800

TRUSTEES R Biggins, R L Jones, Rt Rev P Foster, Rev R M Powley, Canon G Robinson, Rev C J Samuels, Ms W Steadman

NOTES All our income is fully committed

HOW TO APPLY To the address under Who To Apply To in writing with an initial telephone call

WHO TO APPLY TO Canon G V M Robinson, Clerk, Chester Diocesan Moral Aid Charity, 69 Marian Drive, Great Boughton, Chester, Cheshire CH3 5RY *Tel* 01244 315828

CC NO 213298 **ESTABLISHED** 1962

....

■ The Chiron Trust

WHAT IS FUNDED Support is given in the fields of conservation and environment, health facilities, vocational training, advice centres, and support for volunteers and voluntary organisations

WHAT IS NOT FUNDED No funding for expeditions or travel bursaries

WHO CAN BENEFIT Registered charities benefiting: volunteers; at risk groups; those disadvantaged by poverty; socially isolated people; victims of famine, war and man-made or natural disasters, and those who are terminally ill

WHERE FUNDING CAN BE GIVEN England, particularly North East, North West and Eastern regions and London

TYPE OF GRANT Buildings, core costs, running costs and start-up costs will be considered. Funding is available for up to three years

RANGE OF GRANTS £250–£1,000

FINANCES
- Year 1997
- Income £113,747
- Grants £144,323

Does the trust you have chosen match your needs? Haphazard applications waste postage and time

....
103

TRUSTEES D M Tinson, C J Du B Tinson, I R Marks

NOTES In writing, no application forms

WHO TO APPLY TO Mrs D M Tinson, The Chiron Trust, 30 Fitzwalter Road, Colchester, Essex CO3 3SY

CC NO 287062   **ESTABLISHED** 1983

■The Chorley Relief Fund

WHAT IS FUNDED The advancement of welfare

WHERE FUNDING CAN BE GIVEN Chorley

FINANCES
- Year 1996
- Grants £1,919
- Income £4,363

HOW TO APPLY To the Correspondent in writing

WHO TO APPLY TO R Parkinson, Clerk, The Chorley Relief Fund, 40 Judeland, Chorley, Lancashire PR7 1XJ

CC NO 224431   **ESTABLISHED** 1990

■The Chrimes Family Charitable Trust

WHAT IS FUNDED Infrastructure development; hospice at home; and respite and care for carers. The Trustees give preference to support of community welfare on Merseyside and North Wales. Elsewhere only work, in this field, of originality or outstanding excellence is supported

WHAT IS NOT FUNDED No grants to individuals, arts, conservation or education and training

WHO CAN BENEFIT Volunteers; carers and disabled people. Those suffering from arthritis and rheumatism; asthma; autism; cancers; hearing and sight loss; and terminal illnesses

WHERE FUNDING CAN BE GIVEN Priority to Merseyside, Wirral, Conwy and Gwynedd

RANGE OF GRANTS £50–£500

FINANCES
- Year 1997
- Grants £21,984
- Income £18,396

TRUSTEES Mrs Anne Williams, Mrs H G Kirkham Prosser

HOW TO APPLY No application form. Letters appreciated. No deadlines

WHO TO APPLY TO Mrs Anne Williams, The Chrimes Family Charitable Trust, Northfield, Upper Raby Road, Neston, South Wirral L64 7TZ

CC NO 210199   **ESTABLISHED** 1955

■The Chronicle Cinderella Fund

WHAT IS FUNDED To provide holidays and outings for disadvantaged or sick women and children under 18 years

WHO CAN BENEFIT Organisations running holidays for disadvantaged children and individuals on referral from agencies only

WHERE FUNDING CAN BE GIVEN Lancashire (pre-1974)

TYPE OF GRANT One-off

SAMPLE GRANTS £250 to Lancashire Youth Clubs Association
£250 to South West Burnley Community Development Trust
£200 to East Lancashire Deaf Society
£155 to the Hawthorns Centre, Chorley
£150 to Barnardos, Chorley
£150 to Marton Mere Community Association
£150 to Lancaster Young Carers
£150 to Leigh CAB
£120 to Preston and Chorley Integrate
£90 per child to Harvest Trust

FINANCES
- Year 1996–97
- Grants £5,775
- Income £8,129

NOTES The Trustees meet quarterly in January, April, July and October

HOW TO APPLY On application form available from the Correspondent, to be completed by the referral agency. There will be no response to applications without an sae

WHO TO APPLY TO Richard C Davey, The Chronicle Cinderella Fund, 15 Victoria Road, Fulwood, Preston, Lancashire PR2 8PS
Tel 01772 717461 *Fax* 01772 718710
E-mail cclancashire@mcmail.com

CC NO 233743   **ESTABLISHED** 1964

■City of Manchester Common Good Trust

WHAT IS FUNDED General charitable purposes

WHO CAN BENEFIT Individuals and organisations

WHERE FUNDING CAN BE GIVEN Manchester

FINANCES
- Year 1997
- Income £6,817

HOW TO APPLY Application forms obtained from the Correspondent

WHO TO APPLY TO Lord Mayor's Secretary, City of Manchester Common Good Trust, Manchester City Council, Town Hall, Manchester M60 2JR

CC NO 203936   **ESTABLISHED** 1961

104

Think carefully about every application. Is it justified?

■ The Claremont Association

WHAT IS FUNDED General charitable purposes

WHO CAN BENEFIT Individuals and organisations

WHERE FUNDING CAN BE GIVEN Blackpool

FINANCES
- Year 1994–95
- Income £3,262
- Grants £3,900

HOW TO APPLY To the Correspondent in writing

WHO TO APPLY TO Mrs K Hayward, President, The Claremont Association, 5 Banbury Avenue, Blackpool, Lancashire FY2 0TX

CC NO 1023687   **ESTABLISHED** 1993

■ The Emily Clover Trust

WHAT IS FUNDED To relieve need, hardship or distress

WHAT IS NOT FUNDED No grants for adult or further education, or adventure holidays or expeditions

WHO CAN BENEFIT Registered charities and individuals

WHERE FUNDING CAN BE GIVEN Within a ten mile radius of St Oswald's Church, Bidston

TYPE OF GRANT One-off

FINANCES
- Year 1994–95
- Income £3,000
- Grants £4,500

TRUSTEES Rev S Mansfield, J L Berry, A Cobham, S Osborne, A D Perrin, H Smith, L F Chetterden

HOW TO APPLY To the Correspondent in writing. Applications are generally considered at quarterly meetings

WHO TO APPLY TO L F Chettenden, The Emily Clover Trust, 31 Brookside Crescent, Upton, Wirral L49 4LE *Tel* 0151-677 2119

CC NO 246108   **ESTABLISHED** 1983

■ Robert Clutterbuck Charitable Trust

WHAT IS FUNDED Personnel within the armed forces and ex-services men and women. Sport and recreational facilities. Natural history. The welfare, protection and preservation of animal life

WHAT IS NOT FUNDED Applications for payments to individuals are not considered

WHO CAN BENEFIT The Trustees only consider applications from registered charities. Organisations benefiting ex-service and service people, and sportsmen and women

WHERE FUNDING CAN BE GIVEN Mainly UK. Special consideration will be given to charities associated with the counties of Cheshire and Hertfordshire

TYPE OF GRANT Payments normally from income, generally for the purchase of specific items

RANGE OF GRANTS £130–£20,000; typical £2,000–£3,000

SAMPLE GRANTS £4,810 to Barrowmore, Great Barrow, Chester for conversion of a flat for a disabled woman
£4,500 to College of St Barnabas Centenary Appeal, Lingfield, Surrey for cost of new staircase
£3,500 to Trefoil House, Edinburgh for new floor in games room
£3,325 to Training Ship Stirling, Edinburgh for sponsorship of 25 sea cadets for one week on sail training ship
£3,000 to St John the Baptist Church at Godley-Cum-Newton Green, Cheshire for new floor for the conversion of a former school to a community centre
£3,000 to Buckmore Park Scout Centre, Chatham for purchase of a second hand land rover
£2,300 to Coventry Boys' Club for extension of internal games area and purchase of camping and sports equipment
£2,000 to SSAFA Forces Help, Cheshire Branch for administration expenses
£2,000 to David Lewis Organisation, Alderley Edge for grant towards cost of recreation/relaxation room
£2,000 to Royal Schools for the Deaf, Manchester for contribution to cost of multi sensory hydrotherapy pool

FINANCES
- Year 1997–98
- Income £49,897
- Grants £44,985

TRUSTEES Major R G Clutterbuck, C N Lindsell, A C Humphries, OBE

HOW TO APPLY To B C Berryman who will acknowledge them. Applications are only considered by Trustees at their meetings. They meet three times a year

WHO TO APPLY TO B C Berryman, Robert Clutterbuck Charitable Trust, Ashleigh Cottage, 207 Staines Road, Laleham, Staines, Middlesex TW18 2RS *Tel* 01784 451651

CC NO 1010559   **ESTABLISHED** 1992

■ The C D Collins Charitable Trust

WHAT IS FUNDED General charitable purposes, especially causes particularly concerned with the elderly

WHO CAN BENEFIT Elderly people

WHERE FUNDING CAN BE GIVEN UK, especially Liverpool

FINANCES
- Year 1994–95
- Income £11,000

TRUSTEES B J Kynaston Gwyer, Susan Mealhouse

HOW TO APPLY To the Correspondent in writing

WHO TO APPLY TO The Clerk, The C D Collins Charitable Trust, 5 Castle Street, Liverpool L2 4XE

CC NO 327746   **ESTABLISHED** 1988

■The Community Trust for Greater Manchester

WHAT IS FUNDED Medicine and health, welfare, education, religion, arts, conservation and environment, people with disabilities, elderly, animal welfare, youth and children. Other charitable purposes will be considered

WHAT IS NOT FUNDED No grants to individuals, or for political organisations

WHO CAN BENEFIT Small local projects, new and established organisations and innovative projects benefiting children, young adults and elderly people, disabled people, at risk groups, those disadvantaged by poverty and socially isolated people. There is no restriction on the disease or medical condition suffered by the beneficiaries

WHERE FUNDING CAN BE GIVEN Greater Manchester

TYPE OF GRANT One-off grants

RANGE OF GRANTS Up to £1,000

FINANCES
- Year 1996–97
- Income £195,352
- Grants £121,644

TRUSTEES His Grace The Duke of Westminster, OBE, TD, DL, Alan Rudden, R Gordon Humphreys, A J Farnworth, John Sandford, C Smith, M Eileen Polding, Lorraine Worsley, Jack Buckley, W T Risby, C Chan, A A Downie

PUBLICATIONS Annual Report. Guidelines. Information Packs

HOW TO APPLY In writing. Application form available

WHO TO APPLY TO R J Carter, The Community Trust for Greater Manchester, PO Box 63, Beswick House, Beswick Row, Manchester M4 4JY *Web Site* http://www.scanline.com/intersect/community/

CC NO 1017504   **ESTABLISHED** 1993

■The Congleton Inclosure Trust

WHAT IS FUNDED The relief of the aged, impotent and poor; the relief of distress and sickness; the provision and support of facilities for recreation or other leisure-time activities; the provision and support of educational facilities; and any other charitable purpose

WHAT IS NOT FUNDED No grants to projects and applicants resident outside the area Where Funding Can Be Given (Congleton)

WHO CAN BENEFIT Local organisations; national organisations with projects in the area Where Funding Can Be Given. Funding may be given to people with many differing social circumstances. There is no restriction on the age or family situation of the beneficiaries, or on their disease or medical condition

WHERE FUNDING CAN BE GIVEN Congleton and the parishes of Hulme Walfield and Newbold with Astbury

TYPE OF GRANT Buildings, capital, core costs, feasibility studies, salaries and start-up costs will be considered. Funding may be given for up to one year

RANGE OF GRANTS £100–£10,000

SAMPLE GRANTS £10,000 to Astbury National Schools for a building project
£8,000 to Mossley Cricket Club for a building project
£4,000 to Congleton Brass towards instruments for local brass band
£3,500 to Congleton Community Trust for educational workshops for young people
£3,500 to Outreach Team for welfare work in the community
£2,500 to VISYON towards supporting young people under stress
£1,500 to Stepping Stones for equipment for pre-school project
£1,000 to Congleton Borough Council to the Mayor for Christmas charity for the elderly

FINANCES
- Year 1997
- Income £66,000
- Grants £37,830

TRUSTEES G Taylor (Chairman), D Bibbey, K P Boon, Rev E Brazier, J C Dale, A Horton, G Humphreys, R Painter, E G Pedley, M A S Roy, E R Tansley, Rev M Walters, A B Watson

HOW TO APPLY Applications should be made on a form available from the address under Who To Apply To. Applications are considered by the Trustees in January, April, July and October and should be received by the first day of the month in which the Trustees meet

WHO TO APPLY TO D A Daniel, Clerk, The Congleton Inclosure Trust, PO Box 138, Congleton, Cheshire CW12 3SZ *Tel* 01260 273180

CC NO 244136   **ESTABLISHED** 1795

■ The Congleton Town Trust

WHAT IS FUNDED The scheme provides that after defraying the cost of administration and managing the charity and it's property the Trustees are to apply their income in making grants, generally or individually, to persons resident within the area administered by the Congleton Town Council (or who can be treated as being so resident) who are in conditions of need, hardship or distress or to organisations able to provide facilities for such persons. This can be given in the areas of: accommodation and housing; support to volunteers; professional bodies; health care; health facilities and buildings; special needs education; training for work; and community services

WHO CAN BENEFIT Individuals and organisations benefiting disabled people; those disadvantaged by poverty; disaster victims; homeless people; and victims of abuse. There is no restriction on the age or family situation of the beneficiaries

WHERE FUNDING CAN BE GIVEN Congleton

TYPE OF GRANT One-off, capital, buildings, core costs, project, salaries and start-up costs. Funding is available for one year or less

SAMPLE GRANTS £9,505 to Heathfield Sports Trust for facilities for the disabled
£3,000 to youth project supporting a youth information shop
£2,500 to Town Mayor Christmas charities
£2,000 to NSPCC for a single parents project in Congleton
£1,500 to XYZ for personal grants for home improvements for a disabled child
£1,000 to Congleton Borough Council for various care and repair schemes for elderly people

FINANCES
- Year 1997
- Income £22,500
- Grants £20,500

TRUSTEES Six members nominated by Congleton Town Council and five co-opted members. G Baxendale, M J Cooper, P Copestick, J Fuller, A J Hurst, Mrs M Johnson, P Mason, J E Thompson, C M Thompson, Mrs J Vale, R Whiston, Mrs M Williamson, D Parker

HOW TO APPLY To the address under Who To Apply To in writing

WHO TO APPLY TO D A Daniel, Clerk, The Congleton Town Trust, Copperfields, Peel Lane, Astbury, Congleton, Cheshire CW12 4RE *Tel* 01260 273180

CC NO 1051122   **ESTABLISHED** 1884

■ The Coward Trust

WHAT IS FUNDED Medical charities

WHAT IS NOT FUNDED Applications from individuals are unlikely to be successful

WHO CAN BENEFIT National and local organisations benefiting the visually impaired, and those suffering from cancers, diabetes, and motor neurone disease

WHERE FUNDING CAN BE GIVEN Lancashire

TYPE OF GRANT One-off

RANGE OF GRANTS £1,000–£4,000

SAMPLE GRANTS £4,000 to Barnardos
£4,000 to British Diabetic Association for research
£4,000 to Derian House Children's Hospice
£4,000 to League of Friends of Teddington Memorial Hospital
£3,000 to Christie Hospital NHS Trust for cancer research
£3,000 to the Leonard Cheshire Foundation
£2,000 to Red Rose Community Trust
£2,000 to St Dunstan's
£1,000 to Motor Neurone Disease Association
£1,000 to Quidenham Children's Hospice

FINANCES
- Year 1997–98
- Income £25,171
- Grants £30,000

TRUSTEES Norman Jamieson, David Sharples, Gerald Sharples

HOW TO APPLY To the address below in writing. The Trustees meet to decide on grants in December each year

WHO TO APPLY TO N Jamieson, FCA, The Coward Trust, 58 Riverside Mead, Stanground, Peterborough, Cambridgeshire PE2 8JN *Tel* 01733 345800

CC NO 519341   **ESTABLISHED** 1987

■ The Lord Cozens-Hardy Trust

WHAT IS FUNDED The Trust has a preference for supporting national, Norfolk and Merseyside charities for medicine, health and welfare

WHAT IS NOT FUNDED Grants only to registered charities, see Where Funding Can Be Given

WHO CAN BENEFIT Organisations benefiting at risk groups, those disadvantaged by poverty and socially isolated people. Research workers and medical professionals may be considered. There is no restriction on the disease or medical condition suffered by the beneficiaries

WHERE FUNDING CAN BE GIVEN UK with a preference for Norfolk and Merseyside

TYPE OF GRANT At the discretion of the Trustees mostly small payments

RANGE OF GRANTS £100–£11,500

SAMPLE GRANTS £11,500 to BMA Medical Education Trust Fund
£1,500 to Lancashire Constabulary – the Lord Cozens-Hardy Travelling Fellowship
£1,250 to Raleigh International
£1,000 to Cley Church
£1,000 to Greshams School General Charitable Trust
£1,000 to Holt and Neighbourhood Housing Society Ltd
£1,000 to Incorporated Liverpool School of Tropical Medicine
£1,000 to Order of St John
£1,000 to Order of St John Hospital
£1,000 to Royal Liverpool Philanthropic Society

FINANCES
- Year 1997
- Income £80,596
- Grants £65,750

TRUSTEES Hon Beryl Cozens-Hardy, Hon Helen R Phelps, John E V Phelps, Mrs L F Phelps

WHO TO APPLY TO The Hon Beryl Cozens-Hardy, OBE, The Lord Cozens-Hardy Trust, The Glebe, Letheringsett, Holt, Norfolk NR25 7YA

CC NO 264237   **ESTABLISHED** 1972

■The Crag House Charitable Trust

WHAT IS FUNDED General charitable purposes

WHO CAN BENEFIT There are no restrictions on the age; professional and economic group; family situation; religion and culture; and social circumstances of; or disease or medical condition suffered by, the beneficiaries

WHERE FUNDING CAN BE GIVEN The Winster and Windermere areas of Cumbria

TYPE OF GRANT Mainly one-off

RANGE OF GRANTS £50–£6,000; typical £200

FINANCES
- Year 1998
- Income £14,073
- Grants £10,324

TRUSTEES J M Hopkinson, Mrs E J Hopkinson, Mrs L C Sefton,

NOTES The Trustees will mainly select grant recipients from amongst causes already known to them

HOW TO APPLY Small, local charities may approach the Trust with a brief letter, but a response will not necessarily be forthcoming

WHO TO APPLY TO J M Hopkinson, Trustee, The Crag House Charitable Trust, Crag House, Winster, Windermere, Cumbria LA23 3NS *Tel* 01539 720049

CC NO 1054944   **ESTABLISHED** 1996

■The Crosby Charitable Trust

WHAT IS FUNDED Medical and other charitable purposes

WHO CAN BENEFIT Individuals and institutions

WHERE FUNDING CAN BE GIVEN The North West

FINANCES
- Year 1996
- Income £10,871

HOW TO APPLY To the Correspondent in writing

WHO TO APPLY TO M J Crosby, Trustee, The Crosby Charitable Trust, Lapwing Cottage, Lapwing Lane, Lower Withington, Macclesfield, Cheshire SK11 9AD

CC NO 326201   **ESTABLISHED** 1982

■Crosthwaite and Lyth Trust

WHAT IS FUNDED The advancement of welfare, education and recreation

WHO CAN BENEFIT Individuals and institutions

WHERE FUNDING CAN BE GIVEN Crosthwaite and Lyth

FINANCES
- Year 1994–95
- Income £2,000
- Grants £3,060

HOW TO APPLY To the Correspondent in writing

WHO TO APPLY TO Mrs L B Stott, Clerk, Crosthwaite and Lyth Trust, Rock Wood, Crosthwaite, Kendal, Cumbria LA8 8HX

CC NO 509732   **ESTABLISHED** 1961

■The Cumberland and Westmorland Provincial Grand Lodge Benevolent Fund

WHAT IS FUNDED The Trust's grant total is distributed amongst masons and their dependants, and to masonic and other charities

WHO CAN BENEFIT Mainly masons and their families

WHERE FUNDING CAN BE GIVEN Cumbria

108

Think carefully about every application. Is it justified?

FINANCES
- Year 1997
- Income £258,675
- Grants £44,268

TRUSTEES J H Gale, J Hale, A F Sewell, J W Tyson

HOW TO APPLY To the address under Who To Apply To in writing

WHO TO APPLY TO K Graham, Secretary, The Cumberland and Westmorland Provincial Grand Lodge Benevolent Fund, Hoylands, Bowscar, Penrith, Cumbria CA11 8RS *Tel* 01768 863860

CC NO 213203   **ESTABLISHED** 1927

■DAG Charitable Trust

WHAT IS FUNDED General charitable purposes and education, principally Jewish

WHO CAN BENEFIT Charitable and educational institutions benefiting children, young adults and Jewish people

WHERE FUNDING CAN BE GIVEN Manchester

FINANCES
- Year 1997
- Income £33,420
- Grants £28,459

TRUSTEES A Vaisfiche, E Vaisfiche

HOW TO APPLY To the address under Who To Apply To in writing

WHO TO APPLY TO The Trustees, DAG Charitable Trust, Messrs Lopian Barnett & Co, Harvester House, 37 Peter Street, Manchester M2 5QD

CC NO 290020   **ESTABLISHED** 1984

■The Darnhill Exhibition Foundation

WHAT IS FUNDED Grants for educational purposes are given to primary schools in the Beneficial Area

WHO CAN BENEFIT Individuals and institutions

WHERE FUNDING CAN BE GIVEN The Parishes of Over, Darnhill, Whettonhall and Morton and those parts of the Parishes of Little Budworth and Weaverham Cum Milton which were previously in the Parishes of Over and Whitegate

FINANCES
- Year 1996
- Income £2,972

HOW TO APPLY To the Correspondent in writing

WHO TO APPLY TO Miss E N Rigby, Clerk, The Darnhill Exhibition Foundation, Clive House, Clive Back Lane, Winsford, Cheshire CW7 3NX

CC NO 525857   **ESTABLISHED** 1964

■The John Grant Davies Trust

WHAT IS FUNDED Financial support is given for combating poverty, to community groups, voluntary organisations and faith communities in the area Where Funding Can Be Given. Preference is given to small grassroots organisations. This includes: infrastructure development; charity or voluntary umbrella bodies; community arts and recreation; health counselling; health education; environmental issues; transport and alternative transport; IT training; literacy; training for community development; playgrounds and recreation grounds; community services; campaigning for social issues; equal opportunities; and advice and information

WHAT IS NOT FUNDED No grants for buildings or holidays or to individuals

WHO CAN BENEFIT Organisations benefiting: people of all ages; unemployed people; and volunteers. There are a few restrictions on the social circumstances of the beneficiaries

WHERE FUNDING CAN BE GIVEN Greater Manchester

TYPE OF GRANT One-off, capital, core costs, feasibility studies, project, research, salaries and start-up costs. Funding is available for up to three years

RANGE OF GRANTS £100–£3,000

SAMPLE GRANTS £2,200 to Old Trafford Community Development Project towards employing a second community development worker
£2,000 to Hulwe Action Resources project towards drop in/advice centre
£2,000 to The Furniture Station for collecting and refurbishing furniture for poor people
£2,000 to After Adoption funding part of salary for worker with women in Styal Prison who are losing or have lost a child
£2,000 to St Ambrose Young Families, Salford towards core costs
£1,800 to Salford Racial Harassment Project to help fund sessional work for self help support groups
£1,500 to STEP (Strategies to Elevate People) for costs of Saturday School for black children
£1,500 to NACRO Football Community Link funding football coaching sessions using local volunteers and local children
£1,500 Copperdale Trust, Benchill towards costs and salaries for community development project
£1,500 to Old Moat Youth Outreach for costs of drop in centre

FINANCES
• Year 1996–97   • Income £39,900
• Grants £31,745

TRUSTEES Jonathan Dale, Katherine Davies, Nora Davies, Craig Russell

NOTES Policy statement accompanies application form

HOW TO APPLY Applications should be made on a form available from the address under Who To Apply To. Grants are made quarterly and deadlines are given

WHO TO APPLY TO Dr N Davies, The John Grant Davies Trust, 1462 Ashton Old Road, Manchester M11 1HL *Tel* 0161-301 5119

CC NO 1041001   **ESTABLISHED** 1994

··

■The Thomas Pearce Davies Welfare Trust

WHAT IS FUNDED Local organisations or national organisations which benefit the inhabitants of the Beneficial Area

WHO CAN BENEFIT Organisations

WHERE FUNDING CAN BE GIVEN Darwen

FINANCES
• Year 1995   • Income £1,897

HOW TO APPLY To the Correspondent in writing

WHO TO APPLY TO Halliwell & Halliwell, Solicitors, The Thomas Pearce Davies Welfare Trust, 21 Railway Road, Darwen, Lancashire BB3 2RG

CC NO 501158   **ESTABLISHED** 1961

··

■The de Avenley Foundation

This trust did not respond to CAF's request to amend its entry and, by 30 June 1998, CAF's researchers did not find financial records for later than 1995 on its file at the Charity Commission. Trusts are legally required to submit annual accounts to the Charity Commission under section 42 of the Charities Act 1993

WHAT IS FUNDED Arts, especially music and setting up concerts

WHAT IS NOT FUNDED No grants to individuals

WHO CAN BENEFIT Registered charities benefiting musicians, artists, textile workers and designers, and writers and poets

WHERE FUNDING CAN BE GIVEN Cumbria and UK

TRUSTEES P R Gibson, P J Bond, B Ainley

WHO TO APPLY TO P R Gibson, The de Avenley Foundation, Stone Cross Mansion, Ulverston, Cumbria LA12 7RY

CC NO 1048672   **ESTABLISHED** 1995

··

■Denton Relief in Sickness Charity

WHAT IS FUNDED To advance health and welfare

WHO CAN BENEFIT Local organisations which are well-known to the Trustees

WHERE FUNDING CAN BE GIVEN Denton

TYPE OF GRANT Mainly recurrent

FINANCES
• Year 1996   • Income £4,021

TRUSTEES K B Almond, M D Dickin, Canon J K Tutton

HOW TO APPLY **The Trustees do not encourage direct applications from members of the public which they would not be in a position to vet adequately**

WHO TO APPLY TO M D Dickin, Secretary, Denton Relief in Sickness Charity, Booth, Ince & Knowles, Solicitors, 1 Market Street, Denton, Manchester M34 3BX

CC NO 223597   **ESTABLISHED** 1964

■The Nancy Derbyshire Trust

WHAT IS FUNDED The provision of almshouses for poor people of good character who have lived within seven miles of the almshouse building for at least five years. To relieve other poor people who have similar qualifications

WHO CAN BENEFIT Individuals, almshouses

WHERE FUNDING CAN BE GIVEN Blackburn

TYPE OF GRANT Recurring

FINANCES
- Year 1996
- Income £8,829
- Grants £2,000

TRUSTEES J C Barker (Chairman), R B Prest, Miss J Towers, Mrs J Knowles, Mrs N Sutherland

NOTES **The income of the Trust is at present fully utilised in maintaining and providing accommodation at the Almshouses at St Silas Road, Blackburn and there is presently no surplus income for distribution elsewhere**

WHO TO APPLY TO J C Barker, The Nancy Derbyshire Trust, Forbes and Partners, 2–6 Wellington Street St John, Blackburn, Lancashire BB1 8DD *Tel* 01254 54374

CC NO 237996   **ESTABLISHED** 1964

■Edward Dixon Memorial Fund

WHAT IS FUNDED General charitable purposes

WHAT IS NOT FUNDED Grants will not be made to individuals

WHO CAN BENEFIT Organisations

WHERE FUNDING CAN BE GIVEN The boundaries of the old Southport County Borough

SAMPLE GRANTS NCH Action for children
Birkdale School for Hearing Impaired Children
Francis Taylor Foundation
Southport and District Cerebral Palsy Association

FINANCES
- Year 1996–97
- Income £2,100

- Grants £1,500

TRUSTEES D H Hobley, N I Broad

HOW TO APPLY To the Correspondent in writing. Applications considered when received, though grants are only distributed in June

WHO TO APPLY TO D H Hobley, Edward Dixon Memorial Fund, Lithgow Nelson & Co, 399 Lord Street, Southport PR9 0AS
Tel 01704 531888 *Fax* 01704 548343

CC NO 266214   **ESTABLISHED** 1972

■Drugwatch Trust

WHAT IS FUNDED To increase public awareness of the dangers and methods of relief to prevent drug abuse

WHO CAN BENEFIT Individuals and organisations

WHERE FUNDING CAN BE GIVEN Cheshire

FINANCES
- Year 1995–96
- Income £8,875
- Grants £4,298

WHO TO APPLY TO Vivian A Knight, Drugwatch Trust, 57 Curzon Park South, Chester, Cheshire CH4 8AA

CC NO 702821   **ESTABLISHED** 1990

■The Duchy of Lancaster Benevolent Fund (461)

WHAT IS FUNDED General charitable causes

WHAT IS NOT FUNDED Areas outside the County Palatine and charities and organisations which do not have any links with the Duchy of Lancaster. No grants to individuals

WHO CAN BENEFIT People resident in the County Palatine and with links to the Duchy of Lancaster. Particularly children, young adults, older people and disabled people. There are no restrictions on the age; professional and economic group; family situation; religion and culture; and social circumstances of; or disease or medical condition suffered by, the beneficiaries

WHERE FUNDING CAN BE GIVEN The County Palatine of the Duchy of Lancaster, which covers Lancashire, Greater Manchester and Merseyside, and places elsewhere in the country which have a link to the Duchy of Lancaster such as its estates and church livings

TYPE OF GRANT Mainly one-off grants for specific projects. Recurrent grants occasionally given

RANGE OF GRANTS £50–£20,000

Does the trust you have chosen match your needs? Haphazard applications waste postage and time

111

FINANCES
- Year 1998
- Income £320,208
- Grants £272,643

TRUSTEES Richard McCombe, QC, The Hon Mr Justice Blackburne, Sir Michael Peat, KCVO, M K Ridley, CVO, Lord Shuttleworth, JP, A W Waterworth, JP, Col J B Timmins, OBE, TD, JP, Mrs Irene Short (Chairman of Lancaster County Council)

HOW TO APPLY There is no application form. Applications should be by letter, including as much information as possible. All applications are acknowledged

WHO TO APPLY TO F N J Davies, Secretary, The Duchy of Lancaster Benevolent Fund, Duchy of Lancaster Office, 1 Lancaster Place, Strand, London WC2E 7ED *Tel* 0171-836 8277 *Fax* 0171-836 3098

CC NO 1026752   **ESTABLISHED** 1993

Commentary

The estates and jurisdiction known as the Duchy of Lancaster have belonged to the reigning monarch since 1399 when John of Gaunt's son came to the throne as Henry IV. As the Lancaster Inheritance it goes back as far as 1265 when Henry III granted his youngest son Edmund lands and possessions following the Baron's war. In 1267 Henry gave Edmund the County, Honor and Castle of Lancaster and created him the first Earl of Lancaster. In 1351 Edward III created Lancaster a County Palatine.

The Chancellor of the Duchy of Lancaster is responsible for the administration of the Duchy, the appointment of justices of the peace in Lancashire, Greater Manchester and Merseyside and ecclesiastical patronage in the Duchy gift.

It is a principle of English Law that title to property must 'vest' in an identifiable person or body. No property or goods are ownerless. Title vests ultimately in the Crown. If legal ownership cannot be established by anyone else, it falls to the Crown to deal with the assets concerned. In the County Palatine title vests in The Queen in Right of Her Duchy of Lancaster and the Duchy Solicitor, acting as a Corporation Sole under the Administration of Estates Act 1925, discharges duties carried out by the Treasury Solicitor's Department in the remainder of England and Wales (with the exception of Cornwall where such duties are carried out by the Solicitor to the Duchy of Cornwall).

Most of the duties arise on intestacy when no beneficiary entitled at law to claim an estate can be found; or on the dissolution of a company which still owns assets. Whatever remains undistributed is the property of The Queen in Right of Her Duchy. Gifts may be made, on the Chancellor's authority, to those who might reasonably have expected to benefit on a deceased's death; or in the case of dissolved companies, to those who could have claimed ownership had the company not been dissolved. Remaining monies help meet the costs of Palatinate administration and historical obligations and the balance is paid to the Duchy of Lancaster Benevolent Fund. The application of funds is made in this way as a matter of Duchy policy with The Queen's express consent by way of a Royal Sign Manual.

None of the costs incurred in managing the Duchy's assets which produce revenue for the Privy Purse are charged against Bona Vacantia.

The Fund will support general charitable purposes within the County Palatine. It is felt that as the money comes originally from that area, it should be returned to that area for the benefit of its residents. The Fund does not hold any preferences concerning which causes are funded; as long as the application is for a charitable cause the Trustees will consider it. The Fund chooses to group their donations under five main headings, but these do not reflect any funding preferences. The headings are: youth and education; handicapped, the elderly and infirm; community help; religious causes; and miscellaneous.

The Fund does support statutory bodies in the sense that it makes grants to schools and universities, etc, but it will not replace statutory funding. It will not consider co-funding projects as it is entirely independent and it is up to the applicant to find all the funding that they need. Grants are usually one-off and range from under £1,000 to over £20,000. Recurrent grants are sometimes given for major projects of £2,000–£5,000 per year for up to five years. Loans are not made but infrastructure costs are supported as long as they have a charitable purpose, for example, in 1997 the Fund gave £20,000 to the Lord Mayor of Manchester's Emergency Fund for rebuilding work in the wake of the IRA bomb.

Applications to the fund should be by letter, including as much information as possible. Large institutions in particular should try to identify a specific project for which they would like funding, rather than simply asking for money. There is no application form. All applications are acknowledged, then passed to the relevant Lord Lieutenant for the area of the County Palatine in which they are based. The Lord Lieutenants are advised by a small panel of advisers, who look at the suitability of applications and advise on what should be done about them. The Lord Lieutenants can authorise grants of up to £2,500, but grants larger than that must be authorised by all the Trustees. All applications are considered on a continual basis, regardless of their size, so large grants do not have to wait for the bi-annual Trustees' meetings, they just need to be approved by each Trustee. Applications are assessed as to whether or not it is for general charitable purposes within the County Palatine. Visits may be made before and after a donation is approved. Discreet enquiries will be made where necessary

SAMPLE GRANTS
The top ten grants awarded in 1998 were:
£20,000 to Invalids at Home
£15,000 to the Prince's Youth Business Trust
£5,000 to Chethams Library
£5,000 to The Salvation Army
£5,000 to Broughton House
£5,000 to Northern College of Music
£5,000 to Blackburn Cathedral Lantern Tower Appeal
£5,000 to Foxton Youth and Community Centre
£5,000 to The Salvation Army
£5,000 to Christie's Against Cancer

■The Dwek Family Charitable Trust

WHAT IS FUNDED The advancement of Judaism and charitable purposes of benefit to the community

WHO CAN BENEFIT Jewish people and community organisations

WHERE FUNDING CAN BE GIVEN Manchester

SAMPLE GRANTS £18,600 to Bodycote Educational Trust
£5,500 to Ta'ali-A History
£5,000 to JNF Charitable Trust
£5,000 to Manchester Jewish Social Services
£3,000 to North Cheshire Jewish School
£2,694 to Jewish Cultural Centre
£1,850 to Barnardo's
£1,500 to Shaarc Scdck Synagogue
£1,250 to Delamere Forest School
£1,250 to Withington Congregation of Spanish and Portuguese Jews

FINANCES
- Year 1997
- Income £151,028
- Grants £66,013

TRUSTEES J C Dwek, J Dwek, A J Leon

HOW TO APPLY To the address under Who To Apply To in writing

WHO TO APPLY TO J C Dwek, Trustee, The Dwek Family Charitable Trust, Suite One, Courthill House, 66 Water Lane, Wilmslow, Cheshire SK9 5AP

CC NO 1001456   **ESTABLISHED** 1989

■The Eagle Charity Trust

WHAT IS FUNDED To advance medicine and welfare

WHO CAN BENEFIT Organisations

WHERE FUNDING CAN BE GIVEN UK in particular Manchester

FINANCES
- Year 1994
- Income £1,000
- Grants £6,000

TRUSTEES D Gifford, E Gifford, L A Gifford, R M E Gifford, S A Nowalowski, E U Williams

HOW TO APPLY To the Correspondent in writing

WHO TO APPLY TO C Roberts, Clerk, The Eagle Charity Trust, 477 Chester Road, Manchester M16 9HF

CC NO 802134   **ESTABLISHED** 1989

■The East Lancashire Masonic Benevolent Institution (Incorporated)

WHAT IS FUNDED Masonic charities and medical, disability and welfare charities in the area Where Funding Can Be Given

WHO CAN BENEFIT Organisations benefiting: at risk groups; disabled people; those disadvantaged by poverty and socially isolated people. There are no restrictions on the disease or medical condition suffered by the beneficiaries

WHERE FUNDING CAN BE GIVEN East Lancashire

SAMPLE GRANTS £4,500 to Province of West Lancashire 1997 MTGB Festival
£4,000 to Province of Cumberland and Westmorland 1997 Grand Charity Festival
£2,500 to Province of Hertfordshire 1998 RMBI Festival
£1,000 to Tameside Hospice Appeal
£750 to Highfield Hall Community Association
£750 to Manchester Initiative (Help the Redundant)
£525 Ocean Youth Club
£500 to Age Concern
£500 to Beechwood Cancer Care
£500 to Boys and Girls Welfare Society

FINANCES
- Year 1997
- Income £565,927
- Grants £195,714

HOW TO APPLY To the address under Who To Apply To in writing

WHO TO APPLY TO C Wood, Hon Secretary, The East Lancashire Masonic Benevolent Institution, Freemasons Hall, Bridge Street, Manchester M3 3BT *Tel* 0161-832 6256

CC NO 225151   **ESTABLISHED** 1964

■ John Eddleston's Charity

WHAT IS FUNDED Funding is divided between the advancement of religion, relief in need and educational grants, both to schools and individuals under 25

WHO CAN BENEFIT Individuals (under 25) and organisations benefiting children, young adults, students, and those in need. There is no restriction on the religion or culture of the beneficiaries

WHERE FUNDING CAN BE GIVEN The Ecclesiastical Parish of St Aidan, Billinge

RANGE OF GRANTS £150–£11,824

SAMPLE GRANTS £11,824 for upkeep of land
£5,000 to Billinge Parish Council
£3,500 to St Aidans School
£3,000 to an individual
£2,000 to Billinge County Primary School
£1,661 to an individual
£1,500 to Billinge Chapel End Primary School
£1,500 to Billinge and Winstanley St Mary's CP School
£1,498 for legal fees for an individual
£500 to 5th Wigan Brownie Guides
£500 to Billinge and Winstanley RC School

FINANCES
• Year 1996   • Income £130,032
• Grants £44,435

TRUSTEES T R Ellis, Canon K M Forrest, C E Mather, C Stockley, W N Tyrer, N F Wilson, E M Wright

HOW TO APPLY To the address under Who To Apply To in writing. Applications are considered by the Trustees in March

WHO TO APPLY TO A H Leech & Sons, Secretaries to the Trustees, John Eddleston's Charity, Greenbank House, 152 Wigan Lane, Wigan WN1 2LA

CC NO 503695   **ESTABLISHED** 1987

■ Eden Arts Trust

WHAT IS FUNDED To promote and develop the arts and art projects involving the community; to encourage new groups

WHAT IS NOT FUNDED Artists and community groups who are not based within Eden District or whose work is not for the benefit of the residents of Eden District

WHO CAN BENEFIT Individuals and organisations benefiting: young adults and older people; actors and entertainment professionals; musicians; textile workers and designers; volunteers; and writers and poets

WHERE FUNDING CAN BE GIVEN Eden district, Cumbria

TYPE OF GRANT Small local arts and crafts projects, days and events, feasibility studies

RANGE OF GRANTS £50–£2,000, average grant £500

SAMPLE GRANTS £2,300 to Appleby Jazz Society for Appleby Jazz Festival
£2,000 to Quondam Theatre for development work
£1,500 to East Cumbria Countryside Commission for public art project
£1,300 to Penrith Music Club towards annual programme
£1,000 to Upfront for exhibition programme

FINANCES
• Year 1997   • Income £65,622
• Grants £18,619

TRUSTEES Mrs E Thomson

WHO TO APPLY TO N Jones, Eden Arts Trust, 2 Sandgate, Penrith, Cumbria CA11 7TP *Tel* 01768 899444

CC NO 1000476   **ESTABLISHED** 1990

■ James Eden's Foundation

WHAT IS FUNDED Individuals in further education receive the majority of the grant total, while children and youth charities in the area Where Funding Can Be Given also benefit

WHO CAN BENEFIT Individuals and local organisations benefiting children, young adults and students

WHERE FUNDING CAN BE GIVEN The Metropolitan Borough of Bolton

TYPE OF GRANT One-off and recurrent

SAMPLE GRANTS £1,200 to an individual for further education
£1,000 to an individual for further education
£700 each to three individuals for further education
£650 to Bolton Lads and Girls Club
£450 to Bolton YMCA

FINANCES
• Year 1996–97   • Income £13,112
• Grants £9,100

TRUSTEES N G Coates (Chairman), A J Mitchell, B H Leigh-Bramwell, P J Senior, E R Walker, T J Arkwright, A R Taylor

HOW TO APPLY To the address under Who To Apply To in writing

WHO TO APPLY TO J G Smith, Secretary, James Eden's Foundation, Deloitte and Touche Private Clients Ltd, PO Box 500, 201 Deansgate, Manchester M60 2AT *Tel* 0161-455 8283

CC NO 526265   **ESTABLISHED** 1964

■ Egton Parish Lands Charity

WHAT IS FUNDED General charitable purposes

WHO CAN BENEFIT Individuals and organisations

WHERE FUNDING CAN BE GIVEN The Parish of Egton with Newland

FINANCES
- Year 1994–95
- Income £5,700
- Grants £1,000

TRUSTEES J Bell, J V Dover, J R Hockenhall, N Jones, G J Moore, J R Newby, D Satterthwaite

HOW TO APPLY To the Correspondent in writing

WHO TO APPLY TO Mrs J Ireland, Clerk, Egton Parish Lands Charity, Three Ways, Pennybridge, Ulverston, Cumbria LA12 7RQ *Tel* 01229 861405

CC NO 221424   **ESTABLISHED** 1964

■ The Ellison Marsden Charitable Trust

WHAT IS FUNDED General charitable purposes

WHO CAN BENEFIT Organisations

WHERE FUNDING CAN BE GIVEN UK, especially Manchester

FINANCES
- Year 1994–95
- Income £3,800

HOW TO APPLY To the Correspondent in writing. Only registered charities need apply

WHO TO APPLY TO Mervyn Reed, Trustee, Ellison Marsden Charitable Trust, 14 Langham Court, Mersey Road, Manchester M20 2PX

CC NO 326694   **ESTABLISHED** 1984

■ The Eskdale (Cumbria) Trust

WHAT IS FUNDED For the educational benefit of the students, researchers and the public in particular; (a) to restore the Manchester Mill, Ravenglass; (b) to found and maintain a Railway Museum in Ravenglass; (c) to conserve and control flora and fauna in Ravenglass and Eskdale; (d) to promote the study of using water as a means of providing energy

WHERE FUNDING CAN BE GIVEN Ravenglass, Eskdale and district, Cumbria

TYPE OF GRANT Recurring

FINANCES
- Year 1996
- Income £9,808

WHO TO APPLY TO C W Musson, The Eskdale (Cumbria) Trust, 13 Maude Street, Kendal, Cumbria LA9 4QD

CC NO 505295   **ESTABLISHED** 1976

■ Mabel Evans Trust

WHAT IS FUNDED General charitable purposes in particular to advance education in music and drama

WHO CAN BENEFIT Individuals and organisations

WHERE FUNDING CAN BE GIVEN Wilmslow

FINANCES
- Year 1994
- Income £4,000
- Grants £3,500

HOW TO APPLY To the Correspondent in writing

WHO TO APPLY TO Eric Sykes, Trustee, Mabel Evans Trust, 62 Higher Lane, Lymm, Cheshire WA13 0BG

CC NO 511207   **ESTABLISHED** 1976

■ The Eventhall Family Charitable Trust

WHAT IS FUNDED General charitable purposes

WHAT IS NOT FUNDED Student grants cannot be provided

WHO CAN BENEFIT Institutions and individuals. There are no restrictions on the age; professional and economic group; family situation; religion and culture; and social circumstances of; or disease or medical condition suffered by, the beneficiaries

WHERE FUNDING CAN BE GIVEN North West England

FINANCES
- Year 1997
- Income £159,877
- Grants £66,772

TRUSTEES L Eventhall, C Eventhall, D Eventhall

NOTES The largest donation made in 1997 was to the Heathlands Village and will be continuing support for the next two year. Donations were also made to other charities

WHO TO APPLY TO L H Eventhall, The Eventhall Family Charitable Trust, Greenlands, 23 Beeston Road, Sale, Cheshire M33 5AQ

CC NO 803178   **ESTABLISHED** 1989

Does the trust you have chosen match your needs? Haphazard applications waste postage and time

115

■Famos Foundation Trust

WHAT IS FUNDED Education, religion, international organisations, and general charitable purposes. The Trust will consider funding: the advancement of the Jewish religion; synagogues; Jewish umbrella bodies; church schools; cultural and religious teaching and religious studies

WHAT IS NOT FUNDED Individuals, students

WHO CAN BENEFIT Small local projects and established organisations benefiting children, young adults, clergy and Jews

WHERE FUNDING CAN BE GIVEN UK and overseas, particularly Gateshead, Manchester City, Salford and London

TYPE OF GRANT One-off, core costs and running costs. Funding is given for one year or less

RANGE OF GRANTS £1,000 or less

FINANCES
- Year 1996
- Income £88,778
- Grants £42,272

TRUSTEES Rabbi S M Kaputz

HOW TO APPLY In writing at any time

WHO TO APPLY TO Rabbi S M Kaputz, Famos Foundation Trust, 4 Hanover Gardens, Salford, Lancashire M7 4FQ *Tel* 0161-740 5735

CC NO 271211   **ESTABLISHED** 1976

■George Fearn Trust

WHAT IS FUNDED The support of St George's Church and St George's Schools in Stockport

WHO CAN BENEFIT St George's Church and schools benefiting children and young adults

WHERE FUNDING CAN BE GIVEN The County Borough of Stockport

TYPE OF GRANT At the Trustees' discretion

FINANCES
- Year 1997–98
- Income £19,994
- Grants £20,233

TRUSTEES R J B Green (Chairman), F Gregg, S B Berry, A J Garlick, P R Ball, J R Hardy

HOW TO APPLY To the address under Who To Apply To in writing

WHO TO APPLY TO F Gregg, Secretary, George Fearn Trust, 2 Mount Street, Albert Square, Manchester M2 5NX *Tel* 0161-834 7428

CC NO 223212   **ESTABLISHED** 1911

■Ferguson Benevolent Fund Limited

WHAT IS FUNDED To give grants for such charitable purposes as they deem worthy of their support and, in particular, are connected with the Methodist Church. Preference to charities of which the Trust has special interest, knowledge or association. These include: residential facilities; respite and sheltered accommodation; information technology and computers; infrastructure development; Methodist umbrella bodies; acute health care; respite care and care for carers; support and self help groups; special schools; education and training; and community services

WHAT IS NOT FUNDED No support for trade unions and like bodies. No support to individuals for medical electives, postgraduate studies, expeditions or for private schooling

WHO CAN BENEFIT Mainly to cases of social, medical and educational need, usually through charitable bodies working in fields of social and medical need in the areas specified. Organisations benefiting: people of all ages; unemployed people; those in care, fostered and adopted; Methodists; at risk groups; carers; those disadvantaged by poverty; homeless people; those living in rural and urban areas; and victims of domestic violence. Those suffering from Alzheimer's disease, asthma, diabetes, hearing loss, heart disease, leprosy and polio

WHERE FUNDING CAN BE GIVEN North West England, Greater Manchester, Jersey and overseas

TYPE OF GRANT Buildings, capital, endowments, one-off, project, research and start-up costs. All funding is for up to two years

RANGE OF GRANTS £500–£10,000

SAMPLE GRANTS £3,000 to Children's Hospital Appeal for intensive care equipment in children's hospital
£2,000 to Action and Research for MS for a day centre for physiotherapy and helpline
£2,000 to Henshaws Society for the Blind for refurbishing two homes for blind people in Salford and Blackley
£2,000 to Contact for training and help for single girls' home
£2,000 to Ferries and Port Sunlight Family Groups for all sorts of back up for local families
£2,000 to Share and Care Fleetwood for Christian support for elderly house bound

116

Think carefully about every application. Is it justified?

£2,000 to International Childcare Trust for children on the streets in Kenya
£2,000 to Orbis for flying eye hospital for the third world
£1,000 to Opportunities and Activities for adult education in Fallowfield
£1,000 to Traidcraft for empowering women to do business in Africa

FINANCES
- Year 1997
- Income £31,000
- Grants £47,500

TRUSTEES Mrs E Higginbottom (Chair), Mrs C M A Metcalfe, Ms S Ferguson (Secretary), Mrs P Dobson, P A L Holt, S M Higginbottom

HOW TO APPLY By letter only. No telephone calls

WHO TO APPLY TO Mrs E Higginbottom, Ferguson Benevolent Fund Limited, PO Box 16, Ambleside, Cumbria LA22 9GD

CC NO 228746   **ESTABLISHED** 1963

■ Feryal Rajah Educational Trust

WHAT IS FUNDED Facilities for the training and development of vocational skills to improve job prospects in medicine and related professions; maintenance for those who need financial aid to further their education; setting up a helpline service

WHO CAN BENEFIT Women in conditions of need, hardship and distress

WHERE FUNDING CAN BE GIVEN Within and around the City of Salford

FINANCES
- Year 1997
- Income £10,000

TRUSTEES Hazel Blears, MP, David C Johnston, John Merry

HOW TO APPLY Application forms and leaflets are available from the Correspondent

WHO TO APPLY TO D C Johnston, Secretary to Trust, Feryal Rajah Educational Trust, c/o Education Office, Chapel Street, Salford M3 5LT *Tel* 0161-837 1741

CC NO 1058660   **ESTABLISHED** 1997

■ The Fetal Medicine Foundation

WHAT IS FUNDED Research into: early diagnosis and treatment of fetal abnormalities; the causes and prevention of miscarriages and stillbirth; placental failure and fetal growth retardation; screening for chromosomal abnormalities; problems of multiple pregnancies; development of safer techniques for prenatal diagnosis

WHO CAN BENEFIT Individuals and institutions

WHERE FUNDING CAN BE GIVEN UK, Europe

TYPE OF GRANT Research, salaries, feasibility studies, one-off

SAMPLE GRANTS £2,809 towards educational courses
£1,425 grants for research
£500 in donations

FINANCES
- Year 1995–96
- Income £8,483
- Grants £4,734

TRUSTEES J M Charalambides, K H Nicolaides

HOW TO APPLY In writing to the address below

WHO TO APPLY TO Professor K H Nicolaides, The Fetal Medicine Foundation, 8 Devonshire Place, London W1N 1PB *Tel* 0171-486 0476 *Fax* 0171-486 0294

CC NO 1037116   **ESTABLISHED** 1994

■ The J S and L R Fidler Charitable Trust

WHAT IS FUNDED For the benefit of Jews in the Manchester area

WHO CAN BENEFIT Jews

WHERE FUNDING CAN BE GIVEN UK, with a preference for the Manchester area

FINANCES
- Year 1994–95
- Income £4,800

TRUSTEES E R Fidler, J S Fidler, L R Fidler

WHO TO APPLY TO J S Fidler, Trustee, The J S and L R Fidler Charitable Trust, 3 St Mary's Parsonage, Manchester M3 2RD

CC NO 509088   **ESTABLISHED** 1979

■ The Sir John Fisher Foundation

WHAT IS FUNDED General charitable purposes

WHO CAN BENEFIT There are no restrictions on the age; professional and economic group; family situation; religion and culture; and social circumstances of; or disease or medical condition suffered by, the beneficiaries

WHERE FUNDING CAN BE GIVEN UK, with preference for Cumbria

FINANCES
- Year 1997
- Income £415,419

TRUSTEES B G Robinson, R F Hart Jackson, Mrs D S Meacock

WHO TO APPLY TO R F Hart Jackson, Secretary, The Sir John Fisher Foundation, 8–10 New Market Street, Ulverston, Cumbria LA12 7LW

CC NO 277844   **ESTABLISHED** 1979

■Florence's Charitable Trust

WHAT IS FUNDED The establishment, maintenance and support of places of education. Relief of the elderly. Relief of poverty of any person employed or formerly employed in the shoe trade

WHO CAN BENEFIT Mainly local organisations, or local branches of national organisations, benefiting the elderly, employees or former employees of the shoe trade and those disadvantaged by poverty. Support may be given to children and young adults

WHERE FUNDING CAN BE GIVEN UK, especially Lancashire

TYPE OF GRANT Mainly recurrent grants

RANGE OF GRANTS £50–£25,000

SAMPLE GRANTS £25,000 to St Mary's Church Hall, Bacup
£12,000 to All Saints School
£10,500 to St Mary's RC School, Bacup
£10,000 to Age Concern Victim Support, Rossendale
£2,600 to Fearns High School
£2,500 to Friends of Stacksteads Surgery
£2,500 to Stacksteads Freestyle Karate Club
£1,825 to MENCAP promotions
£1,800 to an individual for the Open University
£1,650 to Waterfoot FC Youth

FINANCES
- Year 1997
- Income £134,927
- Grants £111,779

TRUSTEES C C Harrison (Chairman), R Barker, A Connearn, G D Low, J Mellows, M Thurlwell, R D Uttley

HOW TO APPLY To the address under Who To Apply To in writing

WHO TO APPLY TO A Connearn, Florence's Charitable Trust, 6 Greave Crescent, Bacup, Lancashire OL13 9HH

CC NO 265754   **ESTABLISHED** 1973

■Ford of Britain Trust

WHAT IS FUNDED Currently the main areas of interest are children and young people (with emphasis on education, special needs children, youth organisations); community service; the disabled; social welfare; community arts and recreation; cultural heritage; accommodation and housing; respite care for carers; support and self help groups; ambulances and mobile units; hospices; and social advice centres

WHAT IS NOT FUNDED Organisations outside the area Where Funding Can Be Given and national charities are rarely assisted, except for specific projects in Ford areas. Applications in respect of individuals (including students), charities requiring funds for overseas projects, and wholly religious or politically orientated projects are ineligible. Major building projects and research projects (including medical) are rarely assisted

WHO CAN BENEFIT Organisations benefiting: children; young adults; older people; unemployed people; volunteers; at risk groups; carers; disabled people; those disadvantaged by poverty; ex-offenders and those at risk of offending; homeless people; victims of crime, domestic violence and abuse. There are few restrictions on the disease or medical condition suffered by the beneficiaries

WHERE FUNDING CAN BE GIVEN Charities located in close proximity to Ford Motor Company Limited plants in UK. This includes: Halton, Knowsley, Liverpool City, St Helens, Sefton, Wirral, Northamptonshire, Warwickshire, Essex, Southend, Thurrock, Southampton, Barking and Dagenham, Croydon, Enfield, Hackney, Havering, Redbridge, Tower Hamlets, Waltham Forest, Belfast, Carrickfergus, Craigavon, Lisburn, Newtownabbey, Bridgend, Caerphilly, Cardiff, Vale of Glamorgan, Merthyr Tydfil, Neath and Port Talbot, Rhondda Cynon Taff, Swansea

TYPE OF GRANT Capital, buildings, one-off, running costs, and start-up costs. Funding is available for one year or less

RANGE OF GRANTS Most grants range between £100 and £5,000

FINANCES
- Year 1998
- Income £598,791
- Grants £399,487

TRUSTEES I G McAllister, CBE (Chairman), R A Hill, W G F Brooks, M J Callaghan, Prof Ann P Dowling, J H M Norris, CBE, VL, P G Knight

HOW TO APPLY By letter to the address under Who To Apply To. Guidelines are available

WHO TO APPLY TO R M Metcalf, Director, Ford of Britain Trust, c/o Ford Motor Co Ltd, 1–661 Eagle Way, Brentwood, Essex CM13 3BW
Tel 01277 252551

CC NO 269410   **ESTABLISHED** 1975

■The Forster Charitable Trust

WHAT IS FUNDED General charitable purposes in particular to advance education and the Jewish religion in Manchester

WHO CAN BENEFIT Individuals and organisations

WHERE FUNDING CAN BE GIVEN UK, especially Manchester

FINANCES
- Year 1995
- Income £8,700

HOW TO APPLY To the Correspondent in writing

WHO TO APPLY TO S Forster, Trustee, The Forster Charitable Trust, The Hollies, 119 Park Road, Hale, Altrincham, Cheshire WA15 9JP

CC NO 293043   **ESTABLISHED** 1985

■ Fort Foundation

WHAT IS FUNDED General charitable purposes in particular to advance education in Pendle Borough and District

WHO CAN BENEFIT Individuals and organisations

WHERE FUNDING CAN BE GIVEN North East Lancashire

FINANCES
- Year 1994–95
- Income £6,000
- Grants £650

TRUSTEES E S Fort, D J Evans, I Wilson

HOW TO APPLY To the Correspondent in writing

WHO TO APPLY TO E S Fort, OBE, Fort Foundation, Fort Vale Engineering Ltd, Parkfield Works, Brunswick Street, Nelson, Lancashire BB9 0SG

CC NO 1028639   **ESTABLISHED** 1993

■ France's Charity

WHAT IS FUNDED The welfare of sick and elderly people, support groups for people in need, schools and hospitals in the local area

WHO CAN BENEFIT To benefit people of all ages and those in need. There is no restriction on the disease or medical condition suffered by the beneficiaries

WHERE FUNDING CAN BE GIVEN Leigh

RANGE OF GRANTS £200–£450

SAMPLE GRANTS £450 to Westleigh Old Age Pensioners
£450 to Bedford Old Age Pensioners
£450 to Plank Lane Old Age Pensioners
£450 to St Joseph's Area Citizens
£450 to Higher Fold Old Age Pensioners
£450 to Wigan Road Old People's Welfare Centre
£450 to Hourigan House
£450 to Lyndurst Home
£450 to Abbeyfield Society
£330 to Westleigh High School

FINANCES
- Year 1996
- Income £45,816
- Grants £6,910

HOW TO APPLY To the address under Who To Apply To in writing

WHO TO APPLY TO Mrs O E Williams, Secretary, France's Charity, Stephensons Solicitors, 26 Union Street, Leigh, Lancashire WN7 1AT

CC NO 224803   **ESTABLISHED** 1901

■ A J Freeman Charitable Trust

WHAT IS FUNDED General charitable purposes

WHO CAN BENEFIT Registered charities. There are no restrictions on the age; professional and economic group; family situation; religion and culture; and social circumstances of; or disease or medical condition suffered by, the beneficiaries

WHERE FUNDING CAN BE GIVEN Mainly Manchester

TYPE OF GRANT Single donations towards specific objects

FINANCES
- Year 1996
- Income £45,260

TRUSTEES A J Freeman, J M Levy

WHO TO APPLY TO J M Levy, A J Freeman Charitable Trust, Kuit Steinart Levy & Co, 3 St Mary's Parsonage, Manchester M3 2RD

CC NO 279522   **ESTABLISHED** 1979

■Girl's Welfare Fund

WHAT IS FUNDED To benefit women who are in need or attempting to improve the quality of their lives, and other charitable purposes

WHAT IS NOT FUNDED Grants will not be made for capital work, salaries, or non-productive causes. Applications from outside the Beneficial Area will not be acknowledged

WHO CAN BENEFIT Individuals and organisations

WHERE FUNDING CAN BE GIVEN The former Metropolitan Authority of Merseyside

TYPE OF GRANT One-off, recurrent, project

FINANCES
- Year 1997
- Income £6,415

TRUSTEES Mrs O M Coulshed, Mrs S M O'Leary, Mrs E W Waddington

HOW TO APPLY To the Correspondent in writing. The Trustees meet to consider applications in March, June, September and December

WHO TO APPLY TO Mrs S M O'Leary, Hon Secretary, Girl's Welfare Fund, West Hey, Dawstone Road, Heswall, Wirral L60 4RP

CC NO 220347   **ESTABLISHED** 1980

■The Gladstone Trust

WHAT IS FUNDED To advance health in particular appeals for hospitals and specific causes

WHO CAN BENEFIT Individuals and organisations

WHERE FUNDING CAN BE GIVEN The North of England, primarily the North East

FINANCES
- Year 1996
- Income £4,759

HOW TO APPLY To the Correspondent in writing

WHO TO APPLY TO M P W Lee, The Gladstone Trust, Dibb Lupton Broomhead, Fountain Precinct, Balm Green, Sheffield, South Yorkshire S1 1RZ

CC NO 277580   **ESTABLISHED** 1961

■The Granada Foundation (formerly Northern Arts and Sciences Foundation)

WHAT IS FUNDED Favourable consideration is given to projects of potential benefit to a wide public (eg artists in residence). Fine arts, including painting, drawing, architecture, sculpture, literature, music, opera, drama, ballet and cinema

WHAT IS NOT FUNDED Not able to help individual students with the costs of a course of study or expeditions. Does not support youth clubs and community associations. No general appeals

WHO CAN BENEFIT Arts centres, theatres, galleries, performance groups benefiting: actors and entertainment professionals; musicians; textile workers and designers; and writers and poets

WHERE FUNDING CAN BE GIVEN Preference to North West of England

RANGE OF GRANTS £500–£25,000

SAMPLE GRANTS £25,000 to National Museum and Galleries in Merseyside for the completion of a display gallery in the Conservation Centre, Liverpool
£25,000 to Royal Liverpool Philharmonic Society for refurbishment of great organ and cinema screen in Philharmonic Hall
£18,562 to the 'Granada Power Game' for annual competitive project for young engineers in schools
£12,500 to the Tate Gallery, Liverpool for Phase 2 of the development plan
£7,000 to Brouhaha International Festival (1997), Liverpool
£7,000 to Buxton Festival (1997) for opera productions
£5,000 to North West Museums Service, Blackburn for conservation work for galleries and museums
£5,000 to Manchester Camerata for an educational project
£4,000 to Positive Solutions, Liverpool for training in art organisations
£3,000 to Africa Oye, Liverpool for musical events in parks across Merseyside

FINANCES
- Year 1997
- Income £148,190
- Grants £136,162

TRUSTEES Alexander Bernstein, Robert Scott

WHO TO APPLY TO Mrs Irene Langford, The Granada Foundation, Bridgegate House, 5 Bridge Place, Lower Bridge Street, Chester CH1 1SA

CC NO 241693   **ESTABLISHED** 1965

■Greater Manchester Police Community Charity

WHAT IS FUNDED General charitable purposes including health, welfare, disability, education and community development charities

WHO CAN BENEFIT Individuals and organisations

WHERE FUNDING CAN BE GIVEN The Greater Manchester Police area

TYPE OF GRANT One-off, running and start-up costs

FINANCES
- Year 1994
- Income £12,000
- Grants £14,000

TRUSTEES D Wilmot, Mrs A Fishwick, V J P Scerri, Rt Rev C J Scott, C H Woodcock, Baroness McFarlane of Llandaff, S J V Arditti, R Pizzey, M George

HOW TO APPLY Application forms sent on written request to the Correspondent. Trustees consider applications every quarter

WHO TO APPLY TO Robin Garrido, Greater Manchester Police Community Charity, Greater Manchester Police Headquarters, Chester House, Manchester M16 0RE *Tel* 0161-856 2219

CC NO 515975   **ESTABLISHED** 1985

■The Barry Green Memorial Fund

WHAT IS FUNDED Preference for smaller charities rescuing and caring for cruelly treated animals; animal homes; animal welfare; cats, catteries and other facilities for cats; dogs, kennels and other facilities for dogs; and horses, stables and other facilities for horses

WHAT IS NOT FUNDED No expeditions, scholarships, work outside the UK or individuals

WHO CAN BENEFIT All, but the Trustees have a preference towards smaller charities working at grass roots level

WHERE FUNDING CAN BE GIVEN UK, with preference towards Yorkshire and Lancashire

TYPE OF GRANT Buildings, core costs, one-off, recurring costs, running costs and start-up costs. Funding available for more than three years

RANGE OF GRANTS £100–£15,000

FINANCES
- Year 1997
- Income £165,584
- Grants £42,799

TRUSTEES R Fitzgerald-Hart, M Fitzgerald-Hart

HOW TO APPLY Any time, in writing only

WHO TO APPLY TO Clerk to the Trustees, The Barry Green Memorial Fund, Claro Chambers, Horsefair, Boroughbridge, York YO5 9LD

CC NO 1000492   **ESTABLISHED** 1990

■The Esther and Harry Grosberg Foundation

WHAT IS FUNDED General charitable purposes in particular for the benefit of Jews

WHO CAN BENEFIT Jews

WHERE FUNDING CAN BE GIVEN UK, in particular Manchester

FINANCES
- Year 1995
- Income £9,200
- Grants £4,000

HOW TO APPLY To the Correspondent in writing

WHO TO APPLY TO J A Wild, Adviser to Trustees, The Esther and Harry Grosberg Foundation, Lancaster House, Blackburn Street, Radcliffe, Manchester M26 2JW

CC NO 298331   **ESTABLISHED** 1988

■Gurunanak

WHAT IS FUNDED Relief of poverty and general charitable purposes at the Trustees' discretion

WHO CAN BENEFIT Organisations, particularly those benefiting people disadvantaged by poverty

WHERE FUNDING CAN BE GIVEN UK, with preference for Greater Manchester

FINANCES
- Year 1996
- Income £14,496
- Grants £16,486

TRUSTEES J S Kholi, B S Kohli, A S Dhody, H S Chadha

WHO TO APPLY TO J S Kohli, Gurunanak, NIJ Than, 23a Upper Park Road, Salford M7 0HY

CC NO 1017903   **ESTABLISHED** 1993

■The Hadfield Charitable Trust

WHAT IS FUNDED Charities concerned with social needs, youth employment, help for the aged, the arts and the environment, particularly those working in the fields of: accommodation and housing; support and development; arts, culture and recreation; health; conservation; education and training; and social care and development

WHAT IS NOT FUNDED No grants made for projects which are political, religious or sectarian, except churches and places of worship. No grants to individuals

WHO CAN BENEFIT Organisations benefiting children; young adults and older people; unemployed; parents and children; one parent families; and widows and widowers. There is no restriction on the disease or medical condition suffered by the beneficiaries, however there are some restrictions on their social circumstances

WHERE FUNDING CAN BE GIVEN The County of Cumbria

TYPE OF GRANT Capital projects preferred, buildings will be considered and funding is generally for one year or less

RANGE OF GRANTS Minimum £500

SAMPLE GRANTS £10,000 to Life Education Centre for Cumbria for Life Education vehicle
£5,000 to Age Concern, Carlisle for a minibus
£5,000 to The National Trust for Junior Wardens Scheme in Cumbria
£4,000 to Cumbria Association of Youth Clubs
£4,000 to Calvert Trust, Penrith
£3,000 to Abbeyfield (Lakeland Extra-Care) for building extension
£2,000 to Ulverston and North Lonsdale Citizens Advice Bureau for IT equipment
£2,000 to Ehenside Health and Fitness Centre
£1,000 to The National Trust for Highway Centre, Cumbria
£1,000 to Mountain Bothies Association

FINANCES
- Year 1998
- Income £175,000

TRUSTEES R A Morris (Chairman), A T Morris, W Rathbone, O Turnbull

PUBLICATIONS A leaflet setting out the aims and objectives of the Trust (available on request)

HOW TO APPLY Please write for an application form and further details. Applicants are asked to provide a copy of their latest accounts and will be sent an application form for completion. The Trustees like to monitor the progress of successful grants. All applications will be acknowledged

WHO TO APPLY TO M E Hope, The Hadfield Charitable Trust, c/o Rathbone Bros & Co Ltd, Port of Liverpool Building, Pier Head, Liverpool L3 1NW *Tel* 0151-236 6666 *Fax* 0151-243 7001

CC NO 1067491   **ESTABLISHED** 1998

■Hale and Hale Barns Charitable Trust

WHAT IS FUNDED General charitable purposes in particular the elderly

WHO CAN BENEFIT Elderly

WHERE FUNDING CAN BE GIVEN Hale and Hale Barns

FINANCES
- Year 1994–95
- Grants £1,400
- Income £1,200

HOW TO APPLY To the Correspondent in writing

WHO TO APPLY TO D J McGuire, Chairman, Hale and Hale Barns Charitable Trust, 70 Briony Avenue, Hale, Altrincham, Cheshire WA15 8QA

CC NO 1015421   **ESTABLISHED** 1992

■Keren Hamitzvos

WHAT IS FUNDED Jewish charitable purposes as the Trustees direct

WHO CAN BENEFIT Individuals and organisations

WHERE FUNDING CAN BE GIVEN Manchester, Salford and the London Boroughs of Brent, Hackney, Haringey and Redbridge

FINANCES
- Year 1996
- Grants £2,742
- Income £7,290

WHO TO APPLY TO S Kinn, Keren Hamitzvos, 113 Clapton Common, London E5 9AB *Tel* 0181-800 4038

CC NO 801528   **ESTABLISHED** 1989

■Lord Harewood's Charitable Settlement

WHAT IS FUNDED To consider local and particular areas of interest that are registered charities and are known personally to the Trustees especially in the field of music and the arts

WHAT IS NOT FUNDED No reply will be made to speculative applications

WHO CAN BENEFIT Organisations benefiting: actors and entertainment professional; musicians; textile workers and designers; and writers and poets

WHERE FUNDING CAN BE GIVEN North of England

RANGE OF GRANTS Typically £50–£200

FINANCES
- Year 1995
- Grants £14,000
- Income £14,000

TRUSTEES C A Ussher

HOW TO APPLY No telephone calls and no speculative applications

WHO TO APPLY TO The Estate Office, Lord Harewood's Charitable Settlement, Harewood Yard, Harewood, Leeds LS17 9LF

CC NO 243591   **ESTABLISHED** 1964

■The Harris Charity

WHAT IS FUNDED Charities benefiting young persons under 25

WHO CAN BENEFIT Children and young adults under 25 in the Lancashire area

WHERE FUNDING CAN BE GIVEN Lancashire, preference to Preston area

TYPE OF GRANT Prefer capital projects and provision of equipment

FINANCES
- Year 1997
- Grants £61,773
- Income £114,977

TRUSTEES Mrs C Marshall, Mrs S Jackson, W S Huck, E J Booth, J Cotterall, T W S Croft, E C Dickson, S R Fisher, Mrs A Scott, Mrs R Jolly, S Huck, S B R Smith

HOW TO APPLY Half yearly by 30 September and 31 March

WHO TO APPLY TO P R Metcalf, FCA, The Harris Charity, Richard House, 9 Winckley Square, Preston, Lancashire PR1 3HP
Tel 01772 821021 *Fax* 01772 259441

CC NO 526206   **ESTABLISHED** 1883

■The N and P Hartley Memorial Trust

WHAT IS FUNDED For the benefit of the elderly, children, the disabled and the provision of medical facilities and care for all age groups. Particular attention given to smaller charities and individuals in need

WHO CAN BENEFIT Individuals and community organisations benefiting: disabled people, the elderly and young; and the sick. There is no restriction on the disease or medical condition suffered by the beneficiaries

WHERE FUNDING CAN BE GIVEN West Yorkshire principally, but will consider causes in the remainder of Yorkshire and the Northern counties of England

RANGE OF GRANTS £340–£5,500

SAMPLE GRANTS £5,500 to Kisiizi Hospital
£5,000 to Caring for Life
£2,220 to Winged Fellowship
£2,000 to Leeds and Bradford Asbah
£2,000 to Communication for the Disabled
£1,000 to West Riding Care
£1,000 to Beecroft After School Club
£1,000 to Serious Fun
£1,000 to Disability Aid Fund
£500 to National Asthma Campaign

FINANCES
- Year 1997
- Grants £21,920
- Income £47,712

TRUSTEES Mrs V B Procter, J J Procter, J E Kirman

NOTES The Trustees meet three times each year to discuss requests. Pleased to support old and new causes alike and welcome re-applications from those they have helped in the past

HOW TO APPLY By letter outlining your need. Suitable applicants will be invited to complete a questionnaire for the Trustees' consideration at their bi-annual meeting

WHO TO APPLY TO Mrs V Beryl Procter, The N and P Hartley Memorial Trust, 51 Uppleby, Easingwold, Yorkshire YO6 3BD

CC NO 327570   **ESTABLISHED** 1987

■Haslingden Local Charities Account

WHAT IS FUNDED General charitable purposes in Haslingden

WHO CAN BENEFIT Living in urban area

WHERE FUNDING CAN BE GIVEN Haslingden

FINANCES
- Year 1994–95
- Grants £3,200
- Income £4,500

HOW TO APPLY To the Correspondent in writing

Does the trust you have chosen match your needs? Haphazard applications waste postage and time

123

WHO TO APPLY TO The Treasurer, Haslingden Local Charities Account, Treasurer's Dept, Rossendale Borough Council, PO Box 40, Rawtenstall, Rossendale, Lancashire BB4 7NP

CC NO 222536   **ESTABLISHED** 1952

■The M A Hawe Settlement

WHAT IS FUNDED Welfare of the aged, women and children. Education, disability, homelessness and other charitable purposes

WHO CAN BENEFIT National and local organisations and schemes benefiting: people of all ages; women; students; disabled people; at risk groups; socially isolated people; homeless people; and those disadvantaged by poverty.

WHERE FUNDING CAN BE GIVEN UK, with a preference for Lancashire

TYPE OF GRANT One-off, some recurrent

RANGE OF GRANTS Below £100–£174,230

SAMPLE GRANTS £174,230 to Kensington House Trust Limited for welfare purposes
£7,900 to Children in Need
£1,404 to Holy Cross Church and Soup Kitchen
£586 to Old Folks Home
£380 as 12 miscellaneous donations of under £100
£250 to Motability NW
£180 to Jubilee Trust
£100 to an individual
£50 to Hall Park School

FINANCES
● Year 1995–96   ● Income £440,043
● Grants £185,080

TRUSTEES M A Hawe, Mrs G Hawe, Mark G Hawe

HOW TO APPLY To the address under Who To Apply To in writing

WHO TO APPLY TO M A Hawe, The M A Hawe Settlement, 94 Park View Road, Lytham St Annes, Lancashire FY8 4JF

CC NO 327827   **ESTABLISHED** 1988

■The Hemby Trust

WHAT IS FUNDED This Trust will consider funding: social needs; community facilities and services; youth and employment; schools and colleges; help for the aged; health; the arts, culture and recreation; the environment; and church buildings

WHAT IS NOT FUNDED No grants will be made for political, religious (except churches), pressure groups, sponsorships or to individuals

WHO CAN BENEFIT There are no restrictions on the age; family situation of; or disease or medical condition suffered by, the beneficiaries; and few restrictions on the social circumstances

WHERE FUNDING CAN BE GIVEN The County of Merseyside and Wirral

TYPE OF GRANT Capital grants

TRUSTEES R A Morris, P T Furlong, A T Morris, N A Wainwright

NOTES The Trustees meet four times a year. Applications need to be received one month prior to the meeting

HOW TO APPLY To the Secretary at the address under Who To Apply To

WHO TO APPLY TO M E Hope, Secretary, The Hemby Trust, c/o Rathbone Bros & Co Ltd, Port of Liverpool Building, Pier Head, Liverpool L3 1NW *Tel* 0151-236 6666 *Fax* 0151-243 7001

CC NO Pending   **ESTABLISHED** 1998

■Highland Society of London

WHAT IS FUNDED To establish and support schools in the Highlands and northern parts of Britain. To relieve distressed Highlanders away from their native homes. To preserve antiquities and rescue the valuable remains of Celtic literature. To promote the improvement and general welfare of northern parts of Britain

WHO CAN BENEFIT Individuals and institutions

WHERE FUNDING CAN BE GIVEN Highlands of Scotland and northern parts of Great Britain

SAMPLE GRANTS £1,000 to Royal Caledonian Schools
£400 to widows of Highland soldiers
£150 to Royal Scottish Academy

FINANCES
● Year 1994–95   ● Income £8,389

WHO TO APPLY TO Angus Nicol, Highland Society of London, 5 Paper Buildings, Temple, London EC4Y 7HB

CC NO 244472   **ESTABLISHED** 1965

■Gay & Peter Hartley's Hillards Charitable Trust

WHAT IS FUNDED To give aid to those poor, needy and sick who live in the areas which were served by a Hillards store. Churches, community centres and schools within those areas may also be beneficiaries but it is preferable if they have charitable status themselves. The Trust will consider funding: advice and information on housing; emergency

124

Think carefully about every application. Is it justified?

and short term housing; respite; community development; support to voluntary and community organisations; support to volunteers; Councils for Voluntary Service (CVS); Christian education; religious ancillary buildings; religious umbrella bodies; arts education; health care; ambulances and mobile units; hospices; cancer research; health related volunteer schemes; church buildings; historic buildings; animal homes; animal welfare; schools and colleges; special needs education; speech therapy; community services; and other charitable purposes

WHAT IS NOT FUNDED Personal applications are not usually granted unless they come through another charity. As a body, the Trustees do not give to national charities but the individual Trustees have some discretion in that respect

WHO CAN BENEFIT Local and regional organisations benefiting children; young adults, older people; clergy; ex-service and service people; seafarers and fishermen; students; volunteers; those in care, fostered and adopted; parents and children; one parent families; widows and widowers; Baptists; Christians; Church of England; Methodists; Quakers; Roman Catholics; Unitarians; at risk groups; carers; disabled people; those disadvantaged by poverty; ex-offenders and those at risk of offending; homeless people; those living in urban areas; victims of abuse; victims of crime; and victims of domestic violence. There are few restrictions on the disease or medical condition suffered by the beneficiaries

WHERE FUNDING CAN BE GIVEN Areas served by Hillards stores, mainly the North of England, especially Yorkshire

TYPE OF GRANT Buildings, capital, core costs, one-off, project, research, running costs and start up costs. All funding is for one year or less

FINANCES
- Year 1996
- Income £82,861
- Grants £82,355

TRUSTEES P A H Hartley, CBE, Mrs G Hartley, MBE, S R H Hartley, ASVA, Miss S Hartley, BA, MBA, A C H Hartley, MA, MBA, MSc, Miss A Hartley

HOW TO APPLY Application forms are available from the Secretary to the Trustees upon written request and should be returned before 1st November for consideration in December. Applicants are told if they have not been successful

WHO TO APPLY TO Mrs R C Phillips, Secretary to the Trustees, Gay & Peter Hartley's Hillards Charitable Trust, 400 Shadwell Lane, Leeds LS17 8AW *Tel* 0113-266 1424 *Fax* 0113-237 0051

CC NO 327879   **ESTABLISHED** 1988

■ Hilmarnan Charitable Trust

WHAT IS FUNDED The welfare of the elderly, poor and infirm in the area Where Funding Can Be Given

WHO CAN BENEFIT Organisations benefiting elderly people, those disadvantaged by poverty and infirm people

WHERE FUNDING CAN BE GIVEN Within a ten mile radius of Moot Hall, Main Street, Keswick

FINANCES
- Year 1995–96
- Income £18,445
- Grants £5,100

HOW TO APPLY To the address under Who To Apply To in writing. Applications are normally made to the Trustees via local doctors who may highlight a particular person in need

WHO TO APPLY TO G W B Mendus, Trustees Solicitor, Hilmarnan Charitable Trust, c/o Ogelthorpe & Broatch, 6 Borrowdale Road, Keswick CA12 5DB

CC NO 500918   **ESTABLISHED** 1971

■ Historic Cheshire Churches Preservation Trust

WHAT IS FUNDED Grants are given for the preservation of churches in the Beneficial Area, and for the repair and replacement of furniture and fittings in those churches

WHERE FUNDING CAN BE GIVEN Cheshire

FINANCES
- Year 1997
- Income £8,000

HOW TO APPLY To the Correspondent in writing

WHO TO APPLY TO Kenneth A Paul, FCA, Hon Secretary and Treasurer, Historic Cheshire Churches Preservation Trust, Field House, Woodbank, Chester CH1 6JD
Tel 01244 881449

CC NO 213837   **ESTABLISHED** 1962

■ John Holford's Charity

WHAT IS FUNDED The Trust is concerned mainly with aiding individuals, though small grants may also be given to local schools and youth organisations. This Charity will consider funding holiday accommodation; support to voluntary and community organisations; social care and professional bodies; council for voluntary service; and the purchase of books for education

WHO CAN BENEFIT Primarily individuals of all ages who are: at risk, disabled; disaster victims; ex-offenders and those at risk of offending; homeless; socially isolated or living in urban areas

WHERE FUNDING CAN BE GIVEN Astbury, the Parish of Clutton, the Borough of Congleton, the Parish of Middlewich

TYPE OF GRANT Capital, interest free loans and one-off funding

FINANCES
- Year 1996
- Income £45,000

HOW TO APPLY To the address under Who To Apply To in writing

WHO TO APPLY TO The Clerk, John Holford's Charity, Birch Cullimore, Friars, White Friars, Chester CH1 1XS *Tel* 01244 321066

CC NO 223046   **ESTABLISHED** 1984

■ Maria Holland and St Joseph's Charity

WHAT IS FUNDED The elderly, sick and disabled; schools and local churches, especially Catholic

WHO CAN BENEFIT Regional and local organisations benefiting: persons under the age of 25; the elderly, sick and disabled; and Catholics

WHERE FUNDING CAN BE GIVEN Preston

RANGE OF GRANTS £114–£10,000

SAMPLE GRANTS £10,000 to Catholic Caring Services
£8,000 to Sacred Heart and RC Primary School
£6,000 to Preston and North Lancashire Blind Society
£6,000 to an individual
£5,000 to Age Concern
£5,000 to an individual
£2,697 to an individual
£2,000 to Christ The King High School
£114 to St Wilfrid's RC Primary School

FINANCES
- Year 1995
- Income £28,739
- Grants £46,811

TRUSTEES Mrs G R Vernon, M G Sherry

HOW TO APPLY To the address under Who To Apply To in writing

WHO TO APPLY TO M J Belderbos, Trustees' Solicitor, Maria Holland and St Joseph's Charity, Messrs Oswald Goodier & Co, 10 Chapel Street, Preston PR1 8AY

CC NO 223547   **ESTABLISHED** 1990

■ P H Holt Charitable Trust

WHAT IS FUNDED General charitable purposes in Merseyside and abroad, particularly when original work or work of special excellence is being undertaken

WHAT IS NOT FUNDED No grants to individuals

WHO CAN BENEFIT There are no restrictions on the age; professional and economic group; family situation; religion and culture; and social circumstances of; or disease or medical condition suffered by, the beneficiaries

WHERE FUNDING CAN BE GIVEN Merseyside and overseas

WHO TO APPLY TO The Secretary, P H Holt Charitable Trust, c/o Ocean Transport and Trading plc, India Buildings, Liverpool L2 0RB

CC NO 217332   **ESTABLISHED** 1955

■ The Edward Holt Trust

WHAT IS FUNDED Primarily maintaining block of 10 flats in Didsbury, Manchester, for retired gentlefolk. Preference to charities of which the Trustees have special interest, knowledge or association including cancer, neurological and ageing research

WHAT IS NOT FUNDED None per Trust Deed but administratively no grant applications to be made

WHO CAN BENEFIT Individuals and organisations benefiting older people and those suffering from: Alzheimer's disease; autism; cancers; epilepsy; head and other injuries; mental illness; motor neurone disease and muscular dystrophy

WHERE FUNDING CAN BE GIVEN Bolton, Bury, Manchester, Oldham, Rochdale, Salford, Stockport, Tameside and Trafford

TYPE OF GRANT Buildings, capital, project and research. Funding is available for up to two years

FINANCES
- Year 1997
- Income £250,000
- Grants £100,000

TRUSTEES P Kershaw (Chair), H M Fairhurst, R Kershaw, H W E Thompson, FCA, D J Tully

WHO TO APPLY TO J P Sandford, The Edward Holt Trust, KPMG, St James' Square, Manchester M2 6DS *Tel* 0161-838 4000

CC NO 224741   **ESTABLISHED** 1955

■ The Hoover Foundation

WHAT IS FUNDED Wide range of charities including education (mainly supported through grants to universities, normally for research in the engineering subjects), welfare, medical research and small local charities

WHAT IS NOT FUNDED The Trustees do not make grants to individuals, including students

WHO CAN BENEFIT National registered charities, universities and small local charities working in the areas outlined in the area Where Funding Can Be Given benefiting young adults and students. There is no restriction on the disease or medical condition suffered by the beneficiaries

WHERE FUNDING CAN BE GIVEN Biased towards South Wales, Glasgow and Bolton

TRUSTEES A Bertali, D Lunt

NOTES This Trust replied to CAF's mailing. However, by 30 June 1998, CAF's researchers did not find financial records for later than 1994 filed at the Charity Commission

WHO TO APPLY TO Mrs Marion Hceffey, The Hoover Foundation, Pentrebach, Merthyr Tydfil, Mid Glamorgan CF48 4TU
Tel 01685 721222 *Fax* 01685 725667

CC NO 200274   **ESTABLISHED** 1961

■ Clifford Howarth Charity Trust

WHAT IS FUNDED General charitable purposes

WHAT IS NOT FUNDED No grants to individuals, for scholarships or non-local special projects

WHO CAN BENEFIT Local and national registered charities which were supported by the Founder. There are no restrictions on the age; professional and economic group; family situation; religion and culture; and social circumstances of; or disease or medical condition suffered by, the beneficiaries

WHERE FUNDING CAN BE GIVEN Within Burnley or Rosensdale areas of Lancashire

TYPE OF GRANT One-off

SAMPLE GRANTS £1,000 to local church
£1,000 to RSPCA

FINANCES
- Year 1998
- Income £37,700
- Grants £37,000

TRUSTEES M Fenton, J Howarth, E Howarth

NOTES Grants are distributed annually in February and March

WHO TO APPLY TO The Trustees, Clifford Howarth Charity Trust, c/o Lambert Howarth & Sons Ltd, Healey Royd Works, Healey Royd Road, Burnley, Lancashire BB11 2HL

CC NO 264890   **ESTABLISHED** 1972

■ Richard Threlfall Hurst Charitable Trust

WHAT IS FUNDED Educational institutions and local welfare organisations

WHO CAN BENEFIT Individuals and organisations

WHERE FUNDING CAN BE GIVEN Greater Manchester, especially Bolton

FINANCES
- Year 1995–96
- Income £11,300
- Grants £15,300

TRUSTEES B H Hurst, R H Hurst, R A Speak

HOW TO APPLY To the Correspondent in writing

WHO TO APPLY TO J G Smith, Accountant, Richard Threlfall Hurst Charitable Trust, Deloitte & Touche, Chartered Accountants, PO Box 500, 74 Mosley Street, Manchester M60 2AT

CC NO 247533   **ESTABLISHED** 1966

■ The Joseph Hutchinson Educational Charity

WHAT IS FUNDED The support of community facilities for the benefit of children and youth in the Beneficial Area. Education and repairs to Parish Centre

WHAT IS NOT FUNDED Parish of Hunsonby only

WHO CAN BENEFIT Local organisations

WHERE FUNDING CAN BE GIVEN Parish of Hunsonby

FINANCES
- Year 1996
- Income £2,600

TRUSTEES E A Burne (Churchwarden), M Smith (Churchwarden), M Burne, P R Smith

HOW TO APPLY **Grants are given at the discretion of the Trustees, applications are not required**

WHO TO APPLY TO E A Burne, Trustee, Joseph Hutchinson Educational Charity, Ingledene, Hunsonby, Penrith, Cumbria CA10 1PH
Tel 01768 881296

CC NO 526844   **ESTABLISHED** 1726

■Integreat

WHAT IS FUNDED The relief of young people aged five to 15 who have a disability by bringing them into closer association with able-bodied people. The provision, or assistance in the provision, in the interests of social welfare, of facilities for recreation for young people with and without disabilities. The advancement of education by bringing young people who have a disability into closer association and integration with able-bodied people so that the former will have opportunities for overcome their disabilities and the latter will benefit from such association and integration

WHO CAN BENEFIT Organisations benefiting children and young adults, especially those who are disabled

WHERE FUNDING CAN BE GIVEN UK and Northwest

TRUSTEES P Bailey, BA, MSoc, ScDipEd, Ms S Bell, Ms S Coulter, BA, CQSW, Ms J Crombleholme, MA, MIHSM, R Kapoor, BA, DMS, LIPD, Dr C Sayers, MBChB

WHO TO APPLY TO J P Bailey, Secretary, Integreat, 93 Cheadle Road, Stockport, Cheshire SK8 5DW

CC NO 1064187   **ESTABLISHED** 1997

■The N B Johnson Charitable Settlement

WHAT IS FUNDED General charitable purposes. Each case considered on its merits. Particularly Jewish charities

WHAT IS NOT FUNDED Generally registered charities only. Individuals only considered in very special cases

WHO CAN BENEFIT Registered charities benefiting Jewish people

WHERE FUNDING CAN BE GIVEN Bias to local causes (Manchester area)

TYPE OF GRANT Cash

FINANCES
- Year 1995
- Grants £32,496
- Income £31,228

TRUSTEES N B Johnson, Mrs S J Johnson, L Hyman

HOW TO APPLY At any time to the address under Who To Apply To, but will only be dealt with when Trustees meet every three months and grants are not made in the intervening months

WHO TO APPLY TO L Hyman, The N B Johnson Charitable Settlement, Pannone & Partners, 123 Deansgate, Manchester M3 2BU

CC NO 277237   **ESTABLISHED** 1978

■The Johnson Foundation

WHAT IS FUNDED Medicine and health, welfare, education, environmental resources, infrastructure development and professional bodies

WHAT IS NOT FUNDED No grants to individuals or students

WHO CAN BENEFIT Registered charities benefiting: medical professionals; carers; disabled people; those disadvantaged by poverty; and victims of abuse. Those suffering from various diseases and medical conditions will also be considered

WHERE FUNDING CAN BE GIVEN Merseyside

TYPE OF GRANT One-off, recurrent, core costs, project and research. Funding is available for up to two years

RANGE OF GRANTS £100–£25,000, typical grant £500

128

Think carefully about every application. Is it justified?

SAMPLE GRANTS £25,000 to Age Concern for a Devonshire Centre
£1,000 to Shaftesbury Youth Centre for youth club facilities
£1,000 to Barnstondale for holiday scheme for underprivileged children

FINANCES
- Year 1997–98
- Income £721,689
- Grants £76,208

TRUSTEES P R Johnson, S E Johnson, C W Johnson

PUBLICATIONS Annual Report

HOW TO APPLY To the address under Who To Apply To in writing at any time. Trustees meet monthly

WHO TO APPLY TO P R Johnson, The Johnson Foundation, Westmount, Vyner Road South, Birkenhead, Merseyside L43 7PN *Tel* 0151-653 0566

CC NO 518660   **ESTABLISHED** 1987

- - -

■ Johnson Group Cleaners Charity

WHAT IS FUNDED Support of Merseyside charities which feature poverty, underprivileged, relief of suffering. This includes: Councils for Voluntary Service; care in the community; and holidays and outings

WHAT IS NOT FUNDED No grants to national charities or individuals

WHO CAN BENEFIT Registered local charities benefiting children, young adults and older people; at risk groups; carers; those disadvantaged by poverty; ex-offenders and those at risk of offending; homeless people; victims of abuse and domestic violence and those suffering from substance misuse

WHERE FUNDING CAN BE GIVEN Merseyside

TYPE OF GRANT Core costs, one-off, project and running costs. All funding is for up to two years

SAMPLE GRANTS £9,000 to Victims of Violence to assist with essential running costs
£5,000 to Acorn Venture Urban Farm to assist with essential running costs
£5,000 to Merseyside Council for Voluntary Services to assist with essential running costs
£5,000 to Sefton Young Carers to assist with essential running costs
£2,500 to Sail Training Association berths for underprivileged children in Merseyside
£2,000 to Liverpool Motorists Annual Outing for deprived children's day out at Southport
£1,500 to Ocean Youth Club for berths for underprivileged children in Merseyside
£650 to Sefton Women's and Children's Aid to assist with essential running costs
£302 to Marsh Lane Boxing Club for equipment

£250 to Pacific Celtic Boys Foot Ball Club for jerseys

FINANCES
- Year 1998
- Income £102,145
- Grants £113,640

TRUSTEES Johnson Group Cleaners Trustee Company (No 1) Ltd

HOW TO APPLY To Charity Administrator in writing

WHO TO APPLY TO Miss A F Smith, Charity Administrator, Johnson Group Cleaners Charity, Mildmay Road, Bootle, Merseyside L20 5EW

CC NO 216973   **ESTABLISHED** 1990

- - -

■ Joint Churches Community Project

WHAT IS FUNDED The relief of poverty and sickness, the advancement of education and the provision of recreational facilities in the interests of social welfare by promoting co-operation between local people and the local authorities

WHO CAN BENEFIT Local people, particularly those disadvantaged by poverty and those who are sick

WHERE FUNDING CAN BE GIVEN Greenbank, Kells, Mirehouse and Woodhouse in Cumbria

FINANCES
- Year 1997
- Income £20,150

HOW TO APPLY To the address below in writing

WHO TO APPLY TO Fr Tom Singleton, Chairperson, Joint Churches Community Project, St Mary's Presbytery, High Road, Kells, Whitehaven, Cumbria CA28 9PG

CC NO 1064205   **ESTABLISHED** 1997

- - -

■ J E Joseph Charitable Fund

WHAT IS FUNDED For the general relief of poor and needy Jews in certain cities and places in the area Where Funding Can Be Given, priority being given to those of Sephardi extraction. The Trustees respond to all applications which are first vetted by the Secretary

WHAT IS NOT FUNDED Grants to individuals in exceptional cases only and are usually made to assist towards education and in particular further and higher education. No application from an organisation will be considered without a copy of its most recent set of accounts. Only Jewish individuals or organisations need apply

WHO CAN BENEFIT Jewish community organisations, especially those catering for the socially disadvantaged and youth. Only exceptionally individuals

WHERE FUNDING CAN BE GIVEN UK (principally London and Manchester), Near and Far East, Israel, Palestine

TYPE OF GRANT Outright cash grants frequently on an annual basis. Very occasionally loans

RANGE OF GRANTS £500–£10,000

FINANCES
- Year 1998
- Grants £90,750
- Income £107,098

HOW TO APPLY To the Secretary by letter

WHO TO APPLY TO Timothy Simon, The Secretary, J E Joseph Charitable Fund, 2 New Square, Lincoln's Inn, London WC2A 3RZ

CC NO 209058   **ESTABLISHED** 1946

■ Charity of Mrs Hannah Kennington (Deceased)

WHAT IS FUNDED To benefit local child and youth organisations and institutions. In addition, grants are made to local community organisations

WHAT IS NOT FUNDED Applications from individuals will not be considered

WHERE FUNDING CAN BE GIVEN Appleby

FINANCES
- Year 1995–96
- Income £1,131

HOW TO APPLY To the Correspondent in writing

WHO TO APPLY TO Town Clerk, Charity of Mrs Hannah Kennington, Moot Hall, Appleby, Cumbria CA16 6XE

CC NO 503022   **ESTABLISHED** 1961

■ The Peter Kershaw Trust (413)

This trust failed to supply a copy of its annual report and accounts to CAF as required under section 47(2) of the Charities Act 1993. The information given here was obtained independently by CAF's researchers at the Charity Commission

WHAT IS FUNDED Medical research, grants to medical and other institutions, bursaries for schools

WHAT IS NOT FUNDED No grants to individuals

WHO CAN BENEFIT Registered charities benefiting young adults and older people, carers, those disadvantaged by poverty, homeless and socially isolated people

WHERE FUNDING CAN BE GIVEN Greater Manchester

TYPE OF GRANT One-off or core costs. Also research, running costs, salaries and start-up costs. Funding may be given for up to three years

RANGE OF GRANTS £5,000–£40,000

FINANCES
- Year 1997
- Grants £316,474
- Income £312,554

TRUSTEES H F Kershaw, P Kershaw, R Kershaw, B B Pugh, M L Rushbrooke, H W E Thompson

HOW TO APPLY In writing

WHO TO APPLY TO G J Wallwork, FCA, Secretary, The Peter Kershaw Trust, Higher Town Farm House, 4 Warwick Close, Knutsford, Cheshire WA16 8NA

CC NO 268934   **ESTABLISHED** 1974

Commentary

The Peter Kershaw Trust was established on 23 February 1974 to fund charitable purposes at the discretion of the Trustees. Although the Trust Deed gives the Trustees very wide discretionary powers, the Trust has a policy of giving grants for medical research, and to medical and other institutions. Bursaries are also provided for schools. It is not known if the Trustees have a scale of preference within their funding policies.

The Trust funds statutory bodies in that it gives grants to schools, hospitals and other institutions. However, it is not known if the Trust is prepared to replace statutory funding. The Trust's attitude to co-funding is not known. The Trust prefers to make one-off grants for core costs, running costs, salaries and start-up costs. It is not willing to makes loans.

Applications should be in writing. The decision-making processes for dealing with applications, and whether there is an assessment process for dealing with grant recipients, are not known

SAMPLE GRANTS
The top ten grants made in 1997 were:
£250,000 to MacMillan Fund
£40,000 to David Lewis Appeal Fund
£30,000 to The Big Step
£20,636 to Wrightington Hospital for hip replacement surgery research, joint operations and ceramic heads
£20,000 to Booth Drop-In Centre
£20,000 to Lifeshare
£20,000 to East Cheshire Hospice
£20,000 to Fairbridge in Salford
£20,000 to Wood Street Missions
£12,546 to Withington Girls' School

■ The Ursula Keyes Trust

WHAT IS FUNDED Ranges from medical research to practical support, eg purchase of equipment, wheelchairs and funding for a hospice to a wide range of activities in the medical/social field with an emphasis on medical research, welfare and care work

WHAT IS NOT FUNDED Students or political groups

WHO CAN BENEFIT Individuals and institutions benefiting: at risk groups; those disadvantaged by poverty; socially isolated people; and the sick. There are no restrictions on the disease or medical condition suffered by the beneficiaries

WHERE FUNDING CAN BE GIVEN Chester primarily, occasionally other areas

TYPE OF GRANT Small and large grants

RANGE OF GRANTS Below £1,000–£30,000

SAMPLE GRANTS £30,000 to Chester Cathedral Development Trust
£27,083 to Liverpool University for a medical research fellowship
£25,000 to Hospice of the Good Shepherd
£10,000 to Chester Area MacMillan Nurse Appeal
£5,000 to Hope House
£3,000 to The Drugwatch Trust
£2,000 to Neuro Muscular Centre
£3,998 to nine individuals
£1,673 in donations of under £1,000 to institutions

FINANCES
- Year 1996
- Grants £107,754
- Income £252,250

TRUSTEES Dr A E Elliot, J F Kane, J R Leaman, Dr R A Owen, H M Shaw, P R Wise

HOW TO APPLY Require enquiries and applications in writing

WHO TO APPLY TO P R Wise, Trustee, The Ursula Keyes Trust, 90–92 Telegraph Road, Heswall, Wirral, Merseyside L60 0AQ

CC NO 517200   **ESTABLISHED** 1985

■ Knights House Charity

WHAT IS FUNDED To relieve the poor and needy residents of Widnes

WHO CAN BENEFIT Those disadvantaged by poverty

WHERE FUNDING CAN BE GIVEN Borough of Widnes

FINANCES
- Year 1995–96
- Grants £9,944
- Income £10,203

WHO TO APPLY TO A Hill, Director of Resources, Knights House Charity, Halton Borough Council, Municipal Buildings, Widnes, Cheshire WA8 7QF

CC NO 218886   **ESTABLISHED** 1961

■ The Heinz & Anna Kroch Foundation

WHAT IS FUNDED This Foundation exists to further medical research and to relieve suffering in cases of injustice and individual hardship

WHAT IS NOT FUNDED No grants are made to students or for holidays

Does the trust you have chosen match your needs? Haphazard applications waste postage and time

131

WHO CAN BENEFIT Organisations benefiting: carers; disabled people; those disadvantaged by poverty; homeless people; victims of abuse and domestic violence; victims of war. There are no restrictions on the age or family situation of, or disease or medical condition suffered by the beneficiaries

WHERE FUNDING CAN BE GIVEN UK and Ireland

TYPE OF GRANT Grants do not exceed £15,000. Research and funding of up to three years will be considered

RANGE OF GRANTS £50–£15,000

FINANCES
- Year 1995
- Income £115,000
- Grants £79,000

TRUSTEES Ms A C Kroch, H J Kroch, P A English, C T Richardson, D Kroch-Rhodes

NOTES No grants for holidays or education. Individuals must apply through social services, CAB, welfare rights or other recognised organisations

HOW TO APPLY Throughout the year. No application form. Information by letter. Happy to discuss applications on phone prior to applying

WHO TO APPLY TO Mrs H Astle, Administrator, The Heinz & Anna Kroch Foundation, PO Box 17, Worsley, Manchester M28 2SB *Tel* 0161-793 4201

CC NO 207622   **ESTABLISHED** 1962

■Bryan Lancaster's Trust

WHAT IS FUNDED A Quaker Trust. Helps towards setting up, repairs, running costs and new ventures. Priority is given to projects with Quaker involvement. Preferably for smaller and newer charities in the north-west. Particularly charities working in the fields of: accommodation and housing; infrastructure, support and development; Quaker umbrella bodies; alternative health care, health counselling; respite care, care for carers; support and self help groups; Quaker church buildings; historic buildings; professional and specialist training; bursaries and fees; purchase of books; peace campaigning; advice centres; law centres; and various community facilities and services

WHAT IS NOT FUNDED Applications from students and large medical charities are not considered

WHO CAN BENEFIT Organisations benefiting people of all ages, unemployed people and Quakers. There are few restrictions on the social circumstances of the beneficiaries

WHERE FUNDING CAN BE GIVEN UK with preference towards North West England

TYPE OF GRANT Usually one-off grants towards a specific object and to local, not national, bodies. Buildings, capital, core costs, feasibility studies, running costs and start-up costs. Funding for one year or less will be considered

RANGE OF GRANTS £200–£2,000

FINANCES
- Year 1995
- Income £39,400
- Grants £24,500

TRUSTEES D M Butler, A LeMare, C Cathrow

HOW TO APPLY At any time by letter, no application form. Trustees meet about every two months. No telephone calls. Please enclose sae; no acknowledgement without one

WHO TO APPLY TO David M Butler, Bryan Lancaster's Trust, 9 Greenside, Kendal, Cumbria LA9 5DU

CC NO 222902   **ESTABLISHED** 1719

■The Allen Lane Foundation (260)

WHAT IS FUNDED Social welfare; advice, information and advocacy; community development; mediation; conflict resolution and alternatives to violence; employment and

132

Think carefully about every application. Is it justified?

training; research and education aimed at changing public attitudes or policy

WHAT IS NOT FUNDED No grants are made for academic research, addiction, alcohol or drug abuse, animal welfare or animal rights, arts or cultural or language projects or festivals, holidays or holiday playschemes, sports or recreation, housing, individuals, large general appeals from charities which enjoy widespread public support, medical care, hospices or medical research, museums or galleries, overseas travel, private and/or mainstream education, promotion of sectarian religion, publications, purchase costs of property, building or refurbishment, restoration or conservation of historic buildings or sites, vehicle purchase, work outside the UK, work which will have already taken place before a grant is agreed, and work which the Trustees believe is rightly the responsibility of the state

WHO CAN BENEFIT Organisations whose work may be perceived as unpopular such as refugees and asylum seekers, black and ethnic minority communities, travellers, those with mental health problems and offenders among others

WHERE FUNDING CAN BE GIVEN UK, except Greater London

TYPE OF GRANT Generally for one year only, although longer term funding of up to three years may be offered sometimes. Project or core costs. Also research, running costs and start-up costs

RANGE OF GRANTS £500–£10,000 for single grants, £1,000–£5,000 per annum

FINANCES
- Year 1998
- Income £556,345
- Grants £607,397

TRUSTEES Mrs Christine Teale, Mrs Clare Morpurgo, B C G Whitaker, Charles Medawar, Zoe Teale

NOTES The Trustees regret that applications far outstrip the funds available and not all good or appropriate projects can be offered funding, even though they may fall well within current funding priorities. A rejection may be no reflection on the value of the project. Trustees meet three times a year so applicants should allow up to four months for a positive decision

HOW TO APPLY Application may be sent to the Executive Secretary at any time. Guidance notes are available from the Foundation's office

WHO TO APPLY TO Heather Swailes, Executive Secretary, The Allen Lane Foundation, Room 6A, Winchester House, 11 Cranmer Road, London SW9 6EJ *Tel* 0171-793 1899 *Fax* 0171-793 1989 *E-mail* enquiries@allenlane.demon.co.uk *Web Site* www.allenlane.demon.co.uk

CC NO 248031 **ESTABLISHED** 1966

Commentary

The Allen Lane Foundation was set up in 1966 with a large endowment by the late Sir Allen Lane, the founder of Penguin Books. Upon Sir Allen's death in 1970 the endowment was enlarged by a substantial bequest.

Recently the Trustees decided to be more specific about the unpopular causes which it has, for some years, made a priority. Priority groups for the Foundation include refugees and asylum-seekers; lesbian, gay and bisexual groups; black and ethnic minority communities; those experiencing mental health problems; those experiencing violence or abuse; offenders and ex-offenders; and travellers; other similar groups will also receive consideration. Although the Trustees have not excluded the possibility of making grants in other areas, they also decided upon six broad areas of work as priorities: social welfare; the provision of advice, information and advocacy; community development; mediation, conflict resolution and alternatives to violence; employment and training; and research and education aimed at changing public attitudes or policy.

There are a number of areas that the Foundation stresses that it is unwilling to fund. These include: academic research; addiction; alcohol or drug abuse; animal welfare or animal rights; arts projects; cultural projects; language projects; festivals; holidays or holiday playschemes; sports or recreation; housing; individuals; large general appeals from charities which enjoy widespread public support; medical care; hospices or medical research; museums or galleries; overseas travel; private and/or mainstream education; promotion of sectarian religion; publications; purchase costs of property; building or refurbishment; restoration or conservation of historic buildings or sites; vehicle purchase; work outside the UK or inside Greater London; and work which will have already taken place before a grant is agreed.

The Foundation covers the whole of the UK, except Greater London, with its funding and only make grants inside London in very exceptional circumstances. The Foundation targets about 80 per cent of its grant making on national or regional organisations, rather than on local work. There is a desire to balance grant distribution amongst the various categories mentioned above; there is no particular weighting towards any one field.

The Trustees review the areas in which they wish to fund, the last review in 1997 was used to refine their areas of giving, and these are therefore unlikely to change until 2000 at the earliest.

The Trustees will not fund work which they believe is rightly the responsibility of the state. There is a very positive attitude towards co-funding, partly because the Foundation does not feel it has enough money available to consider funding entire projects.

Grants are made both for project and revenue costs to or through registered charities. They are usually single payments although some grants may be made over a period of two or three years. The Trustees try to avoid any longer term commitments to any one organisation in order to avoid over-dependence upon the Foundation. They also hope to spread resources as fairly as possible between new applicants and those who have already been supported by the Foundation.

Applicants should plan well ahead to allow sufficient time for applications to be assessed. If the project or organisation is not in one of the priority groups or is outside the remit of the Trust, notification will be sent within a few weeks. However, applications being put forward for further consideration go to Trustee meetings which take place only three times a year.

There is no application form; applications should be no longer than four A4 sides (although the budget may be put on an extra page) and should be accompanied by the latest Annual Report and Accounts. The application should answer the following questions: (a) what are the aims of your organisation as a whole? (b) how do you try and achieve these aims? (c) what do you want the grant to help you do and how will you do it? (d) how much will it cost? (e) what other sources of funding are you approaching? (f) how will you assess the success of your work? (g) how will the work, and the way it is done, promote equal opportunities?

The better quality applications are assessed in depth and, after some deliberation, the number to go forward for further consideration is reduced to a more manageable size. It is not unusual at this point for more information to be requested by the Secretary or for a visit to be arranged to discuss the application in more detail. After this the remaining applications will go forward for consideration at a full Trustee meeting. After a Trustee meeting, notification of whether the application has been successful will be forwarded within about a week. If an applicant has been successful, they receive an offer outlining the terms and conditions of the grant. When this has been signed and returned, the Foundation will send a cheque to the organisation.

Post-grant assessment is made in the form of a report at the close of the project or after a year for grants made over a period of two to three years. The Foundation tries to encourage organisations to evaluate their own projects, as it is felt that this is much more valuable to the organisations involved

SAMPLE GRANTS

The top ten grants committed in 1997–98 were
£15,000 to Women's Aid Federation, England
£15,000 to Scottish Refugee Council
£15,000 to Runnymeade Trust
£15,000 to Federation of Prisoners' Families Support Group
£15,000 to National Federation of Credit Unions
£15,000 to Respond
£12,000 to North of England Refugee Service
£12,000 to Welsh Refugee Service
£10,000 to Public Law Project
£10,000 to Neighbourhood Initiatives Foundation

■ The Lankelly Foundation (78)

WHAT IS FUNDED The Foundation's main area of concern is social welfare, and its broad priorities are currently: the support of communities and families who are striving to create an environment in which they can flourish; the support of people whose mental or physical disabilities require special resources; and the support of groups who are marginalised because of poverty, unemployment or crime, including domestic violence

WHAT IS NOT FUNDED Registered charities only. Applications from individuals, including students are ineligible. No grants are made in response to general appeals from large, national organisations, nor to circular appeals of any kind. No grants for: advancement of religion; festivals or theatre production; research and feasibility studies; individual youth clubs; medical research; formal education; endowment funds; other grant making bodies; conferences or seminars; publications, films or video; sport; travel, expeditions or holidays; hospital trusts; individual needs; animal welfare; and the under-fives (other than summer holiday schemes)

WHO CAN BENEFIT Registered charities working in the areas outlined under what is funded, with preference given to enabling small organisations to grow. There are no restrictions on the age or family situation of the beneficiaries. The Trustees will consider organisations benefiting ex-service and service people, the unemployed and those affected by various social circumstances and medical conditions

WHERE FUNDING CAN BE GIVEN UK, except Greater London and Northern Ireland

TYPE OF GRANT One-off and recurring grants, that must always be for a specific purpose. Capital and revenue grants are considered, as are buildings, core costs, project, running and start-up costs, and salaries. Funding may be given for more than three years

FINANCES
- Year 1997–98
- Income £2,657,430
- Grants £3,019,985

TRUSTEES Leo Fraser-Mackenzie, Cecil Heather (Chairman), Mrs Georgina Linton, Wallace J Mackenzie, Lady Merlyn-Rees, A Ramsay Hack, Mrs Shirley Turner

PUBLICATIONS Annual Report and guidelines for applicants

HOW TO APPLY At any time. Trustees meet in April, July, October and January. Applications should be in writing, describing what the organisation does and why it is seeking help from the Foundation and including the Annual Report and Accounts. Applications are acknowledged and dealt with as soon as possible. Those which are put to the Trustees for formal consideration are visited beforehand by a member of staff

WHO TO APPLY TO Peter F Kilgarriff, Director, The Lankelly Foundation, 2 The Court, High Street, Harwell, Didcot, Oxfordshire OX11 0EY *Tel* 01235 820044

CC NO 256987   **ESTABLISHED** 1968

Commentary

The Lankelly Foundation was established in 1968 by an anonymous settlor, who later, in 1977, established the Hambland Foundation. These two Trusts operated virtually as one, and in 1993 the assets of the Hambland Foundation were fully transferred to the Lankelly Foundation. The Hambland Foundation no longer operates as a grant making trust. The Lankelly Foundation works closely, in terms of administration, with the Chase Charity. This cuts down on administration costs, gives staff broader contact with voluntary organisations and allows them to be more flexible in their responses. The Trusts remain however very distinct, and separate application forms are required for each.

The Lankelly Foundation was created with the aim of supporting general charitable purposes. This has however been greatly narrowed down in recent years, and the main focus of the Foundation is now on social need and welfare. The priorities of the Foundation are currently: the support of communities and families who are striving to create an environment in which they can flourish; the support of people whose mental or physical disabilities require special resources;

and the support of groups who are marginalised because of poverty, unemployment or crime, including domestic violence. The following specific areas are supported: alcohol and drugs; children and young people; the elderly; the homeless; penal affairs; community welfare; domestic violence; people with disabilities and special needs; ethnic minorities; neighbourhood work; arts and community arts; and conservation and heritage. The Foundation prefers to help small organisations grow stronger, rather than to support large national organisations which normally have many more sources of funding available to them. Organisations run by, and for, people with special needs are particularly favoured, and received the largest proportion of the total amount of grants given. Also particularly favoured are organisations involved with the homeless and neighbourhood work in clearly defined local areas. Appeals from ethnic minority groups are encouraged, and grants to a total of £216,400 were made to such causes in 1998. Less emphasis is being put on the arts and heritage projects than in past years.

Grants for work involved with alcohol and drugs totalled 1.3 per cent; arts and community arts received 5.3 per cent; projects for children and young people received 13.1 per cent; community welfare projects received 11.2 per cent; organisations involved with disability and special needs received 26.24 per cent; organisations involved with domestic violence received 4.9 per cent; organisations for the benefit of the elderly received 6.9 per cent; heritage and conservation projects received 1.5 per cent; projects for the homeless received 7.4 per cent; neighbourhood work projects received 12.9 per cent; and organisations involved with penal affairs received 9.3 per cent of the total grants made. In 1998, 2,077 applications were received, and around 125 grants were made, totalling £3,064,085.

The Foundation is very clear about what they do not fund: unregistered charities; individuals, including students; general appeals from large, national organisations; circular appeals of any kind; or grants for: the advancement of religion; festivals or theatre production; research and feasibility studies; individual youth clubs; medical research; education; endowment funds; other grant making bodies; conferences or seminars; publications, films or video; sport; travel, expeditions or holidays; hospital trusts; individual needs; animal welfare; under-fives (other than summer holiday schemes).

The funding policies have recently been greatly revised by the Trustees from the original objective of general charitable purposes. The policy changes, which reflect the preferences outlined above, are now being implemented and this is leading to a concentration of resources on the social needs of identifiable communities, including those with special needs, and for supporting families and groups working in local areas.

The Foundation will make grants to organisations throughout the whole of the UK except Greater London and Northern Ireland. Their current policy is to try to ensure that grants made are spread as equally as possible across the country, and the number of grants made to each region is carefully monitored. The number of grants made to London and the South East is currently being reduced to this end. The largest number of applications are received from the South East and Greater London, but the North West receives the greatest number of grants.

The Foundation will not make grants to statutory bodies, or replace statutory funding. It has entered into co-funding projects in the past, but it very much depends on the individual circumstances each time. Co-funding projects with the National Lottery Charities Board are not normally entered into, but this is often because the project does not fit into the Foundation's aims, rather than any particular objection to the National Lottery. The Foundation has entered into match-funding projects, such as with a grant to Revolving Doors Agency towards the cost of a pilot project to assist people with mental health problems who are brought into contact with the criminal justice system.

The Foundation prefers to make one-off or recurrent grants, and they will make them for a wide variety of purposes, including building work, infrastructure costs, capital costs, running costs, core costs, start-up costs, project costs, salaries, training and revenue costs. Loans are not made.

Applications can be made at any time and should be in writing, describing what the organisation does and why it is seeking help from the Foundation. It should contain brief information about the origins and current company/charitable status of the organisation, and should answer the following questions: how much needs to be raised?; how soon does it need to be raised?; what support has already been attracted for that project?; who else has been asked to help? The letter should also include the Annual Report and Accounts. Applications are acknowledged and dealt with as soon as possible. The Trustees meet quarterly to consider applications, and for all applications that are going to be considered in detail, the applicant organisation is visited and a detailed exchange of information takes place. This is found to be mutually beneficial and makes it possible to link organisations that feel alone in their work. First hand information from other sources about the work and the people seeking the support is also sought and taken into account. It may take several months to make a decision. The Foundation has recently started to evaluate grants made in the past, and as a part of this process, grant recipients are occasionally visited

SAMPLE GRANTS
The top ten grants made in 1998 were:
£85,400 to the Forward Day Centre, King's Lynn, Norfolk, to employ an assistant manager/outreach worker over four years
£75,000 to Family Welfare Association, London to support their grants to individuals in need
£69,000 over three years to the Jericho Community Project Limited, Birmingham, to help to establish a 'social business' to provide long term unemployed people with the opportunity of training and work,
£67,000 to the Oxfordshire Mental Health Resource Centre, Oxford over five years towards the cost of Allies – an advocacy project for people with mental health problems
£62,200 over three years to Cutteslowe Community Network, Oxford towards the cost of employing two part-time workers
£60,900 over three years to Insight Arts Trust, London to develop the Connecting Lines Project in a number of prisons around the country, in conjunction with Plan B, a Bradford based charity
£60,000 over two years to ASSIST, Scotland towards the cost of developing an independent needs assessment service for people with mental health problems
£60,000 over two years to the Breakthrough Trust, Birmingham towards the cost of developing training courses, over two years
£60,000 over three years to Family Matters, Gravesend, Kent towards the cost of improving the quality of training and the supervision of volunteer counsellors
£60,000 over three years to Youth Enquiry Service, Plymouth, Devon to employ a volunteer co-ordinator

···
■Peter Lathoms Charity

WHAT IS FUNDED The largest proportion of the grant total is given in grants to individuals for education and relief in need purposes

WHO CAN BENEFIT Individuals and some local organisations benefiting those disadvantaged by poverty and those in need

WHERE FUNDING CAN BE GIVEN The parishes of Bickerstaffe; Bispham and Mawdesley; Burscough; Croston; Dalton and Parbold; Newburgh and Latham; Ormskirk; Rufford; Scarisbrick; Skelmersdale; Ulnes; Walton and Eccleston; Heskin and Wrightington; Welch Whittle

FINANCES
- Year 1996
- Income £30,397
- Grants £15,355

TRUSTEES D B Bennett, A Blundell, W J Brown, Rev R J Brunswick, A Caunce, W M Cox, Mrs

136

Think carefully about every application. Is it justified?

D M Gardner, N Johnson, A K Lewis, J N Lucas, R Moss, W Norcross, M Pennington, Mrs M D Rees, A C Richardson, Mrs H Rosbotham, J W Rothwell, P W Scarisbrick, R Shepherd, J W Shufflebothamm, Rev R D Talbot, O Taylor, M Warburton, W Waterworth, L Watson, J Smith

HOW TO APPLY To the address under Who To Apply To in writing

WHO TO APPLY TO C J Byron, Clerk, Peter Lathoms Charity, 15 Railway Road, Ormskirk, Lancashire L39 2DW

CC NO 228828   **ESTABLISHED** 1964

■ The Eric and Dorothy Leach Charitable Trust

WHAT IS FUNDED Health, conservation, and animal facilities and services

WHAT IS NOT FUNDED No grants to individuals

WHO CAN BENEFIT Organisations benefiting children, young adults and older people

WHERE FUNDING CAN BE GIVEN Principally the North West and North Wales

TYPE OF GRANT Core costs, one-off, project, research, running costs and start-up costs

HOW TO APPLY In writing only

WHO TO APPLY TO R Chamberlain, The Eric and Dorothy Leach Charitable Trust, c/o Swayne, Johnson & Wight Solicitors, High Street, St Asaph, Denbighshire LL17 0RF
Tel 01745 582535 *Fax* 01745 584504

CC NO 1070041   **ESTABLISHED** 1998

■ Leasgill Quarry

WHAT IS FUNDED General charitable purposes

WHO CAN BENEFIT Individuals and organisations

WHERE FUNDING CAN BE GIVEN Heversham and Milnthorpe

FINANCES
- Year 1995–96   ● Income £6,093

HOW TO APPLY To the Correspondent in writing

WHO TO APPLY TO Julie Stannard, Parish Clerk, Leasgill Quarry, Tower View, Heversham, Cumbria LA7 7EW

CC NO 1044972   **ESTABLISHED** 1995

■ The Paul & Evelyn Leboff Charitable Trust

WHAT IS FUNDED The Trustees favour local appeals and support a limited number of national organisations. Regret no further organisations considered, only the existing ones already receiving support. Funding may be given to synagogues and Jewish umbrella bodies; respite care, hospices, cancer and MS research; and special schools

WHO CAN BENEFIT Registered charities including those benefiting the elderly, disadvantaged youth, handicapped and disabled, blind and deaf people

WHERE FUNDING CAN BE GIVEN Hertfordshire and Manchester

TYPE OF GRANT One-off, recurrent and research grants depending on funds available. Funding is for one year or less

RANGE OF GRANTS £25–£1,000 (approximately)

SAMPLE GRANTS £3,368 to Bushey United Synagogue
£2,220 to B'nei B'rith Hillel Foundation
£1,720 to BFIWD
£1,580 to Habad Orphan Aid Society
£1,225 to Rudolph Steiner
£800 to Harbard Orphans
£510 to P Hebrew Congregation
£496 to JNF
£325 to JPAIME
£300 to JIA

FINANCES
- Year 1997   ● Income £20,008
- Grants £18,302

TRUSTEES Mrs E Leboff, A B Leboff, Mrs M A Cohen

HOW TO APPLY Reviewed generally April and October each year. No phone calls accepted, no application form used

WHO TO APPLY TO Mrs E Leboff, The Paul & Evelyn Leboff Charitable Trust, 7 Priory Court, 169 Sparrows Herne, Bushey, Watford, Hertfordshire WD2 1EF

CC NO 264707   **ESTABLISHED** 1972

■ Lord Leverhulme's Charitable Trust (223)

This trust failed to supply a copy of its annual report and accounts to CAF as required under section 47(2) of the Charities Act 1993. The information given here was obtained independently by CAF's researchers at the Charity Commission

WHAT IS FUNDED General charitable purposes. Priority is given to certain charitable organisations and trusts in Cheshire and Merseyside, particularly: educational organisations; welfare charities; youth organisations; churches; and organisations benefiting the elderly and disabled people

WHAT IS NOT FUNDED No grants to individuals

WHO CAN BENEFIT Organisations benefiting students and teachers. There are no restrictions on the age of the beneficiaries, and few on their social circumstances

WHERE FUNDING CAN BE GIVEN UK, especially Cheshire and Merseyside

TYPE OF GRANT Recurrent, one-off and capital

RANGE OF GRANTS £5–£10,000 and above

FINANCES
- Year 1995
- Income £450,318
- Grants £759,272

TRUSTEES Algernon E H Heber-Percy, Anthony H S Hannay

HOW TO APPLY Applications by letter to the Trustees with any relevant supporting documents

WHO TO APPLY TO The Trustees of The Charitable Trust, The Lord Leverhulme Charitable Trust, c/o Coopers & Lybrand, 1 Embankment Place, London WC2N 6NN *Tel* 0171-583 5000

CC NO 212431   **ESTABLISHED** 1957

Commentary

Lord Leverhulme's Charitable Trust was founded by Trust Deed on 20 March 1957 by the Right Honourable Philip William Bryce, Third Viscount Leverhulme, with £100. The Trust was set up for the benefit of any charities in the UK who the Trustees and Lord Leverhulme felt represented causes that were particularly deserving. The investments of the Trust are held mainly in UK equities and unit trusts, allowing the generation of only a small income in comparison with the assets held. The Trust manages two additional funds as part of the Trust: the Lady Lever Art Gallery Annuity Fund, the sole function of which is to provide £30,000 to the Trustees of the Gallery; and the Youth Enterprise Scheme, which sponsors young people in the Wirral and Cheshire areas who are receiving support from the Prince's Youth Business Trust.

At present the Trust gives to a wide range of causes including educational organisations (including schools and universities), welfare charities, youth organisations, churches and organisations benefiting the elderly and disabled. By far the largest grants in 1995 were made to schools and colleges, as in previous years. The funding policies of the Trust are extremely unlikely to change, as they are extremely broadly based, allowing the distribution of the Trust's funds to any registered charity. Funding can be given throughout the UK, but the Trust has a special concentration upon the Cheshire and Merseyside areas, where the Third Viscount Leverhulme has lived for most of his life.

There is no restriction on the type of grant that the Trust can give, and it has in the past given large capital grants and recurring grants as well as one-off contributions. Most grants given are in the range from £5 to £1,000. In 1995, 69 of the 111 grants given fell into this range, while 27 were between £1,000 and £10,000, and 15 were for £10,000 or above. The Trust has no stated attitude towards partnership funding, or towards working with statutory authorities. Nor does the Trust have a given policy on the making of loans, although the terms of its deed do not restrict it from doing so.

There is no application form. Applications should be made in writing to the Trustees, giving full details of the proposed project or of the appeal, and any supporting information that the applicant feels to be relevant should be enclosed. All applications received are formally reviewed and considered by Lord Leverhulme and the Trustees before any decisions are made. The evaluation process of the Trust is not made explicit in the accounts of the Trust, but it may be speculated that there is likely to be at least a simple system of monitoring in place.

The accounts of this charity were submitted to the Charity Commission without being audited

SAMPLE GRANTS
The top ten grants given in 1995 were:
£166,000 to Liverpool University Student Community Action
£117,000 to Hammond School
£50,250 to St George's Church, Thornton Hough
£50,000 to Cheshire Cathedral Development Trust
£50,000 to the Royal College of Surgeons of England
£29,782 to Animal Health Trust
£25,000 to Charter Educational Trust
£25,000 to the Cambridge Foundation
£20,000 to the Parochial Church Council of Altcar Parish Council
£20,000 to the 22nd Cheshire Regiment

■The Linen and Woollen Stock Charity

WHAT IS FUNDED General charitable purposes to local charities

WHO CAN BENEFIT Local charities

WHERE FUNDING CAN BE GIVEN Ashton-in-Makerfield

FINANCES
- Year 1995–96
- Income £7,194

HOW TO APPLY To the Correspondent in writing

Have you read How to use the directory *on page xvi?*

WHO TO APPLY TO Mrs G M Foster, Clerk, Linen and Woollen Stock Charity, 40 Alderton Drive, Ashton-in-Makerfield, Wigan, Lancashire WN4 9LG

CC NO 221789   **ESTABLISHED** 1969

■ Lancaster and Morecambe Lions Club Charity Trust

WHAT IS FUNDED General charitable purposes

WHO CAN BENEFIT Charitable bodies, individuals and organisations

WHERE FUNDING CAN BE GIVEN The territorial area of the Club

TYPE OF GRANT Recurring

SAMPLE GRANTS £2,000 to Macmillan Nurses
£500 to St John's Hospice
£300 to Rumanian Challenge
£65 to Winged Fellowship
£12 Lancaster Youth Club

FINANCES
- Year 1994–95
- Income £13,578
- Grants £9,305

WHO TO APPLY TO Graham Haddington, Lancaster and Morecambe Lions Club Charity Trust, 22 Penny Stone Road, Halton, Lancaster, Lancashire LA2 6QE

CC NO 510818   **ESTABLISHED** 1980

■ Littleborough Nursing Association Fund

WHAT IS FUNDED The elderly and infirm, disabled people, pre-school children's education

WHO CAN BENEFIT Playgroups, sheltered accommodation, hospices

WHERE FUNDING CAN BE GIVEN Littleborough

TYPE OF GRANT Primarily one-off, £200 per organisation

FINANCES
- Year 1996
- Income £1,628
- Grants £1,900

TRUSTEES M Alfred, Ms M Alletson, J N Angus, M Halken, D Howe, G Kelsall, J Kershaw, J Leach, Cllr R Sarginson, M Wilde

HOW TO APPLY To the Correspondent in writing

WHO TO APPLY TO Marilyn Aldred, Littleborough Nursing Association Fund, 26 Hodder Avenue, Shore Littleborough, Lancashire OL15 8EU

CC NO 222482   **ESTABLISHED** 1964

■ The Liverpool Queen Victoria District Nursing Association

WHAT IS FUNDED Organisations working with sick, infirm and disabled people

WHO CAN BENEFIT Disabled people. There are no restrictions on the disease and social circumstances of the beneficiaries

WHERE FUNDING CAN BE GIVEN Merseyside

TYPE OF GRANT Primarily one-off

FINANCES
- Year 1997
- Income £35,879
- Grants £30,567

TRUSTEES M Rathbone, G F Appleton, R Currie, Miss M J Dyke, Canon N Frayling, Mrs L M Newsome, Mrs I Nightingale, Ms M Rangel, Mrs L Spark, R P Bradshaw, Miss V Selwyn-Smith, Cllr Lady D Jones, Cllr R White, K Wright, Ms A Hogg, N Malley

HOW TO APPLY To the address under Who To Apply To in writing stating the aims and activities of your organisation, the purpose of the grant requested and enclosing a recent copy of accounts. The Trustees meet to consider applications in January, May and September

WHO TO APPLY TO The Secretary, Liverpool Queen Victoria District Nursing Assn, Liverpool Council of Social Service Inc, 14 Castle Street, Liverpool L2 0NJ *Tel* 0151-236 7728

CC NO 501196   **ESTABLISHED** 1971

■ Liverpool R C Archdiocesan Trustees Incorporated Special Trusts

This trust did not respond to CAF's request to amend its entry and, by 30 June 1998, CAF's researchers did not find financial records for later than 1995 on its file at the Charity Commission. Trusts are legally required to submit annual accounts to the Charity Commission under section 42 of the Charities Act 1993

WHAT IS FUNDED The education of students wishing to enter the priesthood, church schools

WHO CAN BENEFIT Roman Catholic children and young adults

WHERE FUNDING CAN BE GIVEN Roman Catholic Archdiocese of Liverpool

WHO TO APPLY TO Aaron Kiely, Dept Finance and Development, Liverpool RC Archdiocesan Trustees Inc Special Trusts, The Archdiocese of Liverpool, 152 Brownlow Hill, Liverpool L3 5RQ

CC NO 526575   **ESTABLISHED** 1933

■ Liverpool Sailors' Home Trust

WHAT IS FUNDED Nautical charities in the area Where Funding Can Be Given

WHAT IS NOT FUNDED No grants to individuals

WHO CAN BENEFIT Organisations benefiting: seafarers and fishermen, and ex-service and service people

WHERE FUNDING CAN BE GIVEN Merseyside

TYPE OF GRANT One-off and capital grants will be considered

RANGE OF GRANTS Variable

SAMPLE GRANTS £10,000 to Mersey Mission to Seamen for refurbishment
£10,000 to Bearwood College for educational grant
£10,000 to Sea Cadet Corps – Black Cap
£7,500 to Apostleship of the Sea for refurbishment
£5,000 to Royal National Lifeboat Association, Hoylake and West Kirby
£5,000 to STA Tall Ships
£4,070 to Sea Cadet Corps, TS Storm
£2,000 to Derbyshire Family Association

FINANCES
- Year 1996–97
- Income £63,589
- Grants £56,634

TRUSTEES D G Beazley, P O Copland, M Crowson, F D M Lowry, M A Seaford,

HOW TO APPLY To the address under Who To Apply To in writing. Written applications to be received at latest 20 January of relevant year

WHO TO APPLY TO Mrs L Smith, Secretary, Liverpool Sailors' Home Trust, Unit 3a, Ground Floor, Tower Building, 22 Water Street, Liverpool L2 1AB *Tel* 0151-227 3417 *Fax* 0151-227 3417

CC NO 515183   **ESTABLISHED** 1984

■ The Llay Estate

WHAT IS FUNDED The aged, the infirm, the poor of Chester and counselling organisations working within the Beneficial Area

WHO CAN BENEFIT Individuals and organisations

WHERE FUNDING CAN BE GIVEN St Mary-on-the-Hill, Chester

FINANCES
- Year 1994–95
- Income £3,432

HOW TO APPLY To the Correspondent in writing

WHO TO APPLY TO James Higson Bates, The Llay Estate, 81 Earlsway, Curzon Park, Chester, Cheshire CH4 8AZ

CC NO 215406   **ESTABLISHED** 1963

■ The W M and B W Lloyd Charity Trust

WHAT IS FUNDED Mixed range of support for individual emergencies, disasters, equipment for schools welfare. The advancement of education, medical science and provision of medical equipment and facilities and the provision and improvement of public amenities

WHO CAN BENEFIT Individuals and organisations benefiting: children; young adults; students; and support for individual emergencies and disasters

WHERE FUNDING CAN BE GIVEN Principally the Old Borough of Darwen

TYPE OF GRANT One-off grants

FINANCES
- Year 1997
- Income £64,474
- Grants £61,708

TRUSTEES J N Jacklin, D G Watson, E Aspin

NOTES The Trust has four committees: emergency, education, social amenities and medical. Each committee consider requests specific to its areas of remit. The Trustees meet four times a year for the consideration of requests

WHO TO APPLY TO J N Jacklin, The W M and B W Lloyd Charity Trust, 10 Borough Road, Darwen, Lancashire BB3 1PL

CC NO 503384   **ESTABLISHED** 1974

■ Localtrent Ltd

WHAT IS FUNDED Trustees will consider applications from organisations linked to Orthodox Jewish Faith education and poverty

WHO CAN BENEFIT Charities benefiting Jews, children, young adults, students and those disadvantaged by poverty

WHERE FUNDING CAN BE GIVEN Manchester

FINANCES
- Year 1997
- Income £65,098
- Grants £61,244

TRUSTEES Mrs M Weiss, B Weiss, J L Weiss, P Weiss, Mrs S Feldman

HOW TO APPLY In writing. Trustees meet three or four times each year

WHO TO APPLY TO H Weiss, Secretary, Localtrent Ltd, 44 Waterpark Road, Salford, Manchester M7 4ET

CC NO 326329   **ESTABLISHED** 1982

■ Lord Mayor of Chester Charitable Trust

WHAT IS FUNDED Local registered charities, particularly those working in the fields of: community arts and recreation,; health; conservation; animal welfare; schools and colleges; special needs education; playgrounds; and community services. Support is also given to volunteers, and voluntary and community organisations

WHAT IS NOT FUNDED Non-registered charities are not funded

WHO CAN BENEFIT Registered charities benefiting children and young adults, volunteers, at risk groups and carers. There are no restrictions on the family situation of, or the disease or medical condition suffered by, the beneficiaries

WHERE FUNDING CAN BE GIVEN Chester only

TYPE OF GRANT One-off and capital grants will be considered

RANGE OF GRANTS £25–£1,000

SAMPLE GRANTS £1,000 to Grosvenor Housing Association – Foyer
£650 to Hospice of the Good Shepherd
£650 to Chester and Cheshire Society for the Blind
£500 Chester Gateway – Breaking Down Walls
£500 to Wirral Holistic Care Service
£500 to Tarvin Pre-school Nursery
£500 to Chester Rape Crisis
£250 to 1st Upton by Chester Scouts
£200 to Lady Mayoress's Holiday Fund
£200 to Chester and Wirral Federation of Youth Clubs

FINANCES
- Year 1998
- Grants £6,205

TRUSTEES D Areld, E Plenderleath, P F Durham, M A Johnson

HOW TO APPLY In writing. Initial telephone calls are welcome. Deadline for applications is May of each year

WHO TO APPLY TO W Healiss, PA to the Lord Mayor, Lord Mayor of Chester Charitable Trust, Council of the City of Chester, Town Hall, Chester CH1 2HS *Tel* 01244 402126

CC NO 513175   **ESTABLISHED** 1982

■ Lord Mayor of Manchester's Charity Appeal Trust

WHAT IS FUNDED General charitable purposes for the benefit of the inhabitants of the City of Manchester

WHO CAN BENEFIT There are no restrictions on the age; professional and economic group; family situation; religion and culture; and social circumstances of; or disease or medical condition suffered by, the beneficiaries

WHERE FUNDING CAN BE GIVEN City of Manchester

TRUSTEES The Lord Mayor of Manchester (Gerard Carroll), A Sandford, D Martin

WHO TO APPLY TO E J Treacy, Solicitor, Lord Mayor of Manchester's Charity Appeal Trust, City Solicitors, Town Hall, Albert Square, Manchester M60 2LA

CC NO 1066972   **ESTABLISHED** 1997

■R P McAllister Memorial Trust

WHAT IS FUNDED General charitable purposes

WHO CAN BENEFIT Individuals and organisations

WHERE FUNDING CAN BE GIVEN Isle of Man

FINANCES
- Year 1995–96
- Income £2,547

TRUSTEES W A Gilbey, Rt Rev Monsignor N Gilbey

HOW TO APPLY To the Correspondent in writing

WHO TO APPLY TO W A Gilbey, R P McAllister Memorial Trust, Ballacallin Moor, Crosby, Marown, Isle of Man IM4 2HD

CC NO 262086   **ESTABLISHED** 1971

■The Simon and Suzanne McKenna Charity

WHAT IS FUNDED The relief of poverty, the advancement of education and other charitable purposes

WHAT IS NOT FUNDED Grants will not be made for overseas work, travel overseas, etc

WHO CAN BENEFIT Mainly individuals. Particularly those disadvantaged by poverty, children and young adults

WHERE FUNDING CAN BE GIVEN UK, especially Preston

FINANCES
- Year 1995
- Income £114,870
- Grants £10,000

TRUSTEES J L McKenna, P S McKenna, A M McKenna, J P McKenna, J Clark, M G Said

HOW TO APPLY To the address below in writing

WHO TO APPLY TO D R Hazzard, The Simon and Suzanne McKenna Charity, Messrs Wallwork Nelson and Johnson, Derby House, Lytham Road, Fulwood, Preston PR2 8JE

CC NO 1035881   **ESTABLISHED** 1994

■The Roy McMechan Memorial Fund

WHAT IS FUNDED To advance education and travel

WHAT IS NOT FUNDED Applications for grants for people over the age of twenty or under the age of ten will not be considered

WHO CAN BENEFIT Children and young adults aged between ten and twenty

WHERE FUNDING CAN BE GIVEN South Lakeland District Council area and former Westmorland County area

TYPE OF GRANT Cash payment

FINANCES
- Year 1996
- Income £4,016
- Grants £6,585

HOW TO APPLY To the Correspondent in writing

WHO TO APPLY TO The Clerk, The Roy McMechan Memorial Fund, Hayton Winkley, Solicitors, Stramongate House, 53 Stramongate, Kendal, Cumbria LA9 4AW *Tel* 01539 720136 *Fax* 01539 733312

CC NO 700113   **ESTABLISHED** 1988

■The MacNair Trust

WHAT IS FUNDED To promote the welfare of children, young people and the aged. To preserve lands and buildings of beauty and historical importance in the Beneficial Area

WHO CAN BENEFIT Individuals and institutions

WHERE FUNDING CAN BE GIVEN Marple

FINANCES
- Year 1996
- Income £1,876

TRUSTEES J Astley, D P Atkinson, L Kendrick, H Montgomery, R B Sexton, M H Spreckley, R A Thomas

HOW TO APPLY To the Correspondent in writing. The Trustees meet twice a year

WHO TO APPLY TO D P Atkinson, Hon Treasurer, The MacNair Trust, 25 Stockport Road, Marple, Stockport SK6 6BD

CC NO 503631   **ESTABLISHED** 1961

■Manackerman Charitable Trust

WHAT IS FUNDED Jewish charitable purposes

WHERE FUNDING CAN BE GIVEN Manchester

FINANCES
- Year 1994–95
- Income £7,600
- Grants £3,800

HOW TO APPLY To the Correspondent in writing

WHO TO APPLY TO J Marks, Trustee, Manackerman Charitable Trust, Queens House, Queen Street, Manchester M2 5LA

CC NO 326147   **ESTABLISHED** 1982

■The Manchester and Salford Saturday and Convalescent Homes' Fund

WHAT IS FUNDED Priority is given to health authorities and NHS trusts, with hospices, homes for people with disabilities and welfare organisations also within the Trust's scope

WHO CAN BENEFIT Health authorities and welfare charities benefiting: disabled people; at risk groups; those disadvantaged by poverty; and the socially isolated. There are no restrictions on the disease or medical condition suffered by the beneficiaries

WHERE FUNDING CAN BE GIVEN Manchester and surrounding region

RANGE OF GRANTS £400–£9,000

SAMPLE GRANTS £9,000 to Salford Royal Hospitals NHS Trust
£7,345 to South Manchester University Hospitals NHS Trust
£7,000 to Manchester Central Hospitals and Community Care NHS Trust
£6,250 to North Manchester Healthcare Services NHS Trust
£5,280 to Tameside and Glossop Health Services NHS Trust
£4,290 to Blackpool Victoria Hospital NHS Trust
£4,275 to Blackburn, Hyndburn and Ribble Valley Healthcare, NHS Trust
£4,000 to Trafford Healthcare NHS Trust
£3,510 to Bury General Hospital HA Endowment Account
£3,400 to Preston Acute Hospitals NHS Trust

FINANCES
- Year 1995
- Income £100,000
- Grants £88,099

TRUSTEES Executive Committee: H Tomlinson, W A B Hargreaves, L Martin, Mrs J W Cameron, Mrs R J Carroll, B Cowman, D J Keeley, L Pattison, J Platt, E Sharples, Mrs S Whittaker, Mrs I Widdowson, Mrs G Workmaster, D Kilgannon, Mrs M Elliot

HOW TO APPLY To the address under Who To Apply To in writing

WHO TO APPLY TO Richard Sear, Executive, The Manchester and Salford Saturday and Convalescent Homes' Fund, 43–45 Lever Street, Manchester M60 7HP

CC NO 260031   **ESTABLISHED** 1969

■The Manchester Guardian Society Charitable Trust

WHAT IS FUNDED General charitable purposes. The emphasis is very much on helping the Greater Manchester area

WHAT IS NOT FUNDED The Trustees do not give grants to individuals. They very much prefer the applicant to be a registered charity although this is not mandatory

WHO CAN BENEFIT Preference is usually shown to the smaller charity operating within Greater Manchester. There are no restrictions on the age; professional and economic group; family situation; religion and culture; and social circumstances of; or disease or medical condition suffered by, the beneficiaries

WHERE FUNDING CAN BE GIVEN Greater Manchester

TYPE OF GRANT Primarily small single capital projects not exceeding £5,000

RANGE OF GRANTS £200–£5,000

SAMPLE GRANTS £5,000 to the Big Step
£5,000 to Rainbow Family Trust
£2,000 to Dean and Canon of Manchester Cathedral
£2,000 to Emmanuel Community
£1,700 to Rathbone Society
£1,600 to Church Lads and Church Girls Brigade
£1,500 to Daubhill and Derby Churches
£1,500 to Disabled Living Services
£1,500 to FWA Limited
£1,500 to Overward Project

FINANCES
- Year 1997
- Income £110,707
- Grants £85,566

TRUSTEES P R Green, G D Thomas, D A Sutherland, W R Lees-Jones, Mrs J Powell, D G Wilson, Mrs J Harrison, Mrs O Haig, W J Smith, P Goddard, J P Wainwright

PUBLICATIONS An Annual Report and Accounts is prepared and the Annual General Meeting is held either at the September meeting or the November meeting of the Trustees

HOW TO APPLY Applications are considered at quarterly meetings of the Trustees which take place on the first Monday in March, June and September and the last Monday in November. Applications should be received at least 14 days before these dates

WHO TO APPLY TO J A H Fielden, The Manchester Guardian Society Charitable Trust, Cobbetts, Ship Canal House, King Street, Manchester M2 4WB

CC NO 515341   **ESTABLISHED** 1984

■ Manchester Local Medical Committee Compassionate Fund

WHAT IS FUNDED To relieve members of the medical profession, and any other charitable purposes related to medicine or the medical profession

WHO CAN BENEFIT Individuals and hospitals

WHERE FUNDING CAN BE GIVEN Manchester, UK

TYPE OF GRANT Recurring

SAMPLE GRANTS £500 to Macmillan Cancer Relief
£250 to Cameron Fund
£200 to Leisure Link
£100 to St Ann's Hospice
£100 to BASPSCAN

FINANCES
- Year 1994–95
- Income £8,504
- Grants £6,496

TRUSTEES Dr W J Pettit, Dr D Schlosberg, Dr S K Chouksey

WHO TO APPLY TO Dr David Schlosberg, Manchester Local Medical Committee Compassionate Fund, Manchester Medical Committee, Manchester Post Graduate Health Science Centre, Oxford Road, Manchester M13 0BQ

CC NO 221889   **ESTABLISHED** 1964

■ The Manchester Society of Architects

WHAT IS FUNDED To promote and encourage the improvement and development of architecture and the study and acquisition of the artistic, historical and technical knowledge of architecture, and of all ancillary and allied arts and sciences

WHO CAN BENEFIT Individuals and institutions

WHERE FUNDING CAN BE GIVEN Manchester

TYPE OF GRANT Recurring

SAMPLE GRANTS £2,400 for educational grants

FINANCES
- Year 1994–95
- Income £5,037
- Grants £2,400

WHO TO APPLY TO Geoffrey Alsop, The Manchester Society of Architects, 31 Princess Street, Manchester M2 4BF

CC NO 251174   **ESTABLISHED** 1967

■ The Marchon Works Employees Charity Fund

WHAT IS FUNDED Recipients of grants include individuals for wheelchairs and stairlifts, as well as hospitals, community organisations and facilities. Other areas of funding include: residential facilities; respite and sheltered accommodation; infrastructure, support and development; churches; music; health care; schools and colleges; community centres and village halls; recreation grounds; community services; and advice centres

WHAT IS NOT FUNDED No grants for expeditions or scholarships

WHO CAN BENEFIT Individuals and some organisations benefiting: people of all ages; retired people; students; carers; disabled people; those disadvantaged by poverty; ex-offenders and those at risk of offending; and victims of domestic violence. Those suffering from various diseases and medical conditions

WHERE FUNDING CAN BE GIVEN Copeland and Allerdale districts within the County of Cumbria

TYPE OF GRANT One-off donations

RANGE OF GRANTS £10–£1,600

SAMPLE GRANTS The following grants were made to individuals:
£1,492 for a PC and monitor
£1,486 for a stairlift
£1,450 for a stairlift
£1,350 for a stairlift
£962 for bathroom/shower refurbishment
£750 for hydrobath
£567 for a cooker and bath
£500 to West Cumbria Ambulances for Romania as a donation towards fuel costs
£455 for resiting a stairlift

FINANCES
- Year 1996–97
- Income £35,201
- Grants £15,860

TRUSTEES M McLaughlin (Chairman), Mrs A Ryan (Secretary), D Smitham, (Treasurer), Miss C Baxter, Mrs L C Jones, D Douglas, Dr M E Thompson, A Monkhouse, J Moore, J Prince, S Tumelty, A Moore

HOW TO APPLY To the address under Who To Apply To in writing. Initial telephone calls are welcome. There are no application forms, guidelines or deadlines, and no sae is required

WHO TO APPLY TO D Smitham, Treasurer, Marchon Works Employees Charity Fund, Albright & Wilson Ltd, Marchon Works, Whitehaven, Cumbria CA28 9QQ
Tel 01946 68216 *Fax* 01946 68181

CC NO 510504   **ESTABLISHED** 1980

■The Ann and David Marks Foundation

WHAT IS FUNDED To provide aid for Jewish charities in personnel and human resource services; Jewish umbrella bodies; and schools and colleges

WHAT IS NOT FUNDED No grants to individuals

WHO CAN BENEFIT To benefit people of all ages; those in care, fostered and adopted; parents and children; one parent families and Jews

WHERE FUNDING CAN BE GIVEN UK and overseas, with a preference for Manchester

TYPE OF GRANT Buildings, capital one-off and start-up costs. Funding is available for more than three years

RANGE OF GRANTS £40–£2,975

SAMPLE GRANTS £2,975 to Joint Jewish Charitable Trust
£2,555 to North Cheshire Jewish Primary School
£1,068 to Jewish Social Services
£600 to WIZO
£500 to Yeshivas Lubavitch Manchester
£225 to CICJS
£219 to Yeshurun Hebrew Congregation
£200 to Institute of Contemporary Jewish Studies, Jewish Cultural Centre
£200 to Lubavitch South Manchester
£200 to Manchester Charitable Trust

FINANCES
- Year 1995–96
- Income £28,095
- Grants £11,365

TRUSTEES Mrs A Marks, D L Marks, L J Marks, Miss G E Marks

HOW TO APPLY To the address under Who To Apply To in writing, though charities known to the Trustees are more likely to be successful as funds are fully committed for the foreseeable future

WHO TO APPLY TO D L Marks, The Ann and David Marks Foundation, Mutley House, 1 Ambassador Place, Altrincham, Cheshire WA15 8DB *Tel* 0161-941 3183

CC NO 326303   **ESTABLISHED** 1983

■The Mayor of Chorley's Helping Hand Charity

WHAT IS FUNDED Local charities in the Chorley area, according to the wishes of the current Mayor of Chorley. The area of focus for funding varies each year according to the wishes of each new Mayor. Support for 1998–99 is for organisations benefiting young people under the age of 18, who are either resident or studying in Chorely, through provision of area grants or maintenance allowances, to enable them to travel for the furtherance of their education. The area of focus for 1999–2000 is not yet known

WHO CAN BENEFIT In 1998–99, organisations benefiting children, young adults and students under the age of 18

WHERE FUNDING CAN BE GIVEN The Borough of Chorley

TRUSTEES The Mayor of Chorley, the Borough Director of Finance, the Borough Solicitor

HOW TO APPLY To the Mayor's Secretary at the address under Who To Apply To

WHO TO APPLY TO Mayor's Secretary, The Mayor of Chorley's Helping Hand Charity, Town Hall, Chorley, Lancashire PR7 1DP *Tel* 01257 515102

CC NO 1058421   **ESTABLISHED** 1996

■Mayor of Hyde's Trust Fund

WHAT IS FUNDED Local charitable purposes

WHAT IS NOT FUNDED Not for the benefit of individuals

WHO CAN BENEFIT Local organisations

WHERE FUNDING CAN BE GIVEN The old Borough of Hyde

FINANCES
- Year 1996
- Income £1,200
- Grants £1,200

NOTES National and regional applications are not considered

HOW TO APPLY To the Correspondent in writing. Applications should include current accounts

WHO TO APPLY TO J W Lloyd, Hon Secretary, Mayor of Hyde's Trust Fund, 18 Primrose Avenue, Gee Cross, Hyde, Cheshire SK14 5BU *Tel* 0161-368 4740

CC NO 228674   **ESTABLISHED** 1950

■The Mayor of Knowsley Charity Fund

WHAT IS FUNDED General charitable purposes in the area Where Funding Can Be Given

WHO CAN BENEFIT There are no restrictions on the age; professional and economic group; family situation; religion and culture; and social circumstances of; or disease or medical condition suffered by, the beneficiaries

WHERE FUNDING CAN BE GIVEN Knowsley

SAMPLE GRANTS £20,000 to St Helens and Knowsley Hospice
£1,830 to Musical School for musical

scholarships
£607 to Cancer Care
£607 to Sea Cadets
£375 to Roy Castle Fund
£152 to MND

FINANCES
- Year 1996–97
- Income £28,165
- Grants £23,571

TRUSTEES The Mayor, Director of Finance, Knowsley, Borough Solicitor, Knowsley,

NOTES The Mayor of Knowsley Charity Fund is chosen by the Mayor and usually only support one charity per year

HOW TO APPLY To the address under Who To Apply To in writing

WHO TO APPLY TO Paula Deegan, The Mayor of Knowsley Charity Fund, Knowsley MBC, Municipal Buildings, Archway Road, Huyton, Merseyside *Tel* 0151-443 3643 *Fax* 0151-443 3661

CC NO 504656   **ESTABLISHED** 1975

■ The Mayor of Sefton's Charity Fund

WHAT IS FUNDED General charitable purposes in the Borough of Sefton

WHO CAN BENEFIT There are no restrictions on the age; professional and economic group; family situation; religion and culture; and social circumstances of; or disease or medical condition suffered by, the beneficiaries

WHERE FUNDING CAN BE GIVEN Sefton

FINANCES
- Year 1995–96
- Income £19,980
- Grants £16,100

HOW TO APPLY Applications should be made on a form available from the address under Who To Apply To or from on of the Trustees

WHO TO APPLY TO Mrs E Jones, Secretary, The Mayor of Sefton's Charity Fund, Town Hall, Lord Street, Southport PR8 1DA

CC NO 1026227   **ESTABLISHED** 1993

■ The Mayoress of Trafford's Charity Fund

WHAT IS FUNDED The Mayoress chooses a single charity to support the year before she takes office; the charity must benefit the inhabitants of the Borough of Trafford

WHO CAN BENEFIT There are no restrictions on the age; professional and economic group; family situation; religion and culture; and

social circumstances of; or disease or medical condition suffered by, the beneficiaries

WHERE FUNDING CAN BE GIVEN The Borough of Trafford

SAMPLE GRANTS £37,000 to Macmillan Cancer Care to furnish and equip the physiotherapy room at the Trafford Macmillan day care centre

FINANCES
- Year 1997–98
- Income £37,000

HOW TO APPLY To the address under Who To Apply To in writing

WHO TO APPLY TO The Chief Executive, The Mayoress of Trafford's Charity Fund, Trafford Town Hall, Talbot Road, Stretford, Trafford, Manchester M32 0YT *Tel* 0161-912 1212

CC NO 512299   **ESTABLISHED** 1982

■ The Mayor's Relief Fund

WHAT IS FUNDED Disabilities and the homeless

WHO CAN BENEFIT Individuals and institutions

WHERE FUNDING CAN BE GIVEN Barrow-in-Furness

FINANCES
- Year 1994–95
- Income £4,600
- Grants £2,400

TRUSTEES The Mayor of Barrow-in-Furness

HOW TO APPLY In writing c/o The Mayor's Secretary

WHO TO APPLY TO Director of Finance, The Mayor's Relief Fund, Barrow-in-Furness Borough Council, Town Hall, Barrow-in-Furness LA14 2LD

CC NO 503263   **ESTABLISHED** 1961

■ Mersey Basin Trust

WHAT IS FUNDED To conserve, protect and improve water courses, land and buildings within the Mersey Basin Campaign area, to advance the education of the public with regard to the conservation, protection and improvement of the same. Supports voluntary organisations and schools

WHO CAN BENEFIT Organisations, schools and all those involved in environmental conservation

WHERE FUNDING CAN BE GIVEN Northern Mersey Basin: Merseyside, Cheshire, Greater Manchester, Derbyshire and Lancashire

FINANCES
- Year 1997
- Income £433,820

TRUSTEES J E Ashworth, J Gittins, C W Hamilton, Ms E M Jones, Ms L Johnson, B Lythgoe, F Lythgoe, K Parry, W J Rhodes, D Roydes, Mrs A Selby, C Selby, F Smith, H C West, B Williams, P H M Wilmers, E Whewll

NOTES The Mersey Basin Trust includes the Stream Care Project, Waterside Revival, ICI Green Action Grants, Green Generation Grants and Greenlink Awards

WHO TO APPLY TO T Jones, Company Secretary, Mersey Basin Trust, Sunley Tower, Piccadilly Plaza, Manchester M1 4AG

CC NO 1005305   **ESTABLISHED** 1991

■ The Mersey Basin Trust – Greenlink Awards

WHAT IS FUNDED Nature conservation, the tackling of pollution, urban dereliction and waste, the preservation of the built environment

WHO CAN BENEFIT Non-profit making organisations

WHERE FUNDING CAN BE GIVEN Northern Mersey Basin: Merseyside, Cheshire, Greater Manchester, Derbyshire and Lancashire

FINANCES
- Year 1997
- Grants £17,283

HOW TO APPLY To the address under Who To Apply To in writing

WHO TO APPLY TO Carol Worral/Anthony Kelly, The Mersey Basin Trust – Greenlink Awards, Lancashire Enterprise, Enterprise House, 17 Ribblesdale Place, Preston PR1 3NA

CC NO 1005305   **ESTABLISHED** 1991

■ Mersey Basin Trust – ICI Green Action Grants

WHAT IS FUNDED The Trust awards ICI Green Action Grants for environmental projects carried out by voluntary groups and schools in the Runcorn and Northwich areas of Cheshire. The grant is part of the Weaver Valley Initiative. Charities working in the fields of: support to voluntary and community organisations; charity or voluntary umbrella bodies; conservation; ecology; natural history; environmental issues; schools and colleges; and parks will be considered

WHAT IS NOT FUNDED No grants for repairs to buildings, etc

WHO CAN BENEFIT Voluntary, community organisations and schools benefiting people of all ages and students

WHERE FUNDING CAN BE GIVEN Runcorn and Northwich

TYPE OF GRANT Project grants paid retrospectively and funded for up to one year

RANGE OF GRANTS £100–£1,000

SAMPLE GRANTS £1,000 to Witton Area Conservation Group for pond dipping platform
£877 to Witton Area Conservation Group for water level restoration project
£860 to Frodsham Wildlife Conservation Group for woodland sensory trail
£859 to Frodsham Town Council for picnic benches
£677 to Norton Priory Museum Trust for pond dipping platform
£606 to Cloughwood School, Hartford for pondside footpath
£600 to Beechwood Primary School, Runcorn for school nature area
£440 to Frodsham Wildlife Conservation Group for pond creation
£397 to Little Leigh Primary School, Northwich for woodland trail
£350 to Cheshire Countryside Management Service for wildflower meadow creation

FINANCES
- Year 1997–98
- Grants £7,000
- Income £600,000

TRUSTEES Keith Noble, Derek Bullock, Michael O'Brian, Edgar Whewell, John Gittins, Charles Hamilton, Brian Lythgoe, Alan Howarth, Mrs Ann Gardiner, Dr Robin Henshaw, Frank Smith, Ben Williams, Anne Selby, Paul Christie, Anthony Bielderman, Roger Hutchins, David A Roydes, Frank Lythgoe, Cedric Selby, Mrs Diane Rhodes, Peter Glover, Bill Rhodes, John Ashworth, Bert Bowles

PUBLICATIONS *The Campaigner* quarterly newsletter

HOW TO APPLY Application should be made on a form available either by writing or telephone call. The awards panel meets quarterly

WHO TO APPLY TO Mark Turner, Mersey Basin Trust – ICI Green Action Grants, Sunley Tower, Piccadilly Plaza, Manchester M1 4AG *Tel* 0161-228 6924

CC NO 1005305   **ESTABLISHED** 1991

■ Mersey Basin Trust – Stream Care Project

WHAT IS FUNDED The care and improvement of local watercourses through the encouragement of the local community. The Trust offers advice and support to local groups

WHERE FUNDING CAN BE GIVEN Mersey Basin Campaign Area (Cheshire, part of Lancashire, Greater Manchester, Merseyside and part of Derbyshire)

FINANCES
- Year 1997
- Income £36,964
- Grants £11,103

NOTES In 1997, Stream Care supported 46 groups carrying out practical projects and an additional 25 groups received advice and non-financial support. The Trust also produced a new exhibition for display at various venues and events

HOW TO APPLY To the address under Who To Apply To in writing

WHO TO APPLY TO Mark Turner, Mersey Basin Trust – Stream Care Project, Sunley Tower, Piccadilly Plaza, Manchester M1 4AG

CC NO 1005305   **ESTABLISHED** 1991

■ Mersey Basin Trust – Waterside Revival Grants

WHAT IS FUNDED The conservation and improvement of waterside sites, open to the public by funding local voluntary groups to organise and carry out the improvement and management of such sites

WHO CAN BENEFIT Local, voluntary groups involved in waterside conservation

WHERE FUNDING CAN BE GIVEN Mersey Basin Campaign Area (Cheshire, part of Lancashire, Greater Manchester, Merseyside, High Peak in Derbyshire)

FINANCES
- Year 1998
- Grants £8,000

HOW TO APPLY Applications should be made on a form available from the address under Who To Apply To, whereupon a visit to the site will be made. At present, there is one grant panel per annum to consider applications, held in July. Telephone enquiries welcomed

WHO TO APPLY TO Gwen White, Mersey Basin Trust – Waterside Revival Grants, Sunley Tower, Piccadilly Plaza, Manchester M1 4AG *Tel* 0161-228 6924

CC NO 1005305   **ESTABLISHED** 1991

■ Merseyside Development Foundation

WHAT IS FUNDED Education, health and welfare

WHO CAN BENEFIT Organisations benefiting: children and young adults; at risk groups; those disadvantaged by poverty and socially isolated people. There is no restriction on the disease or medical condition suffered by the beneficiaries

WHERE FUNDING CAN BE GIVEN Merseyside

FINANCES
- Year 1997
- Income £62,972
- Grants £17,540

TRUSTEES Directors: Mrs C R Behrend, A R Dronfield, Mrs C J Murphy, M McDonagh, Mrs E Taylor

HOW TO APPLY The Foundation only considered applications via people known to them. Advice and information is available

WHO TO APPLY TO Dr M A Williams, Merseyside Development Foundation, 2nd Floor, Spinney House, Church Street, Liverpool L1 3AS

CC NO 1002626   **ESTABLISHED** 1990

■ Mole Charitable Trust

WHAT IS FUNDED To favour Jewish causes, educational institutions and organisations to relieve poverty

WHO CAN BENEFIT Individuals, registered charities and institutions benefiting children, young adults, Jews and those disadvantaged by poverty

WHERE FUNDING CAN BE GIVEN Manchester

RANGE OF GRANTS £200–£54,000

SAMPLE GRANTS £54,000 to Yeshivas Shaarei Torah
£17,000 to The Satmar Gemach
£12,000 to Vaad Hatzdoko Charitable Trust
£8,000 to Broom Foundation
£5,000 to Manchester Charitable Trust
£4,700 to Manchester Jewish Grammar School
£3,550 to Bikur Cholim and Gemiluth Chesed Trust
£3,448 to North Salford Synagogue and Beth Hamidrash
£3,000 to Kollel Rabbi Yechiel
£2,000 to Manchester Jewish Soup Kitchen

FINANCES
- Year 1997
- Income £80,516
- Grants £128,743

TRUSTEES M Gross, Mrs L P Gross

WHO TO APPLY TO M Gross, Mole Charitable Trust, 2 Okeover Road, Salford, Manchester M7 4JX

CC NO 281452   **ESTABLISHED** 1980

■ The George A Moore Foundation

WHAT IS FUNDED The Trustees select causes and projects from the applications received during the year and also independently research and identify specific objectives where they wish to direct assistance. The type of grants made can vary quite widely from one year to another and care is taken to maintain a rough parity among the various fields covered so that one sphere of activity does not benefit unduly at the expense of another. Areas which are not or cannot be covered by official sources are favoured. Charities working in the fields of: respite and sheltered accommodation; infrastructure development; arts activity; aftercare and respite care; well woman clinics; health facilities and buildings will be considered. Support may also go to historic buildings, memorials, monuments, special schools, care in the community, crime prevention schemes and day centres

WHAT IS NOT FUNDED No assistance will be given to individuals, courses of study, expeditions, overseas travel, holidays or for purposes outside the UK. Because of present long-term commitments and recent grants, the Foundation will not consider appeals for religious property or institutions, or for educational purposes

WHO CAN BENEFIT Only registered charities are considered and the Foundation rarely contributes seedcorn finance to newly established organisations. Projects for young people (teenagers/young adults) are favoured, as are community care projects. Organisations benefiting: ex-service and service people; medical professionals; seafarers and fishermen; parents and children; widows and widowers; Church of England and Methodists. Support may also be given to carers, disabled people, those living in rural areas, victims of crime and those suffering from various diseases and medical conditions

WHERE FUNDING CAN BE GIVEN Principally Yorkshire and the Isle of Man but consideration may be given to some major national charities under certain circumstances

TYPE OF GRANT Grants are generally non-recurrent and the Foundation is reluctant to contribute to revenue appeals. Approximately 75 per cent of the grants made are £500 or below

RANGE OF GRANTS £20–£100,000, average grant £500

SAMPLE GRANTS £100,000 to York Minster Fund for restoration of Great West Door
£50,000 to Prince's Youth Business Trust
£5,000 to Giggleswick School
£2,500 to Sustrans
£1,000 to Anthony Nolan Bone Marrow Trust
£1,000 to Crimestoppers
£1,000 to Methodist Homes for the Aged
£1,000 to Whizz-Kidz
£1,000 to Yorkshire Spinal Injury Centre Appeal
£1,000 to South Parade Baptist Church

FINANCES
- Year 1998
- Income £452,922
- Grants £183,567

TRUSTEES George A Moore, CBE, KStJ, Mrs E Moore, J R Moore, Mrs A L James

HOW TO APPLY Written applications only to the address under Who To Apply To. No guidelines or application forms are issued. The Trustees meet approximately four times a year and an appropriate response is sent out after the relevant meeting

WHO TO APPLY TO Miss L P Oldham, The George A Moore Foundation, Follifoot Hall, Pannal Road, Follifoot, Harrogate, North Yorkshire HG3 1DP

CC NO 262107   **ESTABLISHED** 1970

··

■ John Moores Foundation (210)

WHAT IS FUNDED Women, including girls; black and ethnic minority organisations; race, gender and disability awareness; advice and information to alleviate poverty; tranquilliser users; second chance learning; grass roots community groups; persons with HIV/AIDS, their partners and families. In addition, the following are supported in Merseyside only: people with disabilities; carers; support and training for voluntary organisations; homeless people; unemployed; childcare. In Merseyside the Foundation will also consider small appeals from charitable organisations whose work does not fall into these categories

WHAT IS NOT FUNDED Academic or medical research, animal charities, arts, new buildings, churches for church-based or church-run activities (except community groups running activities in church premises), conservation/environment, employment creation schemes, holidays or expeditions, individuals, medicine and health, national organisations for national services even where used by people living in Merseyside or Northern Ireland, parties and outings, statutory bodies, vehicles

WHO CAN BENEFIT Voluntary organisations and community groups benefiting women and girls, the unemployed, ethnic minority groups, people with HIV and AIDS, and people affected by a wide range of social circumstances

WHERE FUNDING CAN BE GIVEN Merseyside and Northern Ireland

TYPE OF GRANT Core costs, one-off, revenue, project, recurring costs, capital and start-up costs. Funding for up to three years. Volunteers' expenses and help towards salaries

RANGE OF GRANTS In 1996–97 75 per cent of grants were for £5,000 or less, and almost a third of grants were for £1,000 or less

FINANCES
- Year 1997
- Income £813,261
- Grants £792,413

TRUSTEES M T McAleese, B Moores, J Moores

PUBLICATIONS Information About Applying For A Grant, Reports and financial statements

NOTES Some of the larger grants outlined below are exceptional and, therefore, not typical of the grants made in 1997

HOW TO APPLY Applications should be in writing and accompanied by an application form which can be obtained from the Grants Director. Please ensure that your project does not fall into one of the excluded areas, if in doubt and you would like to discuss your application, telephone the Grants Director. Please allow for up to three months for a decision to be made

WHO TO APPLY TO Ms Tara Parveen, Grants Director, John Moores Foundation, Neighbourhood Resource Centre, 79 Gorsey Lane, Wallasey, Merseyside L44 4HF *Tel* 0151-637 0924

CC NO 253481   **ESTABLISHED** 1963

Commentary

John Moores Foundation was set up in 1963 with the intention of providing funds for charitable purposes, and became a registered charity in 1967.

The Foundation funds general charitable purposes, although it prefers to fund groups which support (a) women, including girls; (b) black and ethnic minority organisations; (c) race, gender and disability awareness; (d) advice and information to alleviate poverty; (e) tranquilliser users; (f) second chance learning; (g) grass roots community groups; and (h) people with HIV/AIDS, their partners and families. In addition, the foundation supports the following in Merseyside only: (i) people with disabilities; (j) carers; (k) support and training for voluntary organisations; (l) homeless people; (m) unemployed; (n) childcare. Also specific to Merseyside, the Foundation will consider small appeals from charitable organisations whose work does not fall into these categories. Grant making policy is currently under review though no major changes are anticipated. For up-to-date information applicants are advised to telephone the Foundation's office. The Foundation concentrates its grant making in Merseyside, Skelmersdale, Ellesmere Port, Halton and Northern Ireland.

The Foundation does not fund statutory bodies or embark on co-funded partnerships, although it does partially fund projects which have secured funding from other sources including the Lottery.

There are various types of grants offered, including those for equipment, running costs, one-off project costs, revenue, volunteers' expenses and help towards salaries.

Applications should be made in writing and accompanied by an application form which can be obtained from the Grants Director. Prior to applying, please ensure that your project does not fall into one of the excluded areas stated in What Is Not Funded; if in doubt and you would like to discuss your application, telephone the Grants Director. During the application process, the majority of applicants are visited, although the Foundation may simply telephone for any additional information they require. Although the Trustees meet every six weeks, applicants are advised to allow for up to three months for a decision to be made. Following the distribution of funds, it is the policy of the Trustees to assess recipients, where possible through visits as well as written reports

SAMPLE GRANTS
The top ten grants given in 1997 were:
£83,000 to Merseyside Information and Advice Project, Liverpool
£50,000 to British Red Cross Crisis in Africa Appeal
£50,000 to Crisis, London
£30,000 to Women's Education Fund for Southern Africa, S. Africa
£27,500 to Bronte Youth and Community Centre, Liverpool
£20,000 to South Liverpool Personnel Ltd, Liverpool
£20,000 to Sheila Kay Fund, Liverpool
£16,000 to Liverpool Family Service Unit
£15,337 to Churches Action for Racial Equality (via MARCEA), Liverpool
£15,000 to Women's Educational Training Trust (Blackburne House), Liverpool

■The Moorwoods Charitable Trust

WHAT IS FUNDED Projects which benefit children and other charitable purposes

WHAT IS NOT FUNDED Major existing charities

WHO CAN BENEFIT New projects

WHERE FUNDING CAN BE GIVEN Sheffield, Manchester and their surrounding areas, overseas

TYPE OF GRANT Core funding

SAMPLE GRANTS £4,000 to Whirlaw Hall Farm Trust
£3,000 to Darnast Unity Centre

FINANCES
- Year 1994–95
- Income £8,000
- Grants £12,000

TRUSTEES Alan Aikin, Alison Haslam

HOW TO APPLY To the Correspondent in writing

WHO TO APPLY TO A Aikin, The Moorwoods Charitable Trust, Moorwood Farm, Moorwood Lane, Owler Bar, Sheffield S17 3BS *Tel* 0114-236 3324 *Fax* 0114-262 0122

CC NO 703169   **ESTABLISHED** 1990

■ The Morgan Crucible Company plc Charitable Trust

WHAT IS FUNDED Small, specialist charities preferred in fields: health care, medical research, children, support for disabled or ill. Donations made direct, not through intermediate charities

WHAT IS NOT FUNDED No donations are made to individuals, parish churches or youth clubs. The Trust tends to exclude overseas, armed forces, restoration of buildings, private persons, travel, wildlife, countryside

WHO CAN BENEFIT Physically or mentally disabled people, young people in deprived or undesirable circumstances and those disadvantaged by poverty. There is no restriction on the disease or medical condition suffered by the beneficiaries. Medical professionals and research workers will be considered

WHERE FUNDING CAN BE GIVEN Primarily Wirral, Leeds, South Wales, South London, Worcester, Thames Valley

TYPE OF GRANT Donations are made to the same charities for a period of years. One payment per annum

SAMPLE GRANTS £15,800 to the care, including holidays, of people with mental handicaps
£15,160 to direct sponsorship
£6,178 for medical development and research
£5,850 for the care, including holidays, of young people in deprived or undesirable circumstances
£4,900 to local (Windsor area) good causes
£3,950 for adventure or training holidays or courses for character building
£2,800 to the arts
£2,008 to character reform
£1,900 for education
£1,275 for community services

FINANCES
- Year 1997
- Grants £59,821
- Income £68,000

TRUSTEES Sir James Spooner, Dr E B Farmer

HOW TO APPLY Written only

WHO TO APPLY TO D J Coker, The Morgan Crucible Company plc Charitable Trust, The Morgan Crucible Company plc, Morgan House, Madeira Walk, Windsor, Berkshire SL4 1EP

CC NO 273507   **ESTABLISHED** 1977

■ Nantwich and Acton Grammar School Foundation

WHAT IS FUNDED (a) Support of Malbank School and Sixth Form Centre. (b) Promoting the education (including social and physical training) of persons under 25 years of age who are pupils or former pupils of the said school or any other school serving the area. (c) Arts, culture and recreation is also considered for funding

WHAT IS NOT FUNDED No grants for the relief of public funds

WHO CAN BENEFIT To the benefit of young people under 25 years of age who are pupils or former pupils of Malbank School and Sixth Form Centre, or other schools serving the area Where Funding Can Be Given

WHERE FUNDING CAN BE GIVEN UK and overseas with reference to What is Funded

TYPE OF GRANT Interest free loans, one-off, project and research. Funding is available for up to and over three years

FINANCES
- Year 1997
- Grants £5,875
- Income £16,155

TRUSTEES Mrs L Brookshaw, M Elliott, T Holman, A Kettleday, D Latham, E W Lighton (Chairman), P Taylor (Treasurer)

NOTES Present funding policy is related to early days of the Foundation when capital is being safeguarded. Therefore, grants are of a small scale. Trustees are keen to go beyond the routine academic and travel requests

HOW TO APPLY To the Clerk to the Trustees, with an sae for application form to be returned by 30 April for May consideration, and 31 October for November consideration

WHO TO APPLY TO The Clerk to the Trustees, Nantwich and Acton Grammar School Foundation, Malbank School and VIth Form Centre, Welsh Row, Nantwich, Cheshire CW5 5HD

CC NO 525965   **ESTABLISHED** 1995

■ National Lottery Charities Board (1)

WHAT IS FUNDED Projects submitted from registered charities and/or voluntary sector organisations which are charitable, philanthropic or benevolent and based in the

UK. Awards are currently being offered through a series of main grants programmes (Community Involvement and Poverty and Disadvantage). Small Grants (or Awards For All in Scotland and the East Midlands in England), International Grants and a specialist Health & Social Research programme

WHAT IS NOT FUNDED Duplication of existing services or replacement of statutory provision. The Board is not able to make grants to local authorities, local education trusts, to schools or to charities set up to support statutory bodies. Applications will not be accepted from professional fund-raisers. The Board does not make emergency awards. All grants must be additional to public expenditure

WHO CAN BENEFIT Charitable, benevolent and philanthropic organisations benefiting unemployed people and volunteers. There are no restrictions on the age; family situation; religion and culture; and social circumstances of; or disease or medical condition suffered by, the beneficiaries (The National Lottery Charities Board publish a leaflet called 'Guide to Eligibility')

WHERE FUNDING CAN BE GIVEN UK-wide through mains grants programmes, Small Grants and Health and Social Research programmes. Through the International Grants Programme: in Africa; Asia (including the Pacific, the Caucasus and Central Asian Republics); the Middle East; South and Central America; the Caribbean; Central and Eastern Europe

TYPE OF GRANT Capital grants, revenue grants or a combination of both. Also buildings, core costs, feasibility studies, one-off, project, research, recurring and running costs, salaries and start-up costs. Grants are awarded for projects for up to three years for the main grants programmes and up to five years for International awards

RANGE OF GRANTS £500 minimum; no maximum though the largest grants have been £1.1 million. Average size of grant is £55,868

FINANCES
- Year 1997
- Income £318,000,000
- Grants £319,000,000

TRUSTEES David Sieff (Chairman), Sir Adam Ridley (Deputy Chairman), Tessa Baring, CBE, Amir Bhatia, OBE, Steven Burkeman, June Churchman, OBE, DL, Stella Clarke, CBE, Ann Clark, Kay Hampton, Tom Jones, OBE, Amanda Jordan, Barbara Lowndes, MBE, Monica McWilliams, Garth Morrison, CBE, DL, William Osborne, Ron Partington, John Simpson, OBE, Noel Stewart, OBE, Sir Eric Stroud, Elisabeth Watkins

PUBLICATIONS Range of materials and guidance on applications to the Board available from all Board Offices

NOTES The Board receives 4.6 pence from each lottery ticket purchased

HOW TO APPLY Applications packs for each of the main programmes may be obtained by calling a 24-hour central mailing number 0345 919191. Welsh speakers can ring 0345 273273 (including Small Grants). Application packs for the International programme are available on 0345 778878. Small Grants application forms for Scotland are available on 0645 700777 and England and Northern Ireland on 0345 458458. Completed applications should be returned to the office indicated in the application pack

WHO TO APPLY TO UK Office: Gerald Oppenheim, Director UK and Corporate Planning, National Lottery Charities Board, St Vincent House, 16 Suffolk Street, London SW1Y 4NL *Tel* 0171-747 5299 *Textphone* 0171-747 5347 *Fax* 0171-747 5214 *E-mail* enquiries@nlcb.org.uk *Web Site* www.nlcb.org.uk

REGIONAL OFFICES International grants office: St Vincent House, 16 Suffolk Street, London SW1Y 4NL *Tel* 0171-747 5294 *Fax* 0171-747 5307 *E-mail* mday@nlcb.org.uk
Wales Office: Roy Norris, Director for Wales, Ladywell House, Newtown, Powys SY16 1JB *Tel* 01686 621644 *Textphone* 01686 610205 *Fax* 01686 621534 *E-mail* enquiries@wales.nlcb.org.uk
Northern Ireland Office: Ann McLaughlin, Director for Northern Ireland, 2nd Floor, Hildon House, 30-34 Hill Street, Belfast BT1 2LB *Tel* 01232 551455 *Textphone* 01232 551431 *Fax* 01232 551444 *E-mail* enquiries@ni.nlcb.org.uk
Scotland Office: John Rafferty, Director for Scotland, Norloch House, 36 Kings Stables Road, Edinburgh EH1 2EJ *Tel* 0131-221 7100 *Textphone* 0131-221 7122 *Fax* 0131-221 7120 *E-mail* enquiries@scotland.nlcb.org.uk
England Head Office: Janet Paraskeva, Director for England, Readson House, 96-98 Regent Road, Leicester LE1 7DZ *Tel* 0116-258 7000 *Textphone* 0116-255 5162 *Fax* 0116-255 7398 *E-mail* enquiries@englandhq.nlcb.org.uk
England Regional Offices:
London: Janice Needham, Regional Manager, 3rd Floor, Whittington House, 19-30 Alfred Place, London WC1E 7EZ *Tel* 0171-291 8500 *Textphone* 0171-291 8526 *Fax* 0171-291 8503 *E-mail* enquiries@lon.nlcb.org.uk
South East: Dorothy Buckrell, Regional Manager, 3rd Floor, Dominion House, Woodbridge Road, Guildford, Surrey GU1 4BN *Tel* 01483 462900

Textphone 01483 568764 *Fax* 01483 569893
  E-mail enquiries@se.nlcb.org.uk
South West: John de la Cour and Pippa Warin,
  Regional Managers, Pembroke House,
  Southernhay Gardens, Southernhay East,
  Exeter EX1 1UL *Tel* 01392 849700
  Textphone 01392 490633
  Fax 01392 491134
  E-mail enquiries@sw.nlcb.org.uk
Eastern: Janette Grazette, Regional Manager,
  Great Eastern House, Tenison Road,
  Cambridge CB1 2TT *Tel* 01223 449000
  Textphone 01223 352041
  Fax 01223 312628
  E-mail enquiries@ea.nlcb.org.uk
East Midlands: Mike Wilkins, Interim Regional
  Manager, 3rd Floor, 33 Park Row, Nottingham,
  NG1 6NL *Tel* 0115-934 9300
  Textphone 0115-948 4436
  Fax 0115-948 4435
  E-mail enquiries@em.nlcb.org.uk
West Midlands: Fran Jones, Regional Manager,
  4th Floor, Edmund House, 12-22 Newhall
  Street, Birmingham B3 3NL
  Tel 0121-200 3500
  Textphone 0121-212 3523
  Fax 0121-212 3081
  E-mail enquiries@wm.nlcb.org.uk
Yorkshire and Humberside: Helen Wollaston,
  Acting Regional Manager 3rd Floor, Carlton
  Tower, 34 St Paul's Street, Leeds LS1 2AT
  Tel 0113-224 5300
  Textphone 0113-245 4104
  Fax 0113-244 0363
  E-mail enquiries@yh.nlcb.org.uk
North West (including Merseyside): Andrew
  Freeney, Regional Manager, Dallam Court,
  Dallam Lane, Warrington WA2 7LU
  Tel 01925 626800
  Textphone 01925 231241
  Fax 01925 234041
  E-mail enquiries@nw.nlcb.org.uk
North East: Peter Deans, Regional Manager,
  Ground Floor, Bede House, All Saints Business
  Centre, Broad Chare, Newcastle Upon Tyne
  NE1 2NL *Tel* 0191-255 1100
  Textphone 0191-233 2099
  Fax 0191-233 1997
  E-mail enquiries@ne.nlcb.org.uk

ESTABLISHED 1994

Commentary

The National Lottery Charities Board is one of the
six good causes, and one of the twelve
Distributing Bodies, set up to distribute Lottery
funds. The Board is a Non-Departmental Public
Body, sponsored by the Department for Culture,
Media and Sport but is independent of the
Government. Since the launch of the Board in
August 1994, grants totalling more than £800
million have been made through some 14,500
awards. The Board is the largest, all-purpose
grant-maker in Europe with a grant-making

approach designed to provide the greatest
opportunity for voluntary sector and charitable
organisations to apply for grants. The Board's
grant-making procedures are made as
transparent as possible, especially as it operates
in the glare of public scrutiny to a far greater
extent than most other grant-making trusts.

The Board makes grants in a variety of ways.
These comprise: (a) UK-wide main grants
programmes; (b) UK-wide Small Grants
programmes (or Cross-Distributor programmes
through Awards For All in Scotland and the East
Midlands in England); (c) International
programmes; (d) Specialist programmes to do
with Health and Social Research.

The Board funds projects which help those at
greatest disadvantage in society. The main grants
programmes run so far include: (i) Poverty;
(ii) Youth Issues/Low Income; (iii) Health,
Disability and Care; (iv) New Opportunities and
Choices/Voluntary Sector Development;
(v) Improving People's Living Environment/
Voluntary Sector Development. Those running at
present are (vi) Community Involvement/
Voluntary Sector Development; (vii) Poverty and
Disadvantage. The Small Grants programme was
piloted in Scotland, Wales, and the North-East
and the South West regions of England; and in
July 1998 the Small Grants Scheme was
extended to the rest of England and in Northern
Ireland. In Scotland and the East Midlands the
scheme is known as Awards For All as it involves
all the Lottery Distribution bodies. Under the
Small Grants scheme, awards of between
£500–£5,000 are made for organisations with an
annual income not exceeding £15,000. During
1999 the Awards For All programme will be
extended to the rest of England.

The International Grants programmes make
grants to UK organisations working overseas in
the following geographical areas: Africa; Asia
(including the pacific, the Caucasus and Central
Asian Republics); the Middle East, South and
Central America; the Caribbean; Central and
Eastern Europe. A specialist programme for
Health & Social Research is also being run.

The Board is committed to meeting the widest
possible range of need in a fair and equitable
way. Its grant programmes are designed with this
in mind. Part of the commitment to meeting need
is reflected in the way programmes are run. The
main grants programmes, Community
Involvement and Poverty and Disadvantage, are
being run continuously, replacing the system of
time-limited grant rounds which applied before.
Applicants no longer have to submit applications
to deadlines. Small Grants and Awards For All are
also run continuously.

In addition, the Board is consulting widely with the
Voluntary Sector and carrying out research for its
Strategic Plan. This will show the Board's

commitment to meeting needs and how future grant programmes will reflect this at country level, regional level in England and across all four countries of the UK. All applications are assessed on merit against clear criteria and policies set out in the application pack.

The Board does not fund statutory bodies or replace statutory funding. Awards are made for projects. The Board does not require matching funding and awards can be for the full cost of projects. Awards are made for capital costs, revenue costs and a combination of capital and revenue costs. Awards are made over one, two or three years and are made to registered charities or those organisations which are charitable, benevolent or philanthropic. The Board can not make grants to statutory bodies or individuals and cannot make loans.

Decisions on awards are taken by the five grant-making Committees: England, Scotland; Wales; Northern Ireland and the UK (which also decides on awards under the International and Health and Social Research programmes). Committees are made up of members of the Board who are appointed by the Secretary of State for Culture, Media and Sport. New powers in the National Lottery Act 1998 will mean that in England, grantmaking will be delegated to Regional Awards Committees whilst in Scotland, Wales and Northern Ireland the size of grant-making committees can be increased. Grants Officers (or assessors for the International and specialist grant programmes) undertake the assessment of grant applications.

Applications can only be made by application form. These are available by calling a 24-hour request line on 0345 919191 for the main grants programme. Welsh speakers can apply for application form for both the main grants and small Grants programmes by telephoning 0345 273273. Application forms for the International programme are available on 0345 778878. Small Grants application forms for Scotland are available on 0645 700777 and for England and Northern Ireland on 0345 458458. Application packs contain detailed guidance on how to fill in the form, and applicants are advised to read these carefully before applying.

For projects costing over £200,000 a comprehensive Business Plan must be included with the application form. Copies of audited, or approved accounts are required. Details of an independent referee must be provided, someone who is not part of the applicant organisation but who know its work and the project well. General information about eligibility to apply and the work of the Board is available from Country and Regional offices as well as on the internet: www.nlcb.org.uk.

During the assessment process the applicant may be contacted for clarification on the details of a bid and may be visited. For large bids over £500,000, second-level assessment will also take place using expert opinion from surveyors or accountants as necessary. At the end of the assessment process a detailed portfolio of recommended grants is put forward for decision at Committee level.

The Board monitors all projects which receive grants. Successful applicants are required to complete end of year and end of grant project reports to satisfy the Board that the objectives of the project are being how they have been achieved and who has benefited. Monitoring visits made to all projects which have received funding of over £150,000 and made to all projects which have received funding of over £150,000 and to a 2 per cent sample of those receiving less. The Board continues to monitor and evaluate its own performance in grant-making and has an independent complaints review system. Annual Reports are available on request

SAMPLE GRANTS
At September 1998, the top ten grants awarded were:
£1,106,991 to Shelter
£1,007,762 to Save The Children (UK)
£847,507 to National Association for the Care and Resettlement of Offenders
£833,472 to National Association of Citizens Advice Bureaux
£708,318 to Disabled Living
£663,299 to Population Concern
£650,000 to Columba 1400
£609,060 to Action Aid
£597,595 to Dogs for the Disabled
£597,189 to Skillshare Africa

....

■ The Airey Neave Trust

WHAT IS FUNDED Postgraduate education for refugees or those with exceptional or indefinite leave to remain, resident in the UK and recognised by the Home Office. Refugees needing retraining, teaching English as a second or foreign language, fellowships, refugees bursaries and fees, law research and specialist research will be considered

WHAT IS NOT FUNDED No grants to asylum seekers

WHO CAN BENEFIT Individuals, law faculties and researchers. Organisations benefiting young adults; refugees; academics; legal professionals; post graduate refugees; refugees needing retraining will all be considered

WHERE FUNDING CAN BE GIVEN UK

TYPE OF GRANT Fees for refugees up to £2,000 per annum; research grants up to £20,000 per annum. Feasibility studies. Funding of up to three years is available

SAMPLE GRANTS £31,500 to The Centre for the Study of Terrorism and Political Violence for research into Terrorist Use of Weapons of Mass Destruction

£20,500 to The Queen's University, Belfast for research into Judicial Responsibility in the Criminal Courts

£15,000 to 13 refugees for post-graduate education, subjects covering medicine, law, petroleum geology, telecommunications and business management

FINANCES
- Year 1996–97
- Income £58,517
- Grants £63,500

TRUSTEES Rt Hon Sir Adam Butler, Hugh Tilney, Sir Nigel Mobbs, The Hon Patrick Neave, The Hon Sir William MacAlpine, BT

PUBLICATIONS Among others: *Victims of Terrorism, The International Covenant on Civil and Political Rights and UK Law, The World of Science and The Rule of Law*

NOTES We do not contribute to established institutions

HOW TO APPLY We welcome an initial telephone call. There are application forms for refugees but not for research fellows. There are guidelines for research fellows. There are deadlines, viz: refugees – 31 May, and research – 31 May. We prefer an sae from applicant

WHO TO APPLY TO Mrs Hannah Scott, The Airey Neave Trust, 40 Charles Street, London W1X 7PB *Tel* 0171-495 0554 *Fax* 0171-491 1118

CC NO 297269   **ESTABLISHED** 1979

■ The Newstead Charity

WHAT IS FUNDED Health and disability and community facilities

WHAT IS NOT FUNDED No grants to individuals

WHO CAN BENEFIT Organisations benfiting sick and disabled people. There are no restrictions on the disease or medical condition suffered by the beneficiaries

WHERE FUNDING CAN BE GIVEN Liverpool City, Knowsley and North Wales

TYPE OF GRANT One-off, project and research. Funding for up to one year will be considered

RANGE OF GRANTS Range of grants from £500

FINANCES
- Year 1996–97
- Income £24,000
- Grants £29,000

TRUSTEES K E B Clayton, G D Tasker, W F Glazebrook

HOW TO APPLY Applications in writing only

WHO TO APPLY TO Roberts Legge & Co, The Newstead Charity, 14 Chapel Lane, Formby, Liverpool, Merseyside L37 4DU *Tel* 01704 834490

CC NO 327244   **ESTABLISHED** 1986

■ North and East Lancashire Unitarian Mission

WHAT IS FUNDED To advance missionary efforts in the local areas, support member congregations, train men and women of the churches in the district and discipline of the ministry

WHAT IS NOT FUNDED Unitarian Churches and members of Congregations of Unitarian Churches only

WHO CAN BENEFIT Christians

WHERE FUNDING CAN BE GIVEN Lancashire and parts of Greater Manchester

TYPE OF GRANT Recurring, buildings and salaries

FINANCES
- Year 1995–96
- Income £9,895
- Grants £3,929

WHO TO APPLY TO Mrs N Fletcher, North and East Lancashire Unitarian Mission, 818 Manchester Road, Bury, Lancashire BL9 8DU

CC NO 226163   **ESTABLISHED** 1964

■ North West Arts Board

WHAT IS FUNDED Priorities include maximising access to all artforms throughout the region and encouraging creative and innovative work. The Board works in partnerships to increase the resources in the region's arts economy. Training for community and personal development and training for work may be considered. Publishing and printing may also be funded

WHAT IS NOT FUNDED No grants to profit-making organisations

WHO CAN BENEFIT Arts organisations, groups and individuals who are arts practitioners or wish to promote arts events in the North West of England

WHERE FUNDING CAN BE GIVEN Cheshire, Lancashire, Greater Manchester and Merseyside

TYPE OF GRANT Core costs, feasibility studies, one-off, project, research, recurring costs, running costs and start-up costs will be considered

SAMPLE GRANTS All the following grants were revenue support for core activities:

£1,363,250 to Royal Exchange Theatre

Company, Manchester
£430,000 to Liverpool Playhouse Theatre
£425,100 to Manchester Young People's
Theatre (Contact Theatre)
£255,600 to Bolton Octagon Theatre
£240,550 to Cornerhouse, Manchester (Art
Gallery/Cinema)
£224,400 to Oldham Coliseum Theatre
£210,000 to New Everyman Theatre, Liverpool
£202,500 to NIA Centre, Manchester (Black
Arts Centre)
£173,850 to Dukes Playhouse, Lancaster
£148,800 to Chester Gateway Theatre

FINANCES

- Year 1996–97   - Income £9,612,157
- Grants £8,241,405

TRUSTEES The Board

PUBLICATIONS Annual Report and various other
publications

NOTES Only writers bursaries are available to
students

HOW TO APPLY By application form, timings vary
according to artform. Contact Information Unit
for details

WHO TO APPLY TO Chief Executive, North West
Arts Board, Manchester House, 22 Bridge
Street, Manchester M3 3AB *Tel* 0161-
834 6644 +Minicom: 0161-834 9131
Fax 0161-834 6969 *E-mail* nwarts-
info@mcr1.poptel.org.uk

CC NO 251558   **ESTABLISHED** 1966

··
■ **North West Cancer Research
Fund** (embodying Friends of Liverpool Radium
Institute)

WHAT IS FUNDED Fundamental cancer research
including cost of associated equipment

WHAT IS NOT FUNDED No grants made outside
North West area. No grants for building
projects

WHO CAN BENEFIT All cancer research approved
by and under the direction of the University of
Liverpool Cancer Research Committee. Work
must be for the eventual benefit of cancer
sufferers

WHERE FUNDING CAN BE GIVEN Merseyside,
North Wales, Cheshire, North Shropshire,
Lancashire, Cumbria and the Isle of Man

TYPE OF GRANT Project, research, running costs,
salaries and start-up costs. Usually for three to
five year periods subject to annual review

SAMPLE GRANTS The following grants were given
for fundamental cancer research projects:
£30,000 to researchers at University of
Liverpool
£30,000 to researchers at Liverpool John

Moores University
£30,000 to researchers at University of
Lancaster
£30,000 to researchers at University of
Wales, Bangor

FINANCES

- Year 1997   - Income £675,227
- Grants £864,500

TRUSTEES M S Potts, FCA, P F Sutcliffe, P H
Kenney, J C Lewys-Lloyd, FCA

PUBLICATIONS Annual Report. Publicity leaflet.
Donation leaflet

HOW TO APPLY Telephone the Secretary to
obtain an application form and guidelines for
the awarding of grants. The Committee meets
quarterly. Deadlines for applications will be
advised

WHO TO APPLY TO Miss Lorraine Wells,
Secretary, North West Cancer Research Fund,
The University of Liverpool, Cancer Research
Committee, Faculty of Medicine, Duncan
Building, Liverpool L69 3BX

CC NO 223598   **ESTABLISHED** 1948

··
■ **North West Media Charitable
Trust Limited**

WHAT IS FUNDED General charitable purposes, in
particular, the relief of poverty, hardship and
distress, the relief of the disabled (including
the mentally handicapped); the advancement
of education (encouragement of the arts) and
research; the provision of facilities for
recreation and leisure-time for the benefit of
the public

WHAT IS NOT FUNDED Proposals from
individuals; proposals for projects abroad;
projects that do not fall principally within GTV/
Border regions; other categories the Board
shall determine

WHO CAN BENEFIT Children and young adults
who are homeless; research; mentally or
terminally ill; disabled or in need of health
care. Research workers and students are also
considered

WHERE FUNDING CAN BE GIVEN Granada and
Border TV Regions. This is the North West,
including Dumfries and Galloway and Isle of
Man

TYPE OF GRANT Capital and/or revenue

RANGE OF GRANTS A ceiling on the cost of
projects limits any individual project to
£1,000,000

TRUSTEES Lord Thomas of Macclesfield, R
Mcloughlin, M Davis, J Hartley, N Robinson, J
Macnaught, D Shearer, S Jennings, J Kennedy,
J Marsion, S Ingham, D Clark, R Lancaster, R
Parry, W Martin, A Benzie

NOTES (a) It is anticipated that the Trust will have a limited life. The Board expects to make its final grants in Spring 1999 (b) For precise details of the legal position grant seekers should examine the Memorandum and Articles of Association of the Company

HOW TO APPLY Initial telephone calls are not welcome. Guidelines are available. An sae would be appriciated

WHO TO APPLY TO Mrs A Weisberg, Charity Coordinator, North West Media Charitable Trust Limited, Granada Television, Quay Street, Manchester M60 9EA *Tel* 0161-832 7211 ext 2446

CC NO 1068308   **ESTABLISHED** 1998

■ Northern Arts

WHAT IS FUNDED The Arts including: (a) access; (b) education; (c) audience development; (d) the individual artist; (e) the arts economy; and (f) the value of the arts

WHAT IS NOT FUNDED Students

WHO CAN BENEFIT Any one involved in arts including: actors and entertainment professional; musicians; textile workers and designers; writers and poets; artists; ethnic minority groups; and disabled people

WHERE FUNDING CAN BE GIVEN Cumbria, Northumberland, Durham, Teesside, Tyne and Wear

TYPE OF GRANT One-off and recurring

RANGE OF GRANTS £150–£600,000

SAMPLE GRANTS £664,250 to Northern Stage
£346,960 to Northern Sinfonia
£184,800 to Tyneside Cinema
£179,000 to Welfare State International
£140,000 to Live Theatre
£140,000 to NTC
£100,000 to Northern Gallery for Contemporary Arts
£87,000 to Zone Gallery
£82,000 to Grizedale Society
£80,600 to Sunderland City Council

FINANCES
- Year 1997
- Income £8,082,034
- Grants £6,700,650

TRUSTEES The Board of Directors

PUBLICATIONS Annual Review and programme specific newsletters

NOTES A menu of projects and schemes with detailed guidelines exists

HOW TO APPLY Varies from art form to art form. Potential applicants are advised to outline their proposal in writing, including a budget, with reference to relevant scheme criterion

WHO TO APPLY TO The Chief Executive, Northern Arts, 9–10 Osborne Terrace, Jesmond, Newcastle upon Tyne NE2 1NZ *Tel* 0191-281 6334 *Fax* 0191-281 3276 *E-mail* nab@norab.demon.co.uk

CC NO 517711   **ESTABLISHED** 1961

■ The Northern Rock Foundation

WHAT IS FUNDED Only organisations or projects in the North of the UK. This Foundation will consider funding: infrastructure development; charity or voluntary umbrella bodies; respite accommodation and respite care for carers; community arts and recreation; support and self help groups; hospices; literacy training; care in the community; social counselling; individual rights; and advice centres

WHAT IS NOT FUNDED There are certain organisations, projects and proposals that are excluded from consideration. If you or your project fall into one of these categories please do not apply to the Foundation. Organisations which are not registered charities; charities which trade, have substantial reserves (normally over 75 per cent of annual running costs in unrestricted reserves) or are in serious deficit; national charities which do not have a regional office or other physical representation in the North East and the North; national organisations seeking proportionate expenditure for the North East element of nation-wide projects or provisions; open ended funding agreements; general appeals, sponsorship and marketing appeals; Retrospective grants; endowment funds; replacement of statutory funding; activities primarily the responsibility of central or local government; individuals, including students, and organisations that distribute funds to or purchase equipment for individuals; animal welfare; mainstream educational activity, schools, universities and colleges; curriculum education or equipment to support it; medical research, hospitals (other than hospices) and medical centres, health care treatments and therapies whether provided by statutory authorities or not; environmental projects which do not accord with the main objectives of the Foundation; buildings, fabric appeals for places of worship, etc, except where explicitly invited under the Guidelines in programme descriptions; improvements to buildings owned by local authorities or other statutory bodies where the remaining life of the lease is less than 10 years; promotion of religion; corporate applications for founder membership of a charity; loans or business finance; expeditions or overseas travel; grant-making bodies seeking, to distribute grants on our behalf; academic research unless commissioned by the Foundation; conferences, seminars and other similar activities unless specifically related to an activity supported by the Foundation or of exceptional significance. The following are unlikely to be supported: minibuses and other vehicles (unless a critical part of a bigger project and even then unlikely); holidays and outings; applications for 100 per cent of cost **unless**: (a) all other avenues have been exhausted and (b) the project is unique, experimental, possibly a model for others and has potential for enormous returns if successful and (c) the proposed activity is time-limited or has a credible exit strategy. Applications for very large sums (over £100,000) unless they are for something demonstrably exceptional, experimental or ground-breaking. We will usually prefer applications from organisations that can clearly show management involvement of beneficiaries

WHO CAN BENEFIT Organisations benefiting parents and children as well as one parent families. There is no restriction on age, and a wide range of social circumstances of; and disease or medical condition suffered by, the beneficiaries

WHERE FUNDING CAN BE GIVEN In practice, the North East of England, North West, Cumbria, Yorkshire and Scotland

TYPE OF GRANT Buildings, capital, core costs, one-off, project, recurring costs, running costs, salaries and start-up costs. Funding is available for more than three years

RANGE OF GRANTS £1,000–£150,000, typical grant £5,000–£60,000

SAMPLE GRANTS £150,000 to Percy Hedley Centre towards specialist teaching and therapy facilities for young people with disabilities
£84,557 to Advocacy in Gateshead towards advocacy service for adults with learning difficulties who reside in Gateshead
£83,330 to special needs activities and play provision in York towards a three year lifeskills and work experience programme for young people with disabilities
£79,287 to Carers Support, Derwentside to fund a project providing respite support to carers of people with palliative care needs and core costs
£75,000 to The Princess Royal Trust for Carers to establish the Trust in Newcastle
£71,237 to Hartlepool Voluntary Development Agency towards development of new and existing carers' service in Hartlepool
£69,000 to Disability North to employ a disability equality trainer/consultant
£67,598 to the Neurofibromatosis Association towards the costs of employing family support worker(s) to give specialist support/care to people with neurofibromatosis
£63,000 to Hartlepool MIND towards the establishment of user-led support and information service in Hartlepool

£60,000 to Euryalus Phab Club towards funding an independent living unit in new premises in Jarrow

FINANCES
- Year 1997
- Income £2,024,000

TRUSTEES W R Atkinson (Chairman), R H Dickinson, Josephine, Lady Bonfield, L P Finn, P R M Harbottle, The Lord Howick of Glendale, A E Kilburn, J A Logan, Dorothy, Lady Russell, Miss E E Slattery, J P Wainwright

NOTES The NR Foundation is new and developing. Things change quickly. Enquire or check our Website

HOW TO APPLY Application pack available, includes essential application form

WHO TO APPLY TO Grants Manager, The Northern Rock Foundation, 21 Landsdowne Terrace, Gosforth, Newcastle upon Tyne NE3 1HP
Tel 0191-284 8412
Web Site www.northernrockfoundation.org.uk

CC NO 1063906   **ESTABLISHED** 1997

■Edward C Oldham Charitable Trust

WHAT IS FUNDED General charitable purposes

WHO CAN BENEFIT Individuals and organisations

WHERE FUNDING CAN BE GIVEN Greater Manchester

FINANCES
- Year 1996
- Income £4,224

HOW TO APPLY To the Correspondent in writing

WHO TO APPLY TO P G Livesey, Trustee, Edward C Oldham Charitable Trust, Lower Firwood, Leycester Road, Knutsford, Cheshire WA16 8QR

CC NO 284132   **ESTABLISHED** 1961

■Oldham Charity Carnival Trust

WHAT IS FUNDED General charitable purposes

WHERE FUNDING CAN BE GIVEN Oldham

FINANCES
- Year 1994–95
- Income £4,000

HOW TO APPLY To the Correspondent in writing

WHO TO APPLY TO S K Howard, Treasurer, Oldham Charity Carnival Trust, 2 Bridgefield Crescent, Springhead, Oldham OL4 4PD

CC NO 1043911   **ESTABLISHED** 1995

■Oldham Foundation

WHAT IS FUNDED Main donations to former employees of Oldham Batteries (employed before 1971) and charitable activities where Trustees give personal service or where they know people who do so. Charities working in the fields of: arts, culture and recreation; conservation and environment; and churches will be considered. Support may also be given to hospices, nursing services, cancer research, libraries and museums, day centres, holidays and outings

WHAT IS NOT FUNDED Applications from individuals, including students, are ineligible with the exception of those already selected for schemes like Operation Raleigh. No grants to general appeals from national bodies. Inappropriate appeals are not acknowledged

WHO CAN BENEFIT Organisations benefiting children, young adults, ex-service and service people, Church of England and former employees of Oldham Batteries (employed before 1971). Funding is considered for those disadvantaged by poverty; victims of man-made or natural disasters and those suffering from cancers, HIV and AIDs and mental illness

WHERE FUNDING CAN BE GIVEN North West and South West of England. Charities aided in the area may have objectives overseas

TYPE OF GRANT Annual grant to former employees. Grants usually one-off. Does not provide core funding. General charitable grants with bias towards active participation by Trustees

RANGE OF GRANTS £40–£5,000, typical grant £250/£500/£1,000

SAMPLE GRANTS £5,000 to Sue Ryder Home £5,000 to Cheltenham Festival of Music £5,000 to Cheltenham Festival of Literature £2,000 to Cheltenham Samaritans £2,000 to 24th Leckhampton Scout Group £2,000 to Christchurch Cheltenham Hall Appeal £2,000 to Winstons Wish, Gloucester £2,000 to CABE £1,500 to Parnham House for a bursary award £1,000 to Cheltenham Young Homeless Project

FINANCES
- Year 1998
- Income £77,693
- Grants £96,892

TRUSTEES J Bodden, Mrs D Oldham, J Oldham (Chairman), S Roberts, Prof R Thomas, J Sharpe

HOW TO APPLY Any time. Trustees meet twice a year. Applications should include clear details of projects, budgets, and/or accounts where appropriate. Telephone submissions not accepted

WHO TO APPLY TO Mrs D Oldham, Oldham Foundation, King's Well, Douro Road, Cheltenham, Gloucestershire GL50 2PF

CC NO 269263   **ESTABLISHED** 1974

■Oldham United Charity

WHAT IS FUNDED Local branches of national welfare organisations and individuals in need

WHO CAN BENEFIT Individuals and organisations

WHERE FUNDING CAN BE GIVEN Oldham

FINANCES
- Year 1994–95
- Income £5,000
- Grants £3,800

HOW TO APPLY To the Correspondent in writing

WHO TO APPLY TO B McKnown, Clerk, Oldham United Charity, 85 Union Street, Oldham, Lancashire OL1 1PF

CC NO 221095 **ESTABLISHED** 1987

■ Overton Community Trust

WHAT IS FUNDED General charitable purposes in the area Where Funding Can Be Given

WHO CAN BENEFIT There are no restrictions on the age; professional and economic group; family situation; religion and culture; and social circumstances of; or disease or medical condition suffered by, the beneficiaries

WHERE FUNDING CAN BE GIVEN Frodsham in Cheshire and surrounding area

SAMPLE GRANTS £1,514 to the handicapped
£605 to the community
£500 to the youth
£136 to the elderly

FINANCES
- Year 1996–97
- Income £18,424
- Grants £2,756

HOW TO APPLY To the address under Who To Apply To in writing

WHO TO APPLY TO Miss K Dower, Secretary, Overton Community Trust, 17 Holly Court, Helsby, Cheshire WA6 0PH

CC NO 1050809 **ESTABLISHED** 1995

■ Parkhill Charitable Trust

This trust did not respond to CAF's request to amend its entry and, by 30 June 1998, CAF's researchers did not find financial records for later than 1995 on its file at the Charity Commission. Trusts are legally required to submit annual accounts to the Charity Commission under section 42 of the Charities Act 1993

WHAT IS FUNDED Relief of poverty, Jewish, education and general charitable purposes

WHO CAN BENEFIT Children, young adults, Jewish people and those disadvantaged by poverty

WHERE FUNDING CAN BE GIVEN Manchester

TRUSTEES Deborah Guttentag, Martin S Caller, Jonathan Guttentag

HOW TO APPLY To the address below in writing

WHO TO APPLY TO J Guttentag, Trustee, Parkhill Charitable Trust, 1 Parkhill Drive, Whitefield, Manchester M45 7PD

CC NO 1019828 **ESTABLISHED** 1993

■ Thomas Parkinson (Deceased) Trust

WHAT IS FUNDED Disability; health; youth organisations; and organisations promoting voluntary service

WHO CAN BENEFIT National organisations, local branches of national organisations

WHERE FUNDING CAN BE GIVEN County Borough of Preston

FINANCES
- Year 1996
- Income £2,763

TRUSTEES D G G Davies, J Ward

HOW TO APPLY To the Correspondent in writing

WHO TO APPLY TO D G G Davies, Trustee, Thomas Parkinson (Deceased) Trust, St George's Chamber, 4 Fishergate Walk, Preston, Lancashire PR1 2LH
Tel 01772 253251

CC NO 504458 **ESTABLISHED** 1975

■ Patients' Aid Association Hospital and Medical Charities Trust

WHAT IS FUNDED Provision of equipment and patient amenities to NHS hospitals, hospices, convalescent homes and other medically related charities in the area where the parent Association operates. These include: support to volunteers; health professional bodies; Councils for Voluntary Service; advancement of religion; churches; respite; sheltered accommodation; health; special schools; speech therapy; special needs education; scholarships; medical research; specialist research; and community services

WHAT IS NOT FUNDED Appeals must be from Officials of the appealing body and submitted on official stationery. Appeals not accepted from, or on behalf of, individuals or for provision of vehicles

WHO CAN BENEFIT Mainly NHS hospitals and registered, medically related charities benefiting children; young adults; older people; ex-service and service people; medical professionals, nurses and doctors; musicians; research workers; volunteers; those in care; fostered and adopted; at risk groups; carers; disabled people; those disadvantaged by poverty; disaster victims; ex-offenders and those at risk of offending; gays and lesbians; homeless people; victims of abuse and domestic violence; and victims of war. There are no restrictions on the disease or medical condition of the beneficiaries

WHERE FUNDING CAN BE GIVEN Mainly East and West Midlands, Staffordshire and Shropshire areas

TYPE OF GRANT Mainly medical equipment. Grants not made towards running costs or administration

RANGE OF GRANTS £953–£2,600

SAMPLE GRANTS £2,600 to Muscular Dystrophy, Birmingham for wheelchairs
£2,500 to Whizz Kidz, London for a special walker for the disabled
£2,000 to Portland College, Nottingham for two lightwriters
£1,800 to Royal Institute for the Blind, Birmingham for a bath hoist
£1,640 to Wolverhampton Healthcare NHS Trust for physiotherapy equipment
£1,500 to Norton House Community Care, Keele for an industrial cooker
£1,000 to Martha Trust, Hereford for multi-sensory equipment
£990 to Leukemia Unit, Dudley for a special bed
£963 to St Anthony's Cheshire Home, Wolverhampton for two shower chairs
£953 to Cotswold Care Hospice, Gloucester for special chairs

FINANCES
- Year 1997
- Income £86,278
- Grants £42,139

TRUSTEES T P Horan (Chairman), E P Booth, G F Lewis, T E Ratcliffe, H Reynolds, D Bradley, J Dickie

PUBLICATIONS Brochure concerning Trust

NOTES The Trustees meet four times a year. All appeals are considered before a decision is reached. Full details of the use to which the donations will be put and the cost of the equipment required must be included with the appeal letter

HOW TO APPLY Grant Application Form available on written request giving brief details of requirements and appellant

WHO TO APPLY TO Mrs Patricia Stokes, Secretary, Patients' Aid Association Hospital and Medical Charities Trust, Paycare House, George Street, Wolverhampton WV2 4DX
Tel 01902 713131 *Fax* 01902 710361

CC NO 240378   **ESTABLISHED** 1964

■The Dowager Countess Eleanor Peel Trust (369)

WHAT IS FUNDED General charitable purposes, particularly medical charities, charities for old people, and 'those who have fallen on evil days through no fault of their own'

WHAT IS NOT FUNDED No grants to individuals

WHO CAN BENEFIT Registered charities. There are no restrictions on the age; professional and economic group; family situation; religion and culture; and social circumstances of; or disease or medical condition suffered by, the beneficiaries

WHERE FUNDING CAN BE GIVEN UK, with particular preference for Lancaster

TYPE OF GRANT One-off, capital, project

FINANCES
- Year 1997
- Income £496,915
- Grants £393,050

TRUSTEES R S Parkinson, J W Parkinson, R L Rothwell-Jackson, A G Trower, L H Valner

HOW TO APPLY In writing to the address below

WHO TO APPLY TO The Dowager Countess Eleanor Peel Trust, 6 New Square, Lincoln's Inn, London WC2A 3RP

CC NO 214684   **ESTABLISHED** 1951

Commentary

The Dowager Countess Eleanor Peel Trust was established in 1951 under the terms of the Will of Eleanor Countess Peel. While allowing the Trustees absolute discretion in applying the income of the Trust to charitable purposes, the Trust Deed also enjoins them to have particular regard for medical charities, charities for old people and 'those who have fallen on evil days through no fault of their own', and the charitable bodies specified in the schedule to the Trust

Deed. They cannot give money to charitable bodies substantially controlled by central or local government or charities primarily devoted to children under 18.

Total grants for 1997 amounted to £393,050. Of this, £16,000 went to charities listed in the schedule to the Trust Deed. As far as the over 70 other grants are concerned, the Trust has a small number of organisations which it is committed to supporting over a period of years. Apart from these, all grants were made on a one-off basis. However, organisations can reapply, and in 1997 the vast majority of grant recipients had already received support – often substantial – from the Trust in previous years.

Grants are made throughout the UK, but there is a special emphasis on funding organisations based in Lancaster. The Trust will fund capital expenditure or project costs but not core running costs.

Applications should be made by letter. The Trustees meet at least three times a year, normally in March, July and November, to consider applications.

Grant recipients are always required to report back on how the grant was used. Trustees do occasionally make visits to organisations that have received grants

SAMPLE GRANTS
The top ten grants made in 1997 were:
£99,000 to Jefferiss Research Wing Trust (over three years)
£80,000 to Lancashire and Cumbria Foundation for Medical Research (over three years)
£30,000 to the Peel Medical Research Trust
£10,000 to Cancer Relief MacMillan Fund
£9,500 to Water Aid
£9,000 to Lancaster Royal Grammar School (Peel Further Education Award) (over three years)
£9,000 to the Marie Curie Research Wing Fund
£5,000 to St Lukes Hospital for the Clergy
£5,000 to Little Sisters of the Poor, Leeds and Birmingham
£5,000 to the Churches Conservation Trust

■ Penny in the Pound Fund Charitable Trust

WHAT IS FUNDED Pay out to NHS hospitals amenities for patients

WHAT IS NOT FUNDED No grants towards medical equipment

WHO CAN BENEFIT NHS hospitals and health authorities. There is no restriction on the disease or medical condition suffered by the beneficiaries

WHERE FUNDING CAN BE GIVEN North East England, North West England, North Wales, Midlands and Scottish regions

TYPE OF GRANT Capital

FINANCES
- Year 1995
- Grants £92,203
- Income £92,165

TRUSTEES P B Teare, K W Monti, H F Settle, K Arnold, B E Straveley

HOW TO APPLY Annually in August

WHO TO APPLY TO K Arnold, Finance Officer, Penny in the Pound Fund Charitable Trust, Merseyside Health Benefits Council, 7 Sir Thomas Street, Liverpool L1 6HE

CC NO 257637   **ESTABLISHED** 1968

■ The Pennycress Trust

WHAT IS FUNDED General charitable purposes. Makes distributions to a restricted list of registered charities only, principally in Cheshire and Norfolk

WHAT IS NOT FUNDED No grants to individuals or large national bodies

WHO CAN BENEFIT There are no restrictions on the age, professional and economic group, family situation, religion and culture, and social circumstances of, or disease or medical condition suffered by, the beneficiaries

WHERE FUNDING CAN BE GIVEN Principally Cheshire and Norfolk

TYPE OF GRANT Recurrent and one-off

RANGE OF GRANTS £300–£500

FINANCES
- Year 1997
- Grants £63,000
- Income £67,000

TRUSTEES A J M Baker, Lady Aline Cholmondeley, C G Cholmondeley

HOW TO APPLY Once yearly. Reviewed June/July and December. Sae appreciated

WHO TO APPLY TO A J M Baker, The Pennycress Trust, Heron Place, 3 George Street, London W1H 6AD

CC NO 261536   **ESTABLISHED** 1970

Brigadier and Mrs D V Phelps Charitable Trust (formerly D V Phelps Charitable Trust)

WHAT IS FUNDED General charitable purposes

WHAT IS NOT FUNDED The Trustees do not make grants to individuals

WHO CAN BENEFIT There are no restrictions on the age; professional and economic group; family situation; religion and culture; and social circumstances of; or disease or medical condition suffered by, the beneficiaries

WHERE FUNDING CAN BE GIVEN UK and overseas, with special preference to Merseyside and Norfolk

RANGE OF GRANTS Below £500–£5,950; £500 is usually the upper limit

SAMPLE GRANTS £5,950 to Liverpool Council of Social Service (Inc)
£1,000 to Royal Liverpool University Hospital
£500 to ADAPT
£500 to Assembly House Appeal Fund
£500 to Burlingham House
£500 to CHATTERBOX
£500 to Hillside Animal Sanctuary
£500 to IRIS Fund
£500 to Northern Norfolk Resource Centre – rural

FINANCES
- Year 1997
- Income £143,388
- Grants £21,875

TRUSTEES M A F Leather, M Freeth

NOTES Also includes funds from the Hon Mrs H R Phelps Charitable Trust (now wound up)

HOW TO APPLY Write to the Secretary for application form. Closing date is beginning of March. No acknowledgement given to applications

WHO TO APPLY TO Brigadier and Mrs D V Phelps Charitable Trust, c/o KPMG, Holland Court, The Close, Norwich NR1 4DY

CC NO 249047   **ESTABLISHED** 1966

Pilkington Charities Fund

WHAT IS FUNDED Welfare, illness and disability; a high priority for funding is the C & A Pilkington Trust Fund, which benefits employees and ex-employees of Pilkington. Charities working in the fields of: accommodation and housing; infrastructure, support and development; churches; health; research into medicine, science and technology, and social science; advice and information an social issues; and community facilities and services will be considered

WHAT IS NOT FUNDED Applications from individuals cannot be considered

WHO CAN BENEFIT Local and national organisations benefiting: research workers; retired people; seafarers and fishermen; unemployed people; volunteers; at risk groups; carers; disabled people; those disadvantaged by poverty; disaster victims; homeless people; socially isolated people; victims of abuse, crime and domestic violence; victims of famine, man-made or natural disasters and war. There are no restrictions on the age or family situation of, or the disease or medical condition suffered by the beneficiaries

WHERE FUNDING CAN BE GIVEN UK with preference for Merseyside and St Helens; Overseas

TYPE OF GRANT Buildings, capital, core costs, one-off, project, research, recurring costs. Funding for more than three years will be considered

RANGE OF GRANTS £250–£30,000

SAMPLE GRANTS £30,000 to Intermediate Technology for research
£20,000 to Jefferiss Research Trust for research
£15,000 to St Helens and Knowsley Hospice for general purposes
£10,000 to NSPCC, St Helens for general purposes
£10,000 to Bath Inst, Rheumatic Diseases for general purposes
£10,000 to Human Ageing Trust for research
£10,000 to Liverpool Family Service Units for general purposes
£7,500 to St Helens Housing Association for general purposes
£4,000 to Liverpool School of Tropical Medicine for research
£4,000 to Childrens Society for general purposes

FINANCES
- Year 1996–97
- Income £487,000
- Grants £450,000

TRUSTEES A P Pilkington, Dr L H A Pilkington, Hon Mrs J M Jones,

HOW TO APPLY To the address under Who To Apply To in writing

WHO TO APPLY TO Pilkington Charities Fund, Roberts Legge & Co, 14 Chapel Lane, Formby, Liverpool L37 4DU *Tel* 01704 834490

CC NO 225911   **ESTABLISHED** 1964

The Harry and Mavis Pilkington Foundation for Arts and Leisure

WHAT IS FUNDED To promote literature, music and art, to advance education and to improve amenities in the Beneficial Area

Does the trust you have chosen match your needs? Haphazard applications waste postage and time

163

WHAT IS NOT FUNDED Grants are not made to individuals for educational purposes

WHERE FUNDING CAN BE GIVEN St Helens

TYPE OF GRANT One-off, recurring, running costs and start-up costs

FINANCES
- Year 1995–96
- Income £3,400
- Grants £2,100

TRUSTEES Lady Mavis Pilkington, Chair of the Grants Panel, Chair of Leisure, Chair of Policy and Resources of St Helens Metropolitan Borough Council

HOW TO APPLY To the Correspondent in writing. The Trustees meet every Autumn

WHO TO APPLY TO R L Hart, Secretary, Harry and Mavis Pilkington Foundation, Libraries & Heritage Div, Community Ed & Leisure Dept, Gamble Building, Victoria Square, St Helens, WA10 1DY *Tel* 01744 456990

CC NO 505754 **ESTABLISHED** 1961

■ The Charles Plimpton Foundation

WHAT IS FUNDED Welfare, the elderly and disabled

WHO CAN BENEFIT Individuals and institutions

WHERE FUNDING CAN BE GIVEN North West England

FINANCES
- Year 1994–95
- Income £4,200
- Grants £11,600

HOW TO APPLY To the Correspondent in writing

WHO TO APPLY TO Midland Bank Trust Company, The Charles Plimpton Foundation, Midland Personal Asset Management, Pearl Assurance House, 2 Derby Square, Liverpool L2 9XW

CC NO 519461 **ESTABLISHED** 1987

■ The Police Training Centre, Bruche, Charity

WHAT IS FUNDED Children and youth organisations for the provision of equipment and schools and paediatric departments of hospitals

WHO CAN BENEFIT Individuals and organisations

WHERE FUNDING CAN BE GIVEN North West England

FINANCES
- Year 1994–95
- Income £6,194
- Grants £9,700

HOW TO APPLY To the Correspondent in writing

WHO TO APPLY TO Mrs S J Evans, Committee Secretary, The Police Training Centre, Bruche, Charity, Police Training Centre, Greenway, Bruche, Warrington, Cheshire WA1 3EG

CC NO 511040 **ESTABLISHED** 1981

■ Preston Relief in Need Charity

WHAT IS FUNDED To relieve those in need, hardship or distress

WHO CAN BENEFIT Individuals and institutions

WHERE FUNDING CAN BE GIVEN Borough of Preston

TYPE OF GRANT One-off

FINANCES
- Year 1996–97
- Income £12,700
- Grants £4,562

TRUSTEES The Mayor, Rev Canon R Ladds, R Atkinson, Miss I Black, Mrs D E Chaloner, P R Metcalf, Miss M Rawcliffe, Mrs N Taylor, Mrs J Watson

WHO TO APPLY TO Town Clerk, Preston Relief in Need Charity, Preston Town Council, PO Box 10, Town Hall, Lancaster Road, Preston, Lancashire PR1 2RL *Tel* 01772 906115 *Fax* 01772 906195

CC NO 224848 **ESTABLISHED** 1977

■ The Albert Edward Proctor Charitable Trust

WHAT IS FUNDED Relief of pain and suffering; the young and elderly; and ecclesiastical organisations

WHO CAN BENEFIT Registered charities benefiting children, young adults and the elderly. Support is also given to at risk groups, those disadvantaged by poverty and socially isolated people. Support may be given to the homeless, immigrants and refugees. There is no restriction on the disease or medical condition suffered by the beneficiaries

WHERE FUNDING CAN BE GIVEN Blackpool area only

SAMPLE GRANTS £2,500 to NSPCC, Acorn Centre, Blackpool

FINANCES
- Year 1996
- Income £18,860
- Grants £2,500

TRUSTEES The Royal Bank of Scotland plc

WHO TO APPLY TO Royal Bank of Scotland plc, Trustees, The Albert Edward Proctor Charitable Trust, Preston Trustee Office, 2nd Floor, Guildhall House, Guildhall Street, Preston PR1 3NU

CC NO 295913   **ESTABLISHED** 1984

■ The Proven Family Trust

WHAT IS FUNDED Charities working in the fields of: holiday and respite accommodation; volunteer bureaux; religious and historic buildings; health; and community facilities and services. Other charitable purposes will be considered

WHAT IS NOT FUNDED No grants to individuals

WHO CAN BENEFIT Organisations benefiting children and older people; those in care, fostered and adopted. Support will be given to at risk groups, disabled people, those disadvantaged by poverty, homeless people, and victims of abuse and domestic violence

WHERE FUNDING CAN BE GIVEN Cumbria, Halton, Knowsley, Liverpool, St Helens, Sefton, Warrington, Wigan and Wirral

TYPE OF GRANT One-off

FINANCES
- Year 1998
- Income £37,180
- Grants £32,318

TRUSTEES G R Quigley, Ms D R Proven, M C Taxman, C J Worthington

NOTES The Trustees meet quarterly

HOW TO APPLY In writing at any time

WHO TO APPLY TO Dorothy Proven, Trustee, The Proven Family Trust, 35 The Mount, Papcastle, Cockermouth, Cumbria CA13 0JZ

CC NO 1050877   **ESTABLISHED** 1995

■ Provincial Grand Mark Lodge of Cumberland and Westmorland Benevolent Fund

WHAT IS FUNDED General charitable purposes for the benefit of poor and distressed widows and children or Masonic institutions and other charitable organisations

WHO CAN BENEFIT Masons

WHERE FUNDING CAN BE GIVEN Cumbria

TYPE OF GRANT Recurring

FINANCES
- Year 1996–97
- Income £5,224
- Grants £25,886

TRUSTEES W H Conchie, A F Sewell, J S Kelly, A Routledge

WHO TO APPLY TO A W Jackson, Provincial Grand Mark Lodge of Cumberland and Westmorland Benevolent Fund, Hawkshead Farm, 1 The Nook, Bolton Le Sands, Carnforth, Lancashire LA5 8DR *Tel* 01524 823432

CC NO 240264   **ESTABLISHED** 1965

■ Provincial Insurance Company Trust for Bolton

WHAT IS FUNDED General charitable purposes

WHAT IS NOT FUNDED Building projects, commercial ventures

WHO CAN BENEFIT Individuals and institutions in the Beneficial Area

WHERE FUNDING CAN BE GIVEN Bolton Metropolitan Borough

TYPE OF GRANT Recurring, but mainly one-off

SAMPLE GRANTS £500 to Little Lever Youth Club
£400 to Fernworth and District Special Needs
£350 to Bolton Youth Orchestra
£200 to Woodside Senior School
£150 to Bolton Women's Cricket

FINANCES
- Year 1994–95
- Income £9,159
- Grants £4,969

TRUSTEES D S Porter, LLB (Chairman), Mrs S Badland, L Gent, Mrs G Gerrard, D Sutcliffe, A Watson

HOW TO APPLY On offical application form

WHO TO APPLY TO Mrs S Riley, Provincial Insurance Company Trust for Bolton, c/o Fieldings Porter, Solicitors, Silverwell House, Silverwell Street, Bolton BL1 1PT

CC NO 222819   **ESTABLISHED** 1953

■ The Pye Christian Trust

WHAT IS FUNDED To support Christian evangelistic social and relief work in UK and abroad including: support of local (Lancaster area) churches; Christian outreach and education; missions and evangelists; diocesan boards; Free Church umbrella bodies; and local hospices

WHAT IS NOT FUNDED Campaigning; advocacy; arts; educational training; travel

WHO CAN BENEFIT Registered charities benefiting: people of all ages; Baptists; Christians; evangelists; methodists; those disadvantaged by poverty; and victims of abuse. Those suffering from: kidney disease; sight loss and terminal illness

WHERE FUNDING CAN BE GIVEN UK, mainly North Lancashire. Overseas also considered

TYPE OF GRANT Mainly recurring. Some capital, project and one-off

RANGE OF GRANTS £25–£1,000. Typical grants are £100

SAMPLE GRANTS £4,700 to The Methodist Church for local church expenses Home and Overseas mission, University Chaplaincy, Methodist Homes
£1,750 to The Baptist Church for local and mission work
£1,500 to North West Evangelical Trust for work (Christian) in schools
£1,200 to Tear Fund for overseas relief work
£1,000 to North West Kidney Research
£1,000 to Dayspring Trust for overseas missions
£1,000 to Operation Mobilisation for overseas missions
£800 to Active Service Trust providing services to missionaries
£750 to Water Aid for provision of clean water to villages in third world

FINANCES
- Year 1997
- Income £26,661
- Grants £33,215

TRUSTEES J A Pye, Mrs M Pye

NOTES Income likely to be considerably less for foreseeable future. Therefore grants will be restricted. Preference will be given to many of the causes already supported

HOW TO APPLY By letter with information. No initial telephone calls welcome. There are no application forms, guidelines or deadlines. Sae would be appreciated but not required

WHO TO APPLY TO J A Pye, The Pye Christian Trust, W & J Pye Ltd, Fleet Square, Lancaster, Lancashire LA1 1HA *Tel* 01524 597200

CC NO 501654   **ESTABLISHED** 1972

··

■ Queendeans Association

WHAT IS FUNDED General charitable purposes, including physically disabled, mentally disabled, blind, deaf and local children's charities

WHAT IS NOT FUNDED Anyone outside the area Where Funding Can Be Given should not apply, and such applications will not receive a response

WHO CAN BENEFIT Solely at the discretion of the Committee. Particularly organisations benefiting: children; disabled people; blind and deaf people

WHERE FUNDING CAN BE GIVEN Blackpool and Fylde areas only

TYPE OF GRANT The Trustees do not make cash grants but donate equipment and goods in lieu

RANGE OF GRANTS £214–£10,000

SAMPLE GRANTS £10,000 to Scanner Appeal for medical equipment
£4,135 to South Shore Hospital for a hoist and related equipment
£3,415 to Abbeyfield Home for decor
£2,000 to Guide Dogs for the Blind for two dogs
£1,865 to Schools Safety Campaign for posters, printing, etc
£1,816 to Cheshire Homes for a refrigerator
£1,395 to Highfurlong School for electrical education equipment
£1,153 to Trinity Hospice, the donation of a kiln
£729 to Children's Christmas Party for sweets, meals and entertainment
£500 to Stanley School for musical instruments

FINANCES
- Year 1997
- Income £24,513
- Grants £31,659

TRUSTEES The Association Committee

HOW TO APPLY At any time to the address under Who To Apply To in writing. Telephone contacts are neither accepted or permitted

WHO TO APPLY TO The Secretary, Queendeans Association, Queens Hotel, 469 South Promenade, Blackpool FY4 1AY

CC NO 236277   **ESTABLISHED** 1964

■ The Rainford Trust

WHAT IS FUNDED To consider applications from organisations that aim to enhance the quality of community life. To help initiate and promote special projects by charitable organisations which seek to provide new kinds of employment. To assist programmes whose objects are the provision of medical care, including holistic medicine, the advancement of education and the arts, and the improvement of the environment. Applications from religious bodies and individuals will be considered if they fall within the scope of these aims

WHAT IS NOT FUNDED Funding for the arts is restricted to St Helens only. Applications from individuals for grants for educational purposes will be considered only from applicants who are normally resident in St Helens

WHO CAN BENEFIT Individuals, charitable and voluntary organisations benefiting people of all ages. However, some restrictions on the social circumstances of, and disease and medical conditions suffered by the beneficiaries may be applied

WHERE FUNDING CAN BE GIVEN UK and overseas, with a preference for areas where Pilkington plc have works and offices, especially St Helens, Doncaster, Kings Norton (Birmingham) and St Asaph (Denbighshire)

TYPE OF GRANT Buildings, capital, core costs, project, research, salaries and start-up costs will be considered. Only exceptionally will grants be given in consecutive years, up to a maximum of three years

SAMPLE GRANTS £25,000 to St Helens and Knowsley Hospice towards the building fund
£12,955 to Citadel Arts Gallery, St Helens for revenue funding
£10,000 to Rainford Art Gallery, St Helens for improving the infrastructure of relocated gallery
£3,000 to St Helens Choral Society as two grants (£1,000 and £2,000) for revenue funding
£2,000 to Campaigners for the salary of a youth worker
£2,000 to Age Concern, St Helens towards a music project for the elderly
£2,000 to Allanson Street Primary School, St Helens for the redesign of the playground to make more environmentallly friendly
£2,000 to St Helens Music Centre Association for a summer school workshop

FINANCES
- Year 1997
- Income £157,912
- Grants £130,920

TRUSTEES R E Pilkington, Lady Pilkington, R G Pilkington, Mrs I Ratiu, I S Ratiu, A L Hopkins, Mrs J Graham

HOW TO APPLY At any time. Applications should be accompanied by latest accounts and cost data on projects for which funding is sought. Only successful applications will be acknowledged

WHO TO APPLY TO George Gaskell, Secretary, The Rainford Trust, c/o Pilkington plc, Prescot Road, St Helens WA10 3TT

CC NO 266157   **ESTABLISHED** 1973

■ The Ramsden Hall Trust

WHAT IS FUNDED General charitable purposes for the benefit of the inhabitants of Barrow-In-Furness

WHO CAN BENEFIT There are no restrictions on the age; professional and economic group; family situation; religion and culture; and social circumstances of; or disease or medical condition suffered by, the beneficiaries

WHERE FUNDING CAN BE GIVEN Barrow-in-Furness

WHO TO APPLY TO T J H Bodys, Borough Solicitor, The Ramsden Hall Trust, Town Hall, Duke Street, Barrow-in-Furness, Cumbria LA14 2LD

CC NO 1064867   **ESTABLISHED** 1997

■ Fanny Rapaport Charitable Trust

WHAT IS FUNDED General charitable purposes

WHAT IS NOT FUNDED No grants to individuals

WHO CAN BENEFIT Registered charities only. There are no restrictions on the age; professional and economic group; family situation; religion and culture; and social circumstances of; or disease or medical condition suffered by, the beneficiaries

WHERE FUNDING CAN BE GIVEN North West England favoured

SAMPLE GRANTS £17,000 to donations to 60 charities
£10,000 to the Heathlands Village
£4,250 to the Jewish Philanthropic Association for Israel and the Middle East
£4,000 to Morris Feinmann Homes Trust
£2,000 to Christie Hospital NHS Trust
£1,900 to Manchester Jewish Federation (incorporating Jewish Social Services and Manchester Jew's Benevolent Society)

Does the trust you have chosen match your needs? Haphazard applications waste postage and time

167

£1,000 to Brookvale towards caring for people with special needs
£1,000 to Community Security Trust
£1,000 to Delamere Forest School
£1,000 to Jewish Child's Day

FINANCES
- Year 1997
- Income £43,257
- Grants £44,150

TRUSTEES J S Fidler, N Marks

HOW TO APPLY Trustees hold meetings twice a year in March/April and September/October with cheques for donations issued shortly thereafter. If applicant does not receive a cheque in April/October, application may be assumed to be unsuccessful. No applications acknowledged. Copy of applicant's annual accounts not necessary (unless it forms part of a package)

WHO TO APPLY TO J S Fidler, Fanny Rapaport Charitable Trust, Kuit Steinart Levy, 3 St Mary's Parsonage, Manchester M3 2RD

CC NO 229406   **ESTABLISHED** 1963

■The Eleanor Rathbone Charitable Trust (formerly Miss E F Rathbone Charitable Trust)

WHAT IS FUNDED Preference to charities of which the Trust has special interest, knowledge or association. Interest in charities benefiting women and neglected causes, social work charities, arts and education

WHAT IS NOT FUNDED No grants to individuals or causes with a sectarian interest. No support is given to any activity which relieves a statutory authority of its obligations

WHO CAN BENEFIT Organisations benefiting: children and young adults; women; actors and entertainment professionals; musicians; textile workers and designers; students; writers and poets; at risk groups; those disadvantaged by poverty; and socially isolated people

WHERE FUNDING CAN BE GIVEN UK and overseas, but mainly Merseyside

RANGE OF GRANTS £100–£12,000

SAMPLE GRANTS £12,000 to EFR Holiday Fund
£10,000 to London School of Economic and Political Science
£8,600 to LCSS
£5,676 to Rathbone CI
£5,000 to RUKBA
£5,000 to Bryson House
£5,000 to NMGM
£4,000 to Womankind Worldwide
£4,000 to St Johns Playgroup
£3,750 to Sheila Kay Fund

FINANCES
- Year 1997
- Income £256,977
- Grants £224,004

TRUSTEES Dr B L Rathbone, W Rathbone Jnr, Miss J A Rathbone, P W Rathbone

HOW TO APPLY By letter

WHO TO APPLY TO Lindsay Keenan, The Eleanor Rathbone Charitable Trust, 3 Sidney Avenue, Wallasey, Merseyside L45 9JL

CC NO 233241   **ESTABLISHED** 1947

■The Elizabeth Rathbone Charity

WHAT IS FUNDED General charitable purposes, especially social work charities. Preference to charities of which the Trust has special interest, knowledge or association

WHAT IS NOT FUNDED No grants to individuals seeking support for second degrees

WHO CAN BENEFIT To benefit at risk groups, those disadvantaged by poverty and socially isolated people

WHERE FUNDING CAN BE GIVEN UK, mainly Merseyside

TYPE OF GRANT Mainly donations

RANGE OF GRANTS £85–£5,000

SAMPLE GRANTS £5,000 to National Museums and Galleries
£3,000 to Liverpool Family Service Unit
£3,000 to Glaxo Neurological
£2,500 to Rathbone CI
£2,000 to Research into Ageing
£2,000 to St Helen's and Knowsley Macmillan Nurse Appeal
£2,000 to Garston Adventure Playground
£2,000 to Macmillan Cancer Information Centre
£1,000 to Petrus Community Ltd
£1,000 to Blue Coat School

FINANCES
- Year 1997
- Income £91,607
- Grants £57,021

TRUSTEES S A Cotton, Ms S K Rathbone, Mrs V P Rathbone, R S Rathbone

HOW TO APPLY By letter

WHO TO APPLY TO The Elizabeth Rathbone Charity, Rathbone Bros & Co, Port of Liverpool Building, 4th Floor, Pier Head, Liverpool L3 1NW

CC NO 233240   **ESTABLISHED** 1921

■The Ravensdale Trust

WHAT IS FUNDED The Trustees' policy is to make donations to such charitable institutions as they believe the Settlor, the late Miss M Pilkington would have wished with particular reference to charities dealing with education, health, the arts, religion, social welfare and the environment

WHAT IS NOT FUNDED No grants to individuals

WHO CAN BENEFIT Registered charities benefiting: people of all ages; Christians, Church of England and Unitarians; at risk groups; disabled people; those disadvantaged by poverty; homeless people, victims of abuse, crime and domestic violence. There are few restrictions on the disease or medical condition suffered by the beneficiaries

WHERE FUNDING CAN BE GIVEN UK, with preference for Merseyside and the North West

TYPE OF GRANT Grants are made at the discretion of the Trustees, though generally one-off

RANGE OF GRANTS £100–£3,000

SAMPLE GRANTS £21,000 to Scarisbrick Girl Guides for building project
£3,000 to St Helens URC
£1,500 to YMCA Lakeside
£1,000 to Girl Guides Heritage Centre
£1,000 to Great Ormond Street Hospital
£1,000 to Liverpool Philharmonic
£1,000 to Save the Children Fund, St Helens
£1,000 to Youth Clubs UK
£1,000 to YMCA St Helens
£1,000 to Purcell School

FINANCES
- Year 1996–97
- Income £151,020
- Grants £100,900

TRUSTEES Dr L H A Pilkington, Mrs J M Wailing, Mrs J L Fagan

HOW TO APPLY By letter. No application form. No acknowledgement of applications. Donations are made in June and October of each year

WHO TO APPLY TO Mrs J L Fagan, The Ravensdale Trust, Brabner Holden Banks Wilson, 1 Dale Street, Liverpool L2 2ET *Tel* 0151-236 5821 *Fax* 0151-227 3185

CC NO 265165   **ESTABLISHED** 1973

■The Rawdon-Smith Trust

WHAT IS FUNDED The preservation of the area called the 'Bed of Coniston Water' for the benefit of the public; other charitable purposes including education, welfare, animal welfare, preservation of churches

WHAT IS NOT FUNDED Applications for grants for individuals will not be supported

WHO CAN BENEFIT Local organisations benefiting: children; young adults; students; at risk groups; those disadvantaged by poverty and socially isolated people

WHERE FUNDING CAN BE GIVEN Coniston and the areas surrounding Coniston Water

FINANCES
- Year 1996
- Income £94,394
- Grants £28,797

HOW TO APPLY To the address under Who To Apply To in writing. The Trustees meet to consider applications in February, May and November

WHO TO APPLY TO I Stancliffe, Secretary, The Rawdon-Smith Trust, Campbell House, Coniston, Cumbria LA21 8EF

CC NO 500355   **ESTABLISHED** 1964

■The Robert Rawstone Trust Fund

WHAT IS FUNDED Churches, clubs, community centres and youth groups in the area Where Funding Can Be Given

WHO CAN BENEFIT The community of Freckleton

WHERE FUNDING CAN BE GIVEN Freckleton

TYPE OF GRANT One-off grants

RANGE OF GRANTS £50–£1,600

SAMPLE GRANTS £3,150 to Rawstone Sports Centre
£1,600 to Freckleton C of E Church
£1,600 to Freckleton Methodist Church
£1,600 to Holy Family Church
£1,500 to Freckleton Village Hall
£1,000 to Freckleton Band

FINANCES
- Year 1995–96
- Income £17,370
- Grants £16,000

TRUSTEES 12 members of the Parish Council

HOW TO APPLY To the address under Who To Apply To in writing

WHO TO APPLY TO Mrs M Macdonald, Clerk, The Robert Rawstone Trust Fund, Harford, Preston New Road, Freckleton, Preston PR4 1HN *Tel* 01772 634871

CC NO 508396   **ESTABLISHED** 1979

■The John Rayner Charitable Trust

WHAT IS FUNDED The Charity was formed to apply its income and capital in whole or in part towards the furtherance of such charitable purposes as the Trustees' shall from time to time think fit. Currently the Trustees' policy is to distribute the income of the Trust annually.

The range of charities to benefit shall be at the Trustees discretion, with a preference for small charities in the UK to receive the largest donations. The Trustees will divide the annual income between a small number of charities, sometimes committing funds over a period of years. Charities working in the fields of: accommodation and housing; arts, culture and recreation; health; and community facilities and services. Support may also be given to voluntary and community organisations, special schools, and English as a second or foreign language

WHAT IS NOT FUNDED Applications from anyone other than a registered charity. No grants to individuals

WHO CAN BENEFIT Charities, especially those supporting children, medical research, youth projects, drug addiction. The Trust will also consider charities benefiting: people of all ages; ex-service and service people; musicians; seafarers and fishermen; unemployed people; and volunteers. Support may be given to carers; disabled people; those disadvantaged by poverty; homeless and socially isolated people; those living in urban areas and the victims of abuse, crime and domestic violence. There are few restrictions on the disease or medical condition suffered by the beneficiaries

WHERE FUNDING CAN BE GIVEN UK with preference for the North West of England, Yorkshire and Humberside, Hampshire, London, Swindon and Wiltshire

TYPE OF GRANT Single donations given annually in February/March for buildings, capital, core costs, one-off, project, research and start-up costs. Funding may be given for up to three years

SAMPLE GRANTS £5,000 to Live Music Now! North West towards sponsoring concerts in special schools
£5,000 to The Samaritans for general purposes and a project for the aged
£4,000 to Inspire for work with patients with spinal injuries
£4,000 to Whizz-Kidz towards mobility for disabled children
£3,000 to Demand for design and manufacture for disability
£3,000 to ICRF for cancer research
£2,000 to Merseyside Drugs Council working with drug addiction
£2,000 to Headway for people suffering from head injuries
£2,000 to Children Nationwide for intensive care cots
£2,000 to Guildhall School of Music and Drama for small concerts and a bursary

FINANCES
- Year 1997
- Income £39,000
- Grants £37,000

TRUSTEES Mrs J Wilkinson and others

HOW TO APPLY To the address under Who To Apply To

WHO TO APPLY TO Mrs J Wilkinson, The John Rayner Charitable Trust, 37 Burns Road, London SW11 5GX *Tel* 0171-223 2779 *Fax* 0171-223 2779

CC NO 802363   **ESTABLISHED** 1989

■The Nathaniel Rayner Trust Fund

WHAT IS FUNDED The promotion of evangelical Christianity and also general charitable purposes, particularly the advancement of Christian religion and Christian religious buildings

WHAT IS NOT FUNDED No grants for education, scholarships or expeditions

WHO CAN BENEFIT Registered charities and Christian organisations helping children, young adults, older people, clergy, Baptists, Church of England, Christians, Evangelists and Methodists

WHERE FUNDING CAN BE GIVEN Liverpool

RANGE OF GRANTS £200–£3,000

SAMPLE GRANTS £3,375 to Allerton United Reformed Church
£3,000 to St Columbia United Reformed Church
£3,000 to Lancashire and Cheshire Baptist Association
£2,500 to Highfield United Reformed Church
£1,500 to Northern College
£1,500 to Council for World Mission
£1,125 to St Georges United Reformed Church
£1,000 to Maghill Baptist Church
£1,000 to Dovedale Road Baptist Church
£1,000 to Laird Street Baptist Church

FINANCES
- Year 1996–97
- Income £41,166
- Grants £32,000

TRUSTEES C G Dickie, D E G Faragher, W B Howarth, G C Lindsay, K W Paterson, Miss M Proven, J R Watson

HOW TO APPLY To the address under Who To Apply To in writing

WHO TO APPLY TO G Barrie Marsh, Secretary, The Nathaniel Rayner Trust Fund, Drury House, 19 Water Street, Liverpool L2 0RP *Tel* 0151-236 8989

CC NO 226319   **ESTABLISHED** 1965

■The Red Rose Community Trust

WHAT IS FUNDED General charitable purposes at the discretion of the Trustees

WHO CAN BENEFIT Individuals and organisations

WHERE FUNDING CAN BE GIVEN Area of the franchise of Red Rose Independent Radio Station or the immediate neighbourhood

FINANCES
- Year 1995–96
- Grants £7,031
- Income £9,704

TRUSTEES Pamela Yates, John H Gilmore, Mark Matthews, Domonic Baker, Iiyas Patel

WHO TO APPLY TO Miss H I Fisher, The Red Rose Community Trust, PO Box 301, St Pauls Square, Preston PR1 1YE

CC NO 702300   **ESTABLISHED** 1989

■Riverside Charitable Trust Limited

WHAT IS FUNDED Relief for the poor, aged, the sick and infirm and for educational and other charitable purposes, including health care and health buildings and facilities

WHAT IS NOT FUNDED Political in any form debarred

WHO CAN BENEFIT Individuals and organisations benefiting people of all ages and those who are retired, including those disadvantaged by poverty. There is no restriction on the disease or medical condition suffered by the beneficiaries. Priority to old age pensioners of the Companies that raised the cash and shares. Minimal hard cases as affected by redundancy, and youth education

WHERE FUNDING CAN BE GIVEN Lancashire

TYPE OF GRANT Recurring costs

RANGE OF GRANTS £100–£2,000

SAMPLE GRANTS £8,000 to British Heart Foundation
£7,750 to Cancer Research – Macmillan Fund
£6,000 to Cancer Research
£6,000 to Rossendale Valley Mencap
£6,000 to St Mary's Hospice
£5,000 to Derwen College for the Disabled
£5,000 to Paramedic Bike Appeal Fund
£4,000 to Rossendale Society for the Blind
£3,500 to RNLI
£3,000 to Cancer Chemotherapy

FINANCES
- Year 1997
- Grants £180,026
- Income £185,720

TRUSTEES I B Dearing, Mrs J A Davidson, F Drew, H Francis, Mrs A Higginson, B J Lynch, G Maden

HOW TO APPLY Prefer a request in writing initially

WHO TO APPLY TO Barry J Lynch, Chairman, Riverside Charitable Trust Limited, 20 Dobbin Close, Rossendale, Lancashire BB4 7TH

CC NO 264015   **ESTABLISHED** 1972

■The Rochdale Fund for Relief in Sickness

WHAT IS FUNDED Health and welfare charities benefiting the people of Rochdale

WHO CAN BENEFIT Individuals and organisations benefiting sick and disabled people and those disadvantaged by poverty. There is no restriction on the disease or medical condition suffered by the beneficiaries

WHERE FUNDING CAN BE GIVEN Rochdale

RANGE OF GRANTS £150–£2,802 to organisations

SAMPLE GRANTS £2,802 to Innes School
£1,000 to Cancer Relief Macmillan Fund
£1,000 to Turning Point
£750 to Crossroads Care Attendant Scheme
£750 to Riding for the Disabled
£500 to Winged Fellowship, Southport
£500 to Petrus Community
£500 to Marie Curie Memorial Foundation
£500 to Multiple Sclerosis Society
£500 to Family Service Unit

FINANCES
- Year 1997
- Grants £13,973
- Income £35,657

TRUSTEES J G D Chapple (Chairman), Mrs H E Collins, E T Gartside, J M Porritt, Mrs P S Porritt, Mrs B A Lois Rigg, J M Rigg, A Shackleton

HOW TO APPLY To the address under Who To Apply To in writing

WHO TO APPLY TO The Clerk, The Rochdale Fund for Relief in Sickness, Jackson Brierley Hudson Stoney, Old Parsonage, 2 St Mary's Gate, Rochdale OL16 1AP

CC NO 222652   **ESTABLISHED** 1964

■The Mrs L D Rope Third Charitable Settlement (351)

WHAT IS FUNDED Relief of poverty, advancement of education, advancement of religion and other charitable purposes

WHAT IS NOT FUNDED For unsolicited applications the Trust is unable to fund: (a) new projects or individuals working overseas; (b) charities considered to be relatively wealthy; (c) areas which are the responsibility of statutory bodies; (d) core

Does the trust you have chosen match your needs? Haphazard applications waste postage and time

171

funding for salaries; (e) office running costs; (f) fundraising and professional fees; (g) capital grants; (h) medical research, health care or palliative care; (i) students; (j) fees for private education; (k) environmental and animal welfare appeals; (l) grants for the repayment of debts

WHO CAN BENEFIT For unsolicited applications, charities who work at grass roots level within their community, generally small in size, that are little catered for from other sources, or those that are based in particularly deprived areas. Charities with a large and committed volunteer base and those that have relatively low administration costs, in terms of staff salaries. There are few restrictions on the professional and economic group, religion and culture, and social circumstances of the beneficiaries. There is no restriction on their age or family situation

WHERE FUNDING CAN BE GIVEN North east and north west England; Suffolk; and the London Boroughs of Barking and Dagenham, Brent, Camden, Hackney, Haringey, Havering, Hounslow, Lambeth, Lewisham,Newham, Southwark, and Tower Hamlets. Also Northern Ireland, Wales and Glasgow

TYPE OF GRANT For unsolicited requests with no connection to the Trustees or the principal area Where Funding Can Be Given, grants are usually one-off and small scale. Also interest free loans, project and start-up costs. Funding is given for one year or less

RANGE OF GRANTS £100–£750

FINANCES
- Year 1997
- Income £461,773
- Grants £437,237

TRUSTEES Jeremy P W Heal, Crispin M Rope, Mrs Lucy D Rope

NOTES A summary of the charitable purposes of the Trust are available on request

HOW TO APPLY By letter, as application forms are not provided at present; although it is hoped to develop some in the near future. See below for further details

WHO TO APPLY TO C M Rope, The Mrs L D Rope Third Charitable Settlement, Crag Farm, Boyton, Woodbridge, Suffolk IP12 3LH

CC NO 290533   **ESTABLISHED** 1984

Commentary

The Mrs L D Rope Third Charitable Settlement is a general charitable Trust, established under a Trust Deed dated 22 October 1984, by the Founder, Mrs Lucy D Rope. Although a general charitable trust, the Trust takes regard of the wishes and directions of the Founder, who has indicated the areas in which she wishes the Trust to give support. The Trustees have a keen

interest in helping people in the local area (and in the UK and overseas), where help is most needed, and, in particular, those who find it hard to get funding. The work of the Trust is divided into distinct categories. Firstly, it initiates, supports and pursues certain specific charitable projects selected by the Founder. Secondly, it approves grants to unsolicited applications that fall within the Founder's stated objectives and comply with the Trust's grant-making policies.

According to the Founder's wishes, for self-initiated projects, the Trust makes grants to organisations whose work fall into one or more of four main areas: advancement of religion; advancement of education; relief of poverty; and public and other charitable purposes. For grants for the relief of poverty, causes and individuals are supported when they are personally known to the Founder, members of her family or the other Trustees. Particularly favoured are projects in the UK and the third world who are little catered for by other charities or government and other authorities' grants and benefits. Also supported are those in particularly deprived areas. For grants for the advancement of education, the Trust is keen to support Catholic schools in the general area of Ipswich, a proposed airship museum and projects relating to the interaction of mathematics and physical science with philosophy. For the advancement of religion, the Trust is keen to support the Roman Catholic religion and ecumenical work, both generally and for specific institutions connected historically with the families of William Oliver Jolly and Alice Jolly (the parents of the Founder) and their descendants. General charitable purposes are particularly supported in the south east Suffolk region, and especially in the Parish of Kesgrave and its surrounding areas, including Ipswich. Many grants made fall into more than one of these categories, with the relief of poverty being the most frequently met. Approximately 75 per cent of the Trust's income is directed to charitable projects where the Trust has either initiated the work or where a long-standing relationship over a number of years gave rise to new or continued assistance, but the remaining 25 per cent is open to general application.

For unsolicited applications, the following areas are most likely to be supported: (a) helping people who struggle to live on very little income, including the homeless; (b) helping people who live in deprived inner city and rural areas of the UK, particularly young people who lack the opportunities that may be available elsewhere; (c) charities in the Trust's immediate local area of south east Suffolk; (d) helping to support family life; (e) helping disabled people; (f) Roman Catholic charities and ecumenical projects.

When considering applications, the Trust is keen to support causes and organisations that incur

172

Think carefully about every application. Is it justified?

very low administration expenses, or who are unable to obtain suitable assistance from normal sources or other state or charitable support. Groups able to multiply the value of the original donation received from the Trust are favoured, as are those who are based in particularly deprived areas or have a significant reliance on volunteers. The Trust will occasionally fund individuals, particularly those who are struggling to live on little income. It is very keen to support organisations working at 'grass-root' level within their communities. The Trust does not appear to have any scales of preference within these criteria, it is simply that any application should fall within one or more of these areas and situations, in order to be eligible for funding.

The Trust has certain strict restrictions concerning unsolicited applications. It is unable to help new projects or individuals working overseas, except, very rarely, in circumstances where the applicant has a proven long-term connection to the Trust. This is due to the difficulties involved in the supervision and monitoring of overseas grants. The Trust's overseas giving is now directed through carefully selected charities with which it has had long-standing relationships. Charities considered to be relatively wealthy in comparison with others and that already attract broad support throughout the UK, such as national charities, are not supported because the Trust prefers to support small charities working at 'grass-root' level within their communities and those that have difficulty in obtaining funding from other sources. The larger, wealthier and better known an applicant is, the less likely it is to be supported. Grants are not made to charities concerned with medical research, health care or palliative care. Applications from students, especially post-graduates, are not considered, except occasionally in the case of foreign post-graduate students involved in scientific research, who, for lack of a modest amount, may jeopardise an otherwise considerable educational investment. Only Roman Catholic schools in the immediate locality of the Trust can be considered. Fees for private education are not met. Environmental and animal welfare appeals are not funded; neither are appeals for work in the arts.

Matched funding for National Lottery, statutory or European bids are not offered. On a much smaller scale, causes where a donation may be likely to encourage other donors to come forward, ie some degree of 'added value' is inherent, may be supported. Although grants are made to individuals, grants for the repayments of debts are not made.

The funding policies of the Trust are set by the Founder, who indicates where her priorities for support lie. There have been no major changes to policy recently, but there has been a shift of emphasis from pure grant making towards the aim of initiating projects themselves and seeing them through to achievement. Additionally, there has been a minor change of policy, which requires more resources to be devoted to making visits to charities, in particular local ones, who apply for or receive grants, to ensure that the best use is made of the funds they have available.

In the future the Trust is keen to continue initiating its own projects, rather than purely making grants to organisations that apply to them for funding. Several projects are now underway, and some are becoming close to completion. Some require very long planning periods, such as a proposed new Roman Catholic Primary school and new sports and youth facilities in Kesgrave. The Trust also intends to give priority to longer term objectives rather than short term advantages. Projects to be supported in the immediate future include: public benefit initiatives in the Ipswich area; the Science/Human Dimension Project; and St Stephen's Hospital, Uganda.

The Trust is not prepared to replace statutory funding. The Trust is not keen to participate in co-funding, or match-funding, for example with the National Lottery Charities Board, because they prefer to keep the initiative themselves.

The Trust prefers to make one-off payments which are usually small scale, between £100 and £750, for unsolicited applications, particularly those that fall outside the main areas Where Funding Can Be Given and that have no connections with the Trustees. Much larger grants are made, to a maximum of £90,000 in 1997, but these are generally to organisations to which the Trust already has a link. Of the 12 largest grants made in 1997, five were initiated by the Trust itself. Interest free loans are frequently made, and in 1997, loans were made to the value of £51,665, to a variety of recipients. Recurrent grants are made to self-initiated projects, but seldom as a result of an unsolicited application. If such a situation was to arise, each year's payment would be subject to a strict review and evaluation by the Trust. Smaller charities may be helped with infrastructure costs, such as office equipment costs, but building costs are never supported.

Applications from charities should be by concise letter (preferably one side of A4) explaining the main details of the request. The letter should include the most recent accounts and a budgeted breakdown of the sum to be raised. The Trust also needs to know whether other sources have been applied to and whether these have been successful. Also included should be a list of the trustees and a daytime telephone number. Applications from individuals should be by concise letter, explaining what is needed and why it is thought that the Trust can help. It is helpful if the letter can include details of household income (including benefits) and expenses. A daytime telephone number should be included if possible and the name of at least one personal referee. The letter does not need to be typed and each one is carefully read.

All applications are acknowledged as quickly as possible, and unsuccessful applicants receive a standardised slip. Rejected applications cannot be reconsidered within three years of the original decision. Applications that are to be considered in more detail are then investigated, firstly by telephone and written enquiries, and in some cases visits are made. The Trustees will then consider all appropriate applications, and all grants are approved by the Founder. The grant making committee meets regularly throughout the year, so applications may be sent at any time

SAMPLE GRANTS
The top ten grants made in 1997 were:
£90,000 to Downing College, Cambridge as a major instalment of a grant to endow fellowship
£53,000 to East Anglian Roman Catholic Diocese for the expansion of voluntary aided schools in the Ipswich area
£40,000 to CAFOD for their work with overseas poverty
£39,037 to Science/Human Dimension Project for its work in improving public awareness of important philosophical and general implications of developments in science and mathematics
£35,000 to Worth Abbey for the advancement of religion
£20,000 to Shelter
£15,868 to St Stephen's Hospital, Uganda, for a community health care project
£15,000 to Kesgrave Scouts as the first instalment of funding to assist establishment of the Scouts in their own headquarters
£7,500 to St James' Roman Catholic Church, Ipswich, towards refurbishment of the church, because the congregation is likely to increase due to a large building development
£6,300 to Society of St Vincent de Paul for its work with the poorer members of society.
However, it should be noted that all but two of the above are self-initiated projects

■ Ian Rose Charitable Foundation

This trust did not respond to CAF's request to amend its entry and, by 30 June 1998, CAF's researchers did not find financial records for later than 1995 on its file at the Charity Commission. Trusts are legally required to submit annual accounts to the Charity Commission under section 42 of the Charities Act 1993

WHAT IS FUNDED Welfare, general charitable purposes

WHO CAN BENEFIT There are no restrictions on the age; professional and economic group; family situation; religion and culture; and

social circumstances of; or disease or medical condition suffered by, the beneficiaries

WHERE FUNDING CAN BE GIVEN Blackpool, the Fylde coast area

TRUSTEES K Philbin, I P Rose, J D Rose

HOW TO APPLY To the address below in writing

WHO TO APPLY TO I P Rose, Trustee, Ian Rose Charitable Foundation, 49 Newton Drive, Blackpool, Lancashire FY3 8EW

CC NO 1017911   **ESTABLISHED** 1993

■ Rotary Club of Alderley Edge and Bollin Valley Trust Fund

WHAT IS FUNDED The relief of the poor and needy, or other charitable purposes, institutions, societies or objects

WHAT IS NOT FUNDED Grants are not usually given to individuals

WHO CAN BENEFIT Local clubs, organisations and institutions

WHERE FUNDING CAN BE GIVEN Wilmslow, Alderley Edge and worldwide

TYPE OF GRANT Buildings, capital, core costs, one-off, recurring costs, running costs and start-up costs

SAMPLE GRANTS £1,500 to Barnardos
£250 to Sight Savers
£200 to Water Aid
£25 to Dunblane Fund

FINANCES
- Year 1995–96   • Income £9,868
- Grants £8,499

TRUSTEES Roderick A Moody, Stanley B Horner, Michael Barker, Michael K Batchelor

HOW TO APPLY Applications are acknowledged

WHO TO APPLY TO M K Batchelor, Rotary Club of Alderley Edge and Bollin Valley Trust Fund, 41 Knutsford Road, Wilmslow, Cheshire SK9 6JB *Tel* 01625 524262

CC NO 1031153   **ESTABLISHED** 1983

■ The Rotary Club of New Mills Marple and District Benevolent Fund

WHAT IS FUNDED To benefit the poor and needy, or other charitable purposes, institutions, societies or objects as the club directs

WHO CAN BENEFIT Individuals and organisations

WHERE FUNDING CAN BE GIVEN Local, national and international

TYPE OF GRANT Cash

Have you read How to use the directory *on page xvi?*

SAMPLE GRANTS £2,000 to Manchester Royal
Infirmary Leukaemia Fund
£1,000 to Scouts
£500 to BBC Children in Need
£400 to British Diabetic Association
£400 to local Red Cross
£380 to Save the Children Fund

FINANCES
- Year 1996–97
- Income £9,555
- Grants £6,860

WHO TO APPLY TO Dr Edward H Thomas, Rotary
Club of New Mills Marple and District
Benevolent Fund, 2 Cranford Gardens, Marple,
Stockport, Cheshire SK6 6QQ *Tel* 0161-
427 3500

CC NO 501455   **ESTABLISHED** 1972

■ The Rotary Club of Preston South Trust Fund

WHAT IS FUNDED The relief of the poor and
needy, or other charitable purposes,
institutions, societies or objects as the club
directs

WHAT IS NOT FUNDED No commercial enterprises

WHO CAN BENEFIT Charitable purposes,
institutions, societies

WHERE FUNDING CAN BE GIVEN South Ribble

TYPE OF GRANT Recurring

SAMPLE GRANTS £2,000 to Emmaus Community
£1,300 to St Catherine's Hospice
£900 to Calvert Trust
£100 to Operation Raleigh
£25 to Cancer Help

FINANCES
- Year 1995–96
- Income £5,665
- Grants £6,363

TRUSTEES John Dent, Robin Oatridge, Alan
Atkinson

WHO TO APPLY TO Christopher Thomas, Rotary
Club of Preston South Trust Fund, 6–8 Watkin
Lane, Lostock Hall, Preston, Lancashire
PR5 5RA *Tel* 01772 334738

CC NO 512983   **ESTABLISHED** 1982

■ The Charitable Fund of the Rotary Club of Wallasey

WHAT IS FUNDED Community services, animal
welfare and other charitable purposes

WHO CAN BENEFIT Individuals and organisations

WHERE FUNDING CAN BE GIVEN Wirral

TYPE OF GRANT One-off

SAMPLE GRANTS £500 to Wallasey YMCA
£500 to Manor Child Care Centre
£250 to Wirral Solvent Abuse
£150 to WRVS

FINANCES
- Year 1995–96
- Income £8,804
- Grants £12,451

TRUSTEES President, Vice President, Secretary
and Treasurer of the Wallasey Rotary Club

WHO TO APPLY TO David Foster, Charitable Fund
of Rotary Club of Wallasey, 23 Warrenhurst,
Montpellier Crescent, New Brighton, Wirral
L45 9JZ *Tel* 0151-639 6127

CC NO 515323   **ESTABLISHED** 1984

■ Liverpool Round Table No 8 Charitable Trust

WHAT IS FUNDED General charitable purposes

WHO CAN BENEFIT Individuals and institutions

WHERE FUNDING CAN BE GIVEN Liverpool

TYPE OF GRANT Recurring

FINANCES
- Year 1994–95
- Income £8,527
- Grants £365

WHO TO APPLY TO A Bayliss, Liverpool Round
Table Charitable Trust, Nigel Packer and
Company, 3rd Floor, Royal Liver Buildings, Pier
Head, Liverpool L3 1JH

CC NO 505930   **ESTABLISHED** 1977

■ Maghull Round Table No 318 Charitable Fund

WHAT IS FUNDED General charitable purposes

WHO CAN BENEFIT Charitable purposes at the
Trustees discretion

WHERE FUNDING CAN BE GIVEN Maghull and
district

SAMPLE GRANTS £1,218 for minibus insurance
£500 to Lydiate Guides and Brownies
£280 to Maghull Christmas tree
£100 to Venture Scouts

FINANCES
- Year 1995–96
- Income £4,073
- Grants £2,627

WHO TO APPLY TO J D Sergison, Maghull Round
Table Charitable Fund, 9 Fernbank Drive,
Netherton L30 7RG

CC NO 1048508   **ESTABLISHED** 1995

Does the trust you have chosen match your needs? Haphazard applications waste postage and time

175

■ Sale and District Round Table Charitable Trust Fund

WHAT IS FUNDED General charitable purposes

WHO CAN BENEFIT Charitable purposes at the Trustees discretion

WHERE FUNDING CAN BE GIVEN Sale and district

SAMPLE GRANTS £1,000 to Wythenshawe Hospital
£451 for football trip
£335 to Smoke Watch
£50 to British Red Cross

FINANCES
● Year 1995–96   ● Income £9,926
● Grants £2,767

TRUSTEES Michael Merriman, Simon Harrod, Charles Gaunt

WHO TO APPLY TO C K Varley, Sale and District Round Table Charitable Trust Fund, 9 Henley Drive, Timperley, Altrincham, Cheshire WA15 6RY

CC NO 1048761   **ESTABLISHED** 1995

■ The Rowan Charitable Trust (304)

WHAT IS FUNDED Overseas: agriculture; community development; health; education; environment; human rights; and fair trade. UK: housing and homelessness; social and community care; education; employment; after-care; welfare rights; community development; and environmental improvement

WHAT IS NOT FUNDED No individuals, buildings or building works, or academic research; charitable organisations only

WHO CAN BENEFIT Organisations benefiting children and young adults, medical professionals, students, teachers, and unemployed people. Also carers, disabled people, homeless people, those living in rural areas and blind people

WHERE FUNDING CAN BE GIVEN Overseas – Africa, Asia, Middle East, Pacific Islands, South and Central America; and UK, particularly Merseyside

TYPE OF GRANT One-off, recurring

FINANCES
● Year 1996   ● Income £301,026
● Grants £504,965

TRUSTEES A Baillie, Mrs H Russell, D D Mason

PUBLICATIONS Annual Report and Accounts, Guidelines for Applicants

HOW TO APPLY In writing to the Correspondent. No application forms are issued. Guidelines are issued. Deadline for applications for consideration at January and August Trustees' meetings in December and July respectively

WHO TO APPLY TO The Correspondent, The Rowan Charitable Trust, 9 Greyfriars Road, Reading, Berkshire RG1 1JG *Tel* 0118-959 7111 *Fax* 0118-960 7700

CC NO 242678   **ESTABLISHED** 1964

Commentary

The Rowan Charitable Trust was established in 1964 for general charitable purposes. The Trust's focus is on projects, both overseas and in the UK, which will benefit disadvantaged groups and communities. It will also support advocacy and challenges to powerful economic forces on behalf of the poor or powerless. Two-thirds of the funds available are given as grants each year to charitable organisations overseas; the remaining third is allocated within the UK, with a strong preference for Merseyside.

Overseas, the Trust focuses on projects in the fields of: agriculture – crop and livestock production and settlement schemes; community development – appropriate technology and village industries; health – preventative medicine, water supplies and blindness; education – adult education and materials; environmental – protecting and sustaining ecological systems at risk; human rights – of women, children, and the disabled; fair trade – for primary producers and workers. Overseas project proposals should involve the local community in the planning and implementation; invest in people through training and enabling; have a holistic concern for all aspects of life and a respect for local cultural patterns and beliefs.

In the UK, the Trust supports projects for: housing and homelessness; social and community care; education; employment; after-care; welfare rights; community development; and environment improvement. UK project proposals should demonstrate: an element of self-help; user and community involvement in the planning and delivery of the project; a multi-disciplinary approach; and emphasis on empowerment.

The Trust's funding policies are set by the Trustees. The Trust is prepared to give core-funding, but does not fund statutory bodies, replace statutory funding, cover building costs or make loans. The Trust rarely funds a project in its entirety, participating instead in co-funding with other charitable organisations and the National Lottery.

The Trust makes one-off grants and recurring grants; recurring grants are made to a few large, national organisations and development agencies, including: Christian Aid, UNICEF,

Intermediate Technology, and Barnados. It also gives smaller grants to much smaller organisations and locally-based projects.

Guidelines for applicants are available from the Correspondent. Applications should be made in writing to the Correspondent and should include a brief description of the project (two sides of A4 paper), a budget and the latest Annual Report and Accounts. Unsuccessful applicants will only be notified if an sae is enclosed.

The Trustees meet to allocate grants in February and August each year. Reports are requested from organisations which have received grants

SAMPLE GRANTS
The top ten grants made in 1996 were:
£52,000 to Intermediate Technology
£50,000 to Christian Aid
£20,000 to UNICEF
£20,000 to Personal Service Society
£15,000 to Barnados
£12,500 to Tools for Self Reliance
£10,000 to Lepra
£10,000 to UK Foundation for the South Pacific
£10,000 to Family Service Units
£10,000 to The Children's Society

■The Christopher Rowbotham Charitable Trust

WHAT IS FUNDED To support selected national charities with branches in the North West and North East, and local charities, as stated below. Priority given to smaller charities with low overheads. This Trust will consider funding: infrastructure and development; health care; health education; education and training; and community services

WHAT IS NOT FUNDED Registered charities only. Applications from individuals, including students, are ineligible. No grants made in response to general appeals from large national organisations. No grants overseas. No grants for capital projects

WHO CAN BENEFIT Organisations benefiting: children; young adults; older people; ex-service and service people; medical professionals; retired people; seafarers and fishermen; disabled sportsmen and women; teachers and governesses; unemployed people; and volunteers' There are few restrictions on the social circumstances of, or disease and medical condition suffered by the beneficiaries

WHERE FUNDING CAN BE GIVEN NE England, NW England

TYPE OF GRANT Capital, core costs, one-off, recurring costs, running costs and start-up costs. Funding can be given for up to and over three years. Salaries never considered

RANGE OF GRANTS £100 to £750. Largest grant £3,500

SAMPLE GRANTS £3,500 to Shiplake College
£2,000 to Winged Fellowship for general purposes and respite holidays
£2,000 to Royal Commonwealth Society for the Blind for eye treatment programmes
£1,000 to RUKBA for annuities for retired professionals
£1,000 to Royal Star and Garter Home for disabled ex-service men and women
£1,000 to Instant Muscle for helping unemployed gain employment
£1,000 to Disabled Living Foundation for aids to inform and advise the disabled
£750 to Calvert Trust, Kielder for activities and respite care
£750 to Calvert Trust, Keswick for holidays
£750 to Fairbridge, Tyne and Wear to help young disadvantaged people gain further learning

FINANCES
- Year 1997
- Income £50,000
- Grants £48,000

TRUSTEES Mrs C A Jackson, Mrs E J Wilkinson

NOTES Appeals from the North East should be sent to Mrs Jackson at address below. Appeals from the North West should be sent to Mrs Wilkinson: PO Box 43, Bolton, Lancashire BL1 5EZ

HOW TO APPLY At any time. Trustees meet annually in May. No applications acknowledged. Initial telephone calls are not welcome. There are no application forms, guidelines or deadlines, and no sae is required

WHO TO APPLY TO Mrs C A Jackson, The Christopher Rowbotham Charitable Trust, 18 Northumberland Square, North Shields NE30 1PX

CC NO 261991   **ESTABLISHED** 1970

■The Rowley Trust

WHAT IS FUNDED Charities working for the benefit of women and girls

WHO CAN BENEFIT Individuals, registered charities and organisations benefiting women and girls. There are no restrictions on the age; professional and economic group; family situation; religion and culture; and social circumstances of; or disease or medical condition suffered by, the beneficiaries

WHERE FUNDING CAN BE GIVEN Staffordshire and adjacent counties

FINANCES
- Year 1997
- Income £52,413
- Grants £40,811

HOW TO APPLY Application form and guidelines can be obtained from the Clerk of the Trust, J G Langford

WHO TO APPLY TO J G Langford, The Clerk, The Rowley Trust, 25 Greengate Street, Stafford ST16 2HU *Tel* 01785 252377

CC NO 508630   **ESTABLISHED** 1988

■ The Royal Botanical & Horticultural Society of Manchester and the Northern Counties

WHAT IS FUNDED Financial assistance to local gardens or projects of horticultural interest and local horticultural societies in the North West

WHO CAN BENEFIT Horticultural societies, shows and gardens of horticultural interest

WHERE FUNDING CAN BE GIVEN North West

TYPE OF GRANT Cash payment towards prize money or specific expenditure

RANGE OF GRANTS £25–£2,000

FINANCES
- Year 1997
- Income £17,831
- Grants £16,560

TRUSTEES Incorporated Governors of the Society

HOW TO APPLY Annual by 31 October each year in writing

WHO TO APPLY TO A Pye, MA, FCA, The Royal Botanical & Horticultural Society, PO Box 500, 201 Deansgate, Manchester M60 2AT *Tel* 0161-455 8380 *Fax* 0161-829 3803

CC NO 226683   **ESTABLISHED** 1827

■ Runcorn Community Action Trust

WHAT IS FUNDED General charitable purposes for the benefit of the community, in particular, the relief of poverty, distress, sickness and the protection of health and the advancement of education

WHO CAN BENEFIT Organisations benefiting children, young adults, students, at risk groups, those disadvantaged by poverty and socially isolated people. There is no restriction on the disease or medical condition suffered by the beneficiaries

WHERE FUNDING CAN BE GIVEN Borough of Halton South of the River Mersey

RANGE OF GRANTS Below £1,000–£8,000

SAMPLE GRANTS £8,000 to Brookvale Residents Association
£5,100 to Halton Disability Information Service
£3,216 to The Park CP School
£2,812 to Runcorn and District Mencap
£2,800 to Halton Age Concern
£2,500 to Priory Credit Union
£1,580 to Brookvale United Junior FC
£1,500 to Runcorn Under 8's
£1,222 to Brookvale Community Centre Management Board
£1,140 to Hallwood Park Junior Club

FINANCES
- Year 1997
- Income £73,234
- Grants £59,530

TRUSTEES Rev D Felix, Rev T Barker, Ms D Houghton, B Porter, W Thompson, Ms N Rimmer, Ms E Gwynne, J Patten, D Thomas, J McDonagh, Ms N Hardy, Mrs J Turner

WHO TO APPLY TO Ms J Wood, Runcorn Community Action Trust, 1 Great Ashfield, Hough Green, Widnes, Cheshire WA8 4SA

CC NO 1046581   **ESTABLISHED** 1995

■ Rycroft Children's Fund

WHAT IS FUNDED Welfare of children and young adults

WHO CAN BENEFIT Individuals and organisations benefiting children and young adults

WHERE FUNDING CAN BE GIVEN Cheshire, Derbyshire, Greater Manchester, Lancashire, Staffordshire, South and West Yorkshire. Preference for those resident in the cities of Manchester, Salford and the Borough of Trafford

FINANCES
- Year 1996–97
- Income £41,275
- Grants £39,620

TRUSTEES C P Lees-Jones (Chair), I H D Brown, Mrs J Dixon, Miss M R Mason, A Maddocks, Dr A Robinson

HOW TO APPLY To the address under Who To Apply To in writing

WHO TO APPLY TO J N Smith, Secretary, Rycroft Children's Fund, 10 Heyridge Drive, Northenden, Manchester M22 4HB

CC NO 231771   **ESTABLISHED** 1985

■ The Sainsbury Charitable Fund Ltd

WHAT IS FUNDED Donations to community groups in trading areas, particularly those of a caring nature, children, disabled and the family

WHAT IS NOT FUNDED Grants are not made for expeditions, travel bursaries, sport, individuals, restoration/upkeep of buildings, National Health projects, political or religious causes

WHO CAN BENEFIT Registered charities and self-help groups. National, regional and local organisations benefiting: children; young adults; older people; parents and children; one parent families; widows and widowers; carers; disabled people; victims of man-made and natural disasters; and beneficiaries suffering from asthma, cerebral palsy, cystic fibrosis and diabetes

WHERE FUNDING CAN BE GIVEN UK trading area (England, Aberdeen, Dundee, Edinburgh, Fife, Glasgow, Midlothian, Wrexham, Bridgend, Cardiff, Merthyr Tydfil, Newport, Swansea, Ballymena, Belfast, Coleraine, Craigavon, Derry, Newry and Maine)

TYPE OF GRANT Generally up to £5,000 per project, but smaller grants considered all year round. Project. Funding for one year or less will be considered

RANGE OF GRANTS £200–£5,000

SAMPLE GRANTS £5,000 to Common Purpose for Northern Ireland Bursary
£1,600 to Victims Support London for Volunteers' Conference
£1,500 to Brownlow Community Trust for Northern Ireland Womens Training Scheme
£1,000 to Coleraine Business Education Partnership for Northern Ireland Community Project
£1,000 to Southwark Crossroads for Carers IT Project
£1,000 to Durham Area Disabled Leisure Group for outing for local people
£1,000 to Life Education Centres Swindon for mobile unit for local schools
£550 to Hallam Diocesan Caring Service for parenting scheme
£450 to Cambridge House and Talbot for Southwark Disabled Project
£400 to Ryder-Cheshire Foundation for Swadlincote Disabled Swimming Club

FINANCES
- Year 1998–99
- Income £125,000

TRUSTEES Ms R Thorne, T Wigley, C J Leaver, N F Matthews, M Pattison, D Fry

NOTES All Sainsbury's stores have a community budget to support local fundraising efforts with raffle prizes. Please write to the Store Manager

HOW TO APPLY At any time. Trustees meet quarterly, but grants up to £1,000 considered weekly. No published guidelines. All applications receive a reply. Information required includes aims and objectives, target audience and links with at least one Sainsbury store

WHO TO APPLY TO Mrs S L Mercer, The Sainsbury Charitable Fund Ltd, Stamford House, Stamford Street, London SE1 9LL *Tel* 0171-695 7390 *Fax* 0171-695 0097 *E-mail* slme@tao.j-sainsbury.co.uk

CC NO 245843   **ESTABLISHED** 1965

■ St Helens United Voluntary Organisations Community Trust

WHAT IS FUNDED The provision of welfare through charities in the area Where Funding Can Be Given, especially youth and community organisations, disability groups, victim support schemes and senior citizens' clubs

WHAT IS NOT FUNDED Branches of UK charities may only apply if they are financially independent of a national organisation

WHO CAN BENEFIT Young adults, older people and disabled people

WHERE FUNDING CAN BE GIVEN St Helens

FINANCES
- Year 1994–95
- Grants £16,200
- Income £13,519

TRUSTEES W K Atherton, W H Darlington, Lady M Pilkington, S Warren

NOTES Interested charities may apply for membership of the scheme, which is funded by payroll giving of employees of local companies

HOW TO APPLY To the address under Who To Apply To in writing

WHO TO APPLY TO S Warren, Hon Secretary, St Helens United Voluntary Organisations Community Trust, c/o St Helens YMCA, North Road, St Helens, Merseyside WA10 2TJ

CC NO 235214   **ESTABLISHED** 1964

■ St Joseph's Educational Charity

WHAT IS FUNDED The education of Roman Catholics under 25 years of age

WHO CAN BENEFIT Children and young adults under the age of 25

WHERE FUNDING CAN BE GIVEN Lancaster

FINANCES
- Year 1995
- Income £9,835

TRUSTEES Lancaster Roman Catholic Diocesan Trustees

HOW TO APPLY To the Correspondent in writing

WHO TO APPLY TO St Joseph's Educational Charity, 10 Chapel Street, Preston, Lancashire PR1 8AY

CC NO 526616   **ESTABLISHED** 1967

■ The Francis C Scott Charitable Trust (161)

WHAT IS FUNDED Registered charities in Cumbria and North Lancashire that assist disadvantaged persons. There is an emphasis on community services, support and development

WHAT IS NOT FUNDED No medical research, church restoration, expeditions, individuals, environmental or arts organisations

WHO CAN BENEFIT Youth organisations, those working with disadvantaged persons. There are no restrictions on the age or family situation of the beneficiaries, and grants are given to organisations benefiting those from a range of social circumstances

WHERE FUNDING CAN BE GIVEN Cumbria and North Lancashire

TYPE OF GRANT Capital, revenue, recurrent, buildings, core costs, feasibility studies, one-off, project, research, salaries and start-up costs. Funding for up to three years may be given

FINANCES
- Year 1998
- Income £1,219,607
- Grants £1,138,273

TRUSTEES Mrs S E Bagot, F J R Boddy, W Dobie, I H Pirnie, CB, F A Scott, Miss M M Scott, C C F Spedding, R W Sykes (Chairman), W A Willink

PUBLICATIONS Report on activities in the three years 1993–96, Annual Report and Accounts

NOTES The fund is unlikely to give grants for projects previously funded though statutory sources, normally only give to registered charities

HOW TO APPLY By application form. Trustees meet three times annually

WHO TO APPLY TO D J Harding, Director, Francis C Scott Charitable Trust, Sand Aire House, Kendal, Cumbria LA9 4BE *Tel* 01539 723415

CC NO 232131   **ESTABLISHED** 1963

Commentary

The Francis C Scott Charitable Trust was established in 1963 by Peter F Scott, Francis and Frieda Scott, and their daughter Joan Trevelyan. Francis and his wife shared an interest in supporting music, the arts, youth and social work in Kendal, Westmorland and elsewhere. The Trust was named after F C Scott as recognition for his own charitable activities, and was set up to continue to support the causes he had chosen. A Deed of Trust in October 1963 gave the Trust the opportunity to distribute funds for charitable purposes. The Trust has supported two large projects, Abbot Hall Art Gallery and Museum and Brewery Arts Centre, for a number of years and is involved with two new projects, Whitehaven Breakout, a project intended to benefit young persons 'at risk' and the Ewanrigg Project which caters for family needs in one community.

The Trust supports general charitable purposes, although their priorities are to registered charities in Cumbria and North Lancashire that assist disadvantaged persons. The funding policies derive from those set out in the Trust Deed, although in recent years, the Trustees have chosen to focus their charitable expenditure on disadvantaged people and communities.

The Trust is reluctant to give grants to compensate the withdrawal or expiry of funding previously obtained from statutory sources. However, the Trust may examine the possibilities of partnership funding with the private and/or public sector if it benefits services for the disadvantaged.

The types of grant offered by the Trust include capital and revenue; occasionally recurrent grants are given.

Application forms should be requested in writing from the Director, who is also available to provide preliminary advice by telephone. Following the submission of application forms, in many cases additional information is gathered by a visit from the Director. Requests for grants of up to £2,500 will be reviewed by the Director and the Chairman of the Trustees. Larger and unusual requests will be considered by all of the Trustees and a response may take up to four months. The Trust does not have an assessment procedure to examine grant recipients as many of the successful applicants are either registered charities or known of by the Trust itself. Also, many of the grants are for general purposes and therefore the recipient's expenditure does not need to be examined

SAMPLE GRANTS

The top ten grants given in 1997–98 were:
£105,000 to Whitehaven Breakout Project
£100,000 to Lake District Art Gallery and Museum Trust
£57,461 to Howgill Family Centre – Ewanrigg Family Support Scheme, Maryport
£40,000 to Brathay Hall Trust – Group Sponsorship
£36,000 to Cumbria Association of Youth Clubs
£31,779 to CVA – South Lakeland
£25,000 to Macmillan Cancer Relief
£20,000 to Childline North West
£20,000 to Kendal Brewery Arts Centre
£18,000 to Community Action, Furness

■ The Frieda Scott Charitable Trust

WHAT IS FUNDED A very wide range of registered charities concerned with social welfare, community arts projects, church restoration and upkeep of village halls, within the area Where Funding Can Be Given. Charities working in the fields of: infrastructure support and development; health; conservation; animal welfare; literacy; training for community development; training for work; vocational training; equal opportunities; individual rights; advice centres; and law centres will also be considered

WHAT IS NOT FUNDED No grants to individuals or school appeals. No grants to charities outside the stated geographical area

WHO CAN BENEFIT Small local charities, church restoration, parish halls, youth groups and occasionally locally based work of larger charities. Organisations benefiting: ex-service and service people; medical professionals; retired people; unemployed people; volunteers; and writers and poets. There are no restrictions on the age; family situation; religion and culture; or social circumstances of; or on the disease or medical condition suffered by, the beneficiaries

WHERE FUNDING CAN BE GIVEN The old County of Westmorland and the area covered by South Lakeland District Council

TYPE OF GRANT Buildings, capital, core costs, endowments, feasibility studies, one-off, project, research, recurring costs, running costs, salaries and start-up costs. Funding of up to three years will be considered

RANGE OF GRANTS £200–£5,000 with occasional much larger grants

SAMPLE GRANTS £60,000 to Brewery Arts Centre, Kendal for revenue funding
£20,000 to Cancer Care Lakes Appeal for development of day support centre

£10,000 to Council for Voluntary Action, South Lakeland for core funding
£10,000 to St Martin's Church, Windermere towards appeal funds
£7,500 to Kendal Civic Society, Castle Centenary
£7,000 to Westmorland Music Council for support of local music students
£5,000 to Ambleside and Windermere Methodist Circuit for building repairs for project with young seasonal workers
£5,000 to Carlisle Cathedral Development Trust for disabled access at cathedral
£5,000 to MacMillan Appeal for Royal Lancaster Infirmary for Cancer Treatment Unit
£5,000 to National Trust Lake District Appeal for footpath repairs

FINANCES
- Year 1997
- Income £315,196
- Grants £199,870

TRUSTEES Mrs C Brockbank (Chairman), Mrs J H Barker, Mrs O Clarke, OBE, R A Hunter, Miss C R Scott, P R W Hensman, Mrs M G Wilson

HOW TO APPLY Applications by letter with accompanying Accounts considered three times a year in February, May and October. Initial telephone calls about applications are welcome

WHO TO APPLY TO D J Harding, Secretary, The Frieda Scott Charitable Trust, Sand Aire House, Kendal, Cumbria LA9 4BE
Tel 01539 723415

CC NO 221593   **ESTABLISHED** 1962

■ The Storrow Scott Charitable Will Trust

WHAT IS FUNDED General charitable purposes

WHAT IS NOT FUNDED Only registered charities, no grants to individuals

WHO CAN BENEFIT Registered charities. There are no restrictions on the age; professional and economic group; family situation; religion and culture; and social circumstances of; or disease or medical condition suffered by, the beneficiaries

WHERE FUNDING CAN BE GIVEN The North of England preferred

RANGE OF GRANTS £150–£2,750

SAMPLE GRANTS £2,750 to Northumberland Association of Boys' Clubs
£1,500 to Camphill Village Trust
£1,500 to the Anaphylaxis Campaign
£1,000 to the Percy Hedley Centre
£750 to St Oswald's Hospice, Gosforth
£500 to the Healing Education Trust
£500 to the Northumberland Wildlife Trust
£500 to Harrow School Development Appeal

£500 to Victim Support
£250 to Leonard Cheshire, Northumbria

FINANCES
- Year 1996
- Income £14,944
- Grants £10,150

TRUSTEES G W Meikle, J S North Lewis

WHO TO APPLY TO G W Meikle, The Storrow Scott Charitable Will Trust, Dickinson Dees, Solicitors, Cross House, Westgate Road, Newcastle upon Tyne NE99 1SB

CC NO 328391   **ESTABLISHED** 1989

■ Sir James & Lady Scott Trust

WHAT IS FUNDED To support Settlor's servants and dependants or others connected with him and his family and who are in need, and local charities. This includes residential facilities and services; infrastructure development; charity or voluntary umbrella bodies; religion; arts, culture and recreation; health care; conservation; animal welfare; environmental issues; heritage; education and training; social care and development; and other charitable purposes

WHAT IS NOT FUNDED No schools or medical appeals

WHO CAN BENEFIT Individuals and registered charities benefiting: retired people; unemployed people; and volunteers. There are no restrictions on the age; family situation; religion and culture; the social circumstances of; or disease or medical condition suffered by, the beneficiaries

WHERE FUNDING CAN BE GIVEN Mainly Bolton

TYPE OF GRANT Recurring costs, one-off, buildings, capital, core costs, endowment, feasibility studies, project research, running costs, salaries and start-up costs. Funding is available for one year or less

RANGE OF GRANTS £200–£5,000

SAMPLE GRANTS £6,000 to Octagon Theatre Trust, Bolton for appointment of youth theatre director
£5,000 to North West Life Education Trust for preventive drug and health education
£2,707 to Bolton YMCA for a children's day camp project
£2,500 to Woodside School PTA towards a minibus
£2,000 to Society of St Vincent de Paul, Bolton for a holiday project for needy families
£2,000 to Relate – Bolton Marriage Guidance for training costs for a counsellor

FINANCES
- Year 1997
- Income £114,098
- Grants £41,170

TRUSTEES P F Scott, W L G Swan, C J Scott

HOW TO APPLY By application form accompanied by latest set of audited accounts. An initial telephone call from applicant is welcome

WHO TO APPLY TO D J Harding, The Sir James & Lady Scott Trust, Sand Aire House, Kendal, Cumbria LA9 4BE *Tel* 01539 723415

CC NO 231324   **ESTABLISHED** 1907

■ Sefton and West Lancashire Deaf Children's Society

WHAT IS FUNDED To further the education and relief of deaf children without regard to race, religion, creed, disability, sex or family circumstance

WHO CAN BENEFIT Multiple impairments

WHERE FUNDING CAN BE GIVEN Sefton and West Lancashire

SAMPLE GRANTS £300 to Boros Treatment
£200 to NDCS Jubilee
£25 to Derby Deaf School

FINANCES
- Year 1995
- Income £9,807

WHO TO APPLY TO P J Olson, Sefton and West Lancashire Deaf Children's Society, 4 Esplen Avenue, Great Crosby, Liverpool L23 2SS

CC NO 1033804   **ESTABLISHED** 1993

■ Sefton Community Foundation

WHAT IS FUNDED General charitable purposes for the benefit of the community, in particular, the advancement of education, the protection of mental and physical health and the relief of poverty and sickness

WHO CAN BENEFIT Children, young adults, disabled people and those disadvantaged by poverty. There are no restrictions on the disease or medical condition suffered by the beneficiaries

WHERE FUNDING CAN BE GIVEN Sefton

TRUSTEES C A Batchelor, Cllr W Burke, J Flynn, G Kaye, Cllr P J McVey, M J O'Brien, M J Swift, A White

WHO TO APPLY TO Mrs A White, Sefton Community Foundation, c/o The Old Museum, Church Road, Waterloo, Liverpool L22 5NB

CC NO 1068887   **ESTABLISHED** 1998

■ The Severn Trent Water Charitable Trust Fund

WHAT IS FUNDED The relief of those in need, poverty, hardship or distress and are unable to pay for the supply of water and/or sewerage services provided to premises used or occupied by them

WHO CAN BENEFIT Householders unable to meet charges for water or sewerage services provided by Severn Trent Water

WHERE FUNDING CAN BE GIVEN Area where Severn Trent Water is provided

TYPE OF GRANT (a) To individuals towards water charges and some other household charges. (b) To organisations towards the funding of debt counselling/money advice for householders falling into Who Can Benefit category

RANGE OF GRANTS For individuals average grant £340, no upper or lower limit for water debt. For funding debt counselling typically two to three year award of up to £30,000

FINANCES
- Year 1997–98
- Income £2,000,000
- Grants £909,000

TRUSTEES Hon Alderman Mrs Majorie Brown, CBE, JP, J R A Crabtree, Mrs Liz Pusey, BA, CCAW, Mrs Edna Sadler, JP, Roy Simpson

PUBLICATIONS None as yet except newsletter introducing the Trust, for copies please write to the Trust

HOW TO APPLY By application form for grants to individuals, usually with support/help from money advisor. By application form for grants to fund money advice within the Severn Trent Water geographical area

WHO TO APPLY TO S Braley, Chief Executive, The Severn Trent Water Charitable Trust Fund, Ground Floor, Hammond House, 2259–2261 Coventry Road, Birmingham B26 3PA
Tel 0121-742 1376

CC NO 1064005   **ESTABLISHED** 1997

■ Alfred Shaw Trust

WHAT IS FUNDED Assistance towards the upkeep of All Saints Parish Church. Any surplus income can be used for general charitable purposes in Runcorn in line with the Benefactor's wishes

WHO CAN BENEFIT Church of England, old people, Church of England schools

WHERE FUNDING CAN BE GIVEN Runcorn Old Town (mainly in the Parish of All Saints)

FINANCES
- Year 1994
- Income £8,000

- Grants £1,000

TRUSTEES Mrs M Spruce, J R B Dawson, J Wharne

HOW TO APPLY To the Correspondent in writing

WHO TO APPLY TO Mrs S M Spruce, Trustee, Alfred Shaw Trust, 18 Kenilworth Avenue, Runcorn, Cheshire WA7 4XQ
Tel 01928 567311

CC NO 257976   **ESTABLISHED** 1969

■ The Patricia and Donald Shepherd Charitable Trust

WHAT IS FUNDED General charitable purposes. To donate only to local charities or charities of which the Trustees have personal knowledge, interest or association.

WHAT IS NOT FUNDED No grants to individuals

WHO CAN BENEFIT Mainly local organisations – those in the North of England and Scotland

WHERE FUNDING CAN BE GIVEN North of England and Scotland with preference for the York area

TYPE OF GRANT Mainly one-off

FINANCES
- Year 1995
- Income £85,595
- Grants £63,197

TRUSTEES D W Shepherd, Mrs P Shepherd, Mrs J L Robertson, Patrick M Shepherd, D R Reaston

HOW TO APPLY Applications acknowledged on receipt. No application form is used

WHO TO APPLY TO The Trustees, The Patricia and Donald Shepherd Charitable Trust, PO Box 10, York YO1 1XU

CC NO 272948   **ESTABLISHED** 1973

■ The Skelton Bounty

WHAT IS FUNDED Restricted to Lancashire charities (not national ones unless operating in Lancashire from a permanent establishment within the County predominantly for the benefit of residents from that County) assisting youth, the aged and infirm

WHAT IS NOT FUNDED Religious charities, medical and scientific research and minibus appeals are not encouraged. Grants can only be made to registered charities

WHO CAN BENEFIT Organisations benefiting young and elderly people and the infirm

WHERE FUNDING CAN BE GIVEN Lancashire – meaning the geographical County as it existed in 1934

Does the trust you have chosen match your needs? Haphazard applications waste postage and time

183

TYPE OF GRANT Capital expenditure preferred

RANGE OF GRANTS £200–£7,000

SAMPLE GRANTS £7,000 to Rainbow Family
Trust, Stretford
£5,000 to Ocean Youth Club, Denton
£3,500 to Old Swan Youth Club, Liverpool
£3,000 to Carleton Community Association,
Poulton-le-Fylde
£3,000 to Christ Church Centre, Netherley
£3,000 to Henshaw's Society for the Blind
£2,500 to Royal School for the Blind, Liverpool
£2,312 to Mawdesley Village Hall
£2,000 to Liverpool Personal Service Society
Inc
£2,000 to Merseyside Council for Voluntary
Service

FINANCES
- Year 1997   • Income £70,646
- Grants £64,352

TRUSTEES G P Bowring, S R Fisher, Mrs A
Fishwick, K A Gledhill, Lord Shuttleworth, DL,
FRICS, Sir Kenneth M Stoddart, KCVO, AE,
LLD, JP, DL, Lady Towneley, A W Waterworth,
Sir William L Mather, CVO, OBE, MC, TD, DL

NOTES The Charity comprises three former
charities founded by members of the Shelton
Family. Each member by their wills founded a
charitable trust, all of which were
amalgamated into one charity in 1991

HOW TO APPLY Between 1 January and 31 March
on form obtainable from the address under
Who To Apply To

WHO TO APPLY TO Messrs Cockshott Peck
Lewis, The Skelton Bounty, 24 Hoghton Street,
Southport PR9 0XH

CC NO 219370   ESTABLISHED 1934

■The John Slater Foundation

WHAT IS FUNDED The relief of suffering

WHAT IS NOT FUNDED No grants to individuals

WHO CAN BENEFIT Registered charities. There is
no restriction on the disease or medical
condition suffered by the beneficiaries

WHERE FUNDING CAN BE GIVEN West Lancashire

SAMPLE GRANTS £10,000 to Trinity Hospice,
Blackpool
£10,000 to Blackpool Ladies' Sick and Poor
£9,000 to St Gemma's Hospice, Leeds
£8,500 to Supt Geral Richardson Memorial
Fund
£6,000 to Manorlands Home, Oxenhope
£6,000 to Bury Grammar School
£5,000 to Blackpool and Flyde Society for the
Blind
£5,000 to Mission to Deep Sea Fishermen
£5,000 to Church Road Methodist Day Care
Unit

£4,500 to Fleetwood and Wyre Mentally
Handicapped

FINANCES
- Year 1995   • Income £500,334
- Grants £316,422

TRUSTEES Midland Bank Trust Company Limited

HOW TO APPLY Half-yearly – 1 May and 1
November by letter to the address under Who
To Apply To

WHO TO APPLY TO The Secretary to the Trustees,
The John Slater Foundation, Midland Private
Banking, 4 Dale Street, Liverpool L69 2BZ

CC NO 231145   ESTABLISHED 1963

■The Slater Trust Limited

WHAT IS FUNDED Only local applications
considered for new grants. Charities working in
the fields of: community arts and recreation;
community facilities; clubs; charity or voluntary
and religious umbrella bodies

WHAT IS NOT FUNDED No new grants to
individuals. No new grants at present

WHO CAN BENEFIT Local organisations benefiting
people of all ages

WHERE FUNDING CAN BE GIVEN West Cumbria

TYPE OF GRANT Recurrent

RANGE OF GRANTS £15–£550

SAMPLE GRANTS £550 to Boat Trade Benevolent
Society
£300 to Cumbria Association of Clubs for
Young People for running costs
£250 to The Methodist Church, Cockermouth
£250 to Life Education Centre for Cumbria for
abuse of drugs awareness and education
campaign
£200 to Mines Advisory Group, Cockermouth
for land mine clearance
£200 to NSPCC, Cockermouth Branch
£200 to Cockermouth Cricket Club for Youth
Project Appeal
£200 to Cumbria College of Art to improve
scholarship
£150 to Cockermouth Cottage Hospital
League of Friends
£125 to Save the Children, Cockermouth
Branch

FINANCES
- Year 1997   • Income £15,975
- Grants £11,460

TRUSTEES The Council

NOTES Present commitments restrict availability
of new grants

HOW TO APPLY Applications by letter, which are
not responded to unless a grant is made

WHO TO APPLY TO The Secretary, The Slater Trust Limited, PO Box No 2, Cockermouth, Cumbria CA13 0NP

CC NO 230099 **ESTABLISHED** 1963

■ South Lakeland Communities Charitable Trust

WHAT IS FUNDED Small local initiatives towards sustainable communities, eg in accord with Local Agenda 21 of the 1992 Earth Summit – a document which outlines a local community's vision for an environmentally and socially sustainable and desirable future

WHAT IS NOT FUNDED To be decided

WHO CAN BENEFIT To be decided

WHERE FUNDING CAN BE GIVEN District of South Lakeland

TYPE OF GRANT One-off contributions towards start-up costs

RANGE OF GRANTS To be decided

TRUSTEES J Jeffers, G Henson, L Smyth, E Straughton

WHO TO APPLY TO G Henson, Trustee, South Lakeland Communities Charitable Trust, 22 Castle Garth, Sedbergh, Cumbria LA10 5AN *Tel* 01539 621495

CC NO 167740 **ESTABLISHED** 1998

■ The Stanley Charitable Trust

This trust did not respond to CAF's request to amend its entry and, by 30 June 1998, CAF's researchers did not find financial records for later than 1995 on its file at the Charity Commission. Trusts are legally required to submit annual accounts to the Charity Commission under section 42 of the Charities Act 1993

WHAT IS FUNDED Jewish religious charities

WHAT IS NOT FUNDED Grants are only made to projects and charities known to the Trustees

WHO CAN BENEFIT Charities benefiting Jewish People

WHERE FUNDING CAN BE GIVEN UK, especially Greater Manchester

TRUSTEES A M Alder, I Alder, J Alder

HOW TO APPLY To the address below in writing

WHO TO APPLY TO A M Alder, The Stanley Charitable Trust, 8 Stanley Road, Salford M7 0EG

CC NO 326220 **ESTABLISHED** 1982

■ Sir Halley Stewart Trust (232)

This trust failed to supply a copy of its annual report and accounts to CAF as required under section 47(2) of the Charities Act 1993. The information given here was obtained independently by CAF's researchers at the Charity Commission

WHAT IS FUNDED To promote research that will prevent human suffering, to advance education, to relieve poverty, and to advance religion

WHAT IS NOT FUNDED No grants are made for general funds; for personal education; for the purchase, building or conversion of buildings, nor for established projects which should properly be the responsibility of the state

WHO CAN BENEFIT Young research workers doing pioneering work in social, religious, medical or education fields. Beneficiaries may also include young adults and older people, retired people, academics, medical professionals, scientists and clergy. Also ethnic minority groups, carers, disabled people, ex-offenders, and those disadvantaged by poverty. people suffering from Alzheimer's disease, arthritis and rheumatism, Crohn's disease, tropical diseases, paediatric diseases and prenatal conditions and the terminally ill may also benefit

WHERE FUNDING CAN BE GIVEN UK, West Africa, India

TYPE OF GRANT One-off and project grants. Also feasibility studies, research and salaries will be considered. Funding may be given for up to three years

FINANCES
- Year 1998
- Grants £702,000
- Income £920,000

TRUSTEES Prof John Lennard Jones, MD, FRCP, FRCS (Chairman), Prof Harold C Stewart, CBE, DL, MD, FRCP, FRCS, William P Kirkman, MBE, MA, Prof Phyllida Parsloe, BA, AAPSW, PhD, Michael S Ross Collins, George Russell, JP, CA, Dr Duncan Stewart, MB, BS, D.Obst, RCOG, Rt Hon Lord Stewartby, RD, LittD, FBA, Brian Allpress, FCCA, Prof Philip Whitfield, BA, MA, PhD, Sir Ronald Stewart, BT, DL (Emeritus Trustee), Prof C Hallett (Emeritus Trustee), Prof W Jacobson, MD, ScD, FRCP, FRC Path (Associate Trustee), Miss Barbara Clapham (Associate Trustee)

NOTES *Notes for for those Seeking Grants* available from the Secretary

HOW TO APPLY To the Trust Secretary in writing. An initial telephone call is welcome

WHO TO APPLY TO Mrs P Fawcitt, BSc (Econ), Trust Secretary, Sir Halley Stewart Trust, 88 Long Lane, Willingham, Cambridge, Cambridgeshire CB4 5LD *Tel* 01954 260707

CC NO 208491 **ESTABLISHED** 1924

Commentary

Established as a charitable trust in December 1924 by Sir Halley Stewart, the original purpose of the Trust was to promote a wide range of charitable causes aimed at the prevention of suffering and the building of the Kingdom of God upon Earth. The settlor also gave guidance that he wished the Trust to principally provide grants for research into the prevention of human suffering, with a view to making pioneer research work self-supporting at the earliest possible moment.

The Trust has three main areas where it applies its charitable purposes: (a) medicine; (b) social and educational; and (c) the advancement of religion. The Trust will also give grants to promote 'other charitable purposes beneficial to the community. The Trust deed also laid out three principles which the Trustees were to have in mind when making grants: furthering for every individual the opportunities for education, service and leisure to develop the body, mind and spirit; securing a just environment in all aspects of life; and fostering international goodwill between all races, tribes, peoples and nations to secure the fulfilment of the hope of peace on Earth. The medical programme concentrates upon the support of research for prevention rather than relief of human suffering, to promote innovative projects and promising students (especially but not exclusively at a postgraduate level) and encourage pioneer work that is likely to become self-supporting. Adventurous or unusual projects are favoured, especially where they are in the early stages when they are unlikely to be funded by large organisations. Also favoured are: projects related to the prevention of birth handicaps; those enabling the elderly to retain independence; research designed to prevent or treat tropical infectious or parasitic diseases. As the Trustees are keen that the benefit to human welfare should be apparent within a few years, there is a bias towards applied rather than basic research. The social and educationalprogramme generally gives small to medium-sized grants for the advancement of education and the relief of poverty. Areas in which the Trustees have an interest include charities dealing with: children with disabilities; elderly people suffering from dementia and their carers; homelessness; issues affecting ethnic minorities; and charities dealing with inner city crime. It is also a priority of the Trust to support projects in the UK attempting to bridge cultural and racial divides. In the UK, the Trust is especially interested in innovative projects which have the prospect of secure future funding. Elsewhere in the world, especially in West Africa, the Trust concentrates, at present, upon small-scale, localised projects with a clear focus (rather than large-scale aid work), supporting initiatives which are chosen by local people who will directly benefit from the development of skills to help themselves and others.

The religious grants programme has various aspects, including: (a) theological training in cases where there is a special and specific need (for example in Eastern Europe and Africa); (b) teaching children in the UK about Christianity; (c) encouraging varied groups of people to explore their experience of spirituality and their spiritual needs and strengths; and (d) encouraging the widespread communication of the Christian message through the media.

The medical programme has recently distributed by far the majority of the Trust's grant total: in 1997 £435,000 was given through the medical programme (59 per cent of the grant total), while £255,000 was given through the social and educational programme (35 per cent of the grant total), and £47,000 was given through the religious grants programme (6 per cent of the grant total). Most grants made were for more than £5,000 – 43 grants over £5,000 were given, totalling £673,000. 27 grants under £5,000 and over £1,000 were given, totalling £60,000, and 16 grants made were for under £1,000, totalling £4,000. The funding policies of the Trust are reviewed at regular meetings of the Trustees, although there is rarely any substantial change needed, due to the relative freedom allowed by the objects of the Trust.

Grants may be given to organisations working throughout the UK and overseas. The Trust is not prepared to replace statutory funding, stating that 'established projects which should properly be the responsibility of the State or of other bodies' will not be considered for funding. The Trust has no stated attitude towards partnership funding. The Trust makes grants to organisations only, often for further distribution to individuals involved in research. Grants can be either one-off or recurring to help support a project. The Trust has no stated attitude towards making loans to charities instead of grants.

There are three separate committees of Trustees that deal with each of the programmes, who meet as necessary to consider applications. The medical programme has a slightly different selection procedure for projects. The first step of the application process for the medical programme is the submission of a brief description of the project in lay terms. This is then screened to see that it meets the general guidelines. A detailed application is then requested, which is examined by the Medical Committee, before going to a full Trustee meeting. At the preliminary stage, considerable correspondence and enquiry is often undertaken. For the other programmes, the grants committees meet to consider the applications and to recommend them to go forward to a full Trustee meeting for final approval. The Trustees meet three times a year to approve grants, receive reports from previous grant recipients and conduct any other business of the Trust. The Trust does not supply details of whether it has a post-grant evaluation process

SAMPLE GRANTS
The top ten grants given in 1997 were:
£66,000 to Cambridge University
£50,000 to the London School of Hygiene
£40,000 to Kaloko Trust, Zambia
£35,000 to King's College, London
£33,000 to Warwick University
£32,000 to Royal Free Hospital, London
£20,000 to Plymouth University
£19,000 to Oxford University
£19,000 to United Medical and Dental Schools, London
£18,000 to Nottingham University

■ Stockport Community Trust

WHAT IS FUNDED Relief of poverty, health and sickness, education

WHO CAN BENEFIT Individuals and institutions

WHERE FUNDING CAN BE GIVEN Stockport, Manchester

FINANCES
- Year 1996
- Income £5,337

HOW TO APPLY To the Correspondent in writing

WHO TO APPLY TO Stockport Community Trust, c/o BASF Plc, PO Box 4, Earl Road, Cheadle Hulme, Cheadle, Cheshire SK8 6QG

CC NO 1012836 **ESTABLISHED** 1992

■ The Stockport Educational Foundation

WHAT IS FUNDED Organisations working with young people and educational grants to individuals

WHAT IS NOT FUNDED Grants will not be made to individuals over the age of 25

WHO CAN BENEFIT Individuals and organisations

WHERE FUNDING CAN BE GIVEN Stockport

FINANCES
- Year 1994–95
- Income £2,200
- Grants £900

HOW TO APPLY To the Correspondent in writing

WHO TO APPLY TO A Roberts, Stockport Educational Foundation, 4th Floor, Hilton House, Lord Street, Stockport, Cheshire SK1 3NA

CC NO 525939 **ESTABLISHED** 1967

■ The Alan Jenkin Stokes Memorial Trust

WHAT IS FUNDED The advancement of welfare

WHO CAN BENEFIT Local branches of national organisations and local organisations, there is a priority for children

WHERE FUNDING CAN BE GIVEN England, Scotland and Wales, with a possible preference for Liverpool and the Midlands

TYPE OF GRANT Predominantly recurrent

FINANCES
- Year 1995
- Income £7,200
- Grants £6,000

HOW TO APPLY To the Correspondent in writing

WHO TO APPLY TO Mrs S M Maxwell, Trustee, The Alan Jenkin Stokes Memorial Trust, 39 Primrose Road, Liverpool L18 2HE *Tel* 0151-231 5290

CC NO 218507 **ESTABLISHED** 1964

■ The Swales Scholarship Fund

WHAT IS FUNDED To advance public education and award scholarships to students of agriculture and forestry, in particular at Cumbria College, and to further their education by awarding grants for travelling and/or study within the UK or abroad

WHO CAN BENEFIT Students

WHERE FUNDING CAN BE GIVEN Cumbria, UK and overseas

FINANCES
- Year 1995–96
- Income £8,391
- Grants £10,195

TRUSTEES Joseph E Swale, William J Kirkpatrick, Anthony Mitchell, David Ward

WHO TO APPLY TO D Routledge, The Swales Scholarship Fund, County Treasurers Department, The Court, Carlisle, Cumbria CA3 8NA

CC NO 702552 **ESTABLISHED** 1990

■ The Charles Sykes Trust
(417) (known as The Charles and Elsie Sykes Trust)

WHAT IS FUNDED Animals and birds; blind and partially sighted; children and youth; cultural and environmental heritage; deaf, hard of hearing and speech impaired; disabled and physically handicapped; education; hospices and hospitals; medical research; medical welfare; mental health and mentally handicapped; old people's welfare; overseas

Does the trust you have chosen match your needs? Haphazard applications waste postage and time

187

aid; services and ex-services; social and moral welfare; trades and professions; and sundry

WHAT IS NOT FUNDED No grants to individuals or for their benefit. Preference for north of the country

WHO CAN BENEFIT Registered charities only, benefiting people of all ages, especially the mentally ill and those with sensory impairments. There are no restrictions upon the professional and economic group of the beneficiaries, although service and ex-service people are favoured

WHERE FUNDING CAN BE GIVEN Preference for North of England, occasionally overseas

TYPE OF GRANT Donations in cash, usually one-off for a specific project or part thereof. If on annual list, there is a requirement to submit accounts and report annually

FINANCES
- Year 1997
- Income £434,890
- Grants £313,115

TRUSTEES John Horrocks (Chairman), Mrs Anne E Barker, Harold T Bartrop, Mrs G Mary Dance, Michael G H Garnett, Dr Michael D Moore, Dr M McEvoy, John Ward

HOW TO APPLY To the Secretary in writing, with full details and audited accounts. Acknowledgements given if sae supplied. No guidelines issued

WHO TO APPLY TO David J Reah, Secretary, The Charles Sykes Trust, 6 North Park Road, Harrogate, North Yorkshire HG1 5PA

CC NO 206926   **ESTABLISHED** 1954

Commentary

The Charles Sykes Trust was established in 1954 by an endowment. The Trust is also known as The Charles and Elsie Sykes Trust. Additional endowments of almost £30,000 were credited to the fund during 1997. The stated objects of the Trust are general charitable giving. However, donations are given in the following areas: animals and birds (which received 0.17 per cent of the Trust's donations in 1997); blind and partially sighted (1.63 per cent); children and youth (11.17 per cent); cultural and environmental heritage (3.15 per cent); deaf, hard of hearing and speech impaired (2.97 per cent); disabled and physically handicapped (5.42 per cent); education (2.36 per cent); hospices and hospitals (5.91 per cent); medical research (19.01 per cent); medical welfare (6.53 per cent); mental health and mentally handicapped (4.21 per cent); sundry (13.07 per cent: old people's welfare (4.92 per cent); overseas aid (4.04 per cent); services and ex-service (1.36 per cent); social and moral welfare (12.65 per cent); and trades and professions (1.43 per cent). There is an established list of organisations to whom the

Trust gives regular annual donations, on receipt of satisfactory annual accounts, but provision is also made for special, ie one-off, grants. During 1997 a total of £161,750 special donations were given, ranging in size from £200 to £31,500, to a varied list of 113 organisations representing a wide area of interests. Funding will be given only to registered charities – individuals will not be considered.

Organisations throughout the UK can apply but the North of England is favoured for local projects. The co-funding of projects is not ruled out. Continuous funding in the form of annual donations and one-off payments for special projects are the types of support that the Trust favours. Loans are not considered. It was not apparent whether infrastructure costs would be funded.

Applicants should submit brief details of their project together with a copy of the organisation's most recent accounts. An sae will guarantee a reply. Telephone calls are not welcome.

Trustees meet periodically in subcommittees to advise the board on annual as well as special, or one-off, donations. There is no formal assessment procedure but Trustees may visit an organisation if they feel it would be beneficial to their decision-making process

SAMPLE GRANTS

The top ten grants made in 1997 were:
£31,500 to Harrogate Community House Trust
£11,000 to University of Cambridge School of Clinical Medicine
£5,000 to Abbeyfield York Society 'Open the Door' Appeal
£5,000 to British Red Cross (Disaster Preparedness Programme in Bangladesh)
£4,100 to National Children's Home
£3,500 to Calvert Trust, Keswick
£3,500 to St George's Youth Club & Community Centre, Harrogate
£3,300 to St Michael's Hospice
£2,800 to Royal National Institute for Deaf People
£2,750 to Save the Children

∎ The Elsie Talbot Bridge Will Trust

WHAT IS FUNDED Wildlife, the arts, education, museums and galleries, medical care

WHO CAN BENEFIT Local and regional organisations benefiting children, young adults, students and sick people. There is no restriction on the disease or medical condition suffered by the beneficiaries. Those involved in the arts may benefit

WHERE FUNDING CAN BE GIVEN Southport

FINANCES
- Year 1996
- Income £20,145

TRUSTEES D T Bushell, J Kewley

HOW TO APPLY To the Trustees in writing

WHO TO APPLY TO The Elsie Talbot Bridge Will Trust, 11 St George's Place, Lord Street, Southport, Lancashire PR9 0AL

CC NO 279288   **ESTABLISHED** 1961

∎ The 3i Charitable Trust

WHAT IS FUNDED 3i prefers to support the fundraising efforts of its staff and charities with which staff are involved, together with charities local to any of the 3i offices. Particularly charities working in the fields of: respite and sheltered accommodation; conservation; business schools; and social care and development

WHAT IS NOT FUNDED No grants to individuals

WHO CAN BENEFIT Registered charities only. There is no restriction on the age, or social circumstances of, or the disease or medical condition suffered by the beneficiaries

WHERE FUNDING CAN BE GIVEN Newcastle upon Tyne, Liverpool City, Manchester City, Birmingham City, Solihull, Leeds, London, Aberdeen, Edinburgh, Glasgow and Cardiff

TYPE OF GRANT One-off and project will be considered

SAMPLE GRANTS £100,000 to INSEAD Trust for European Management Education
£50,000 to Royal Opera House Development Appeal
£50,000 to Understanding Industry Trust for education
£25,000 to Cambridge Foundation for education
£13,000 to Birkbeck College for education
£11,450 to Business in the Community for education
£10,000 to London Business School Anniversary Trust for education
£10,000 to North Lambeth Day Centre for homelessness
£7,100 to Percy Hedley Centre for education
£5,422 to NSPCC for support for children in the community

FINANCES
- Year 1998
- Grants £466,550
- Income £310,000

TRUSTEES 3i Trustee Company Limited

PUBLICATIONS Report & Accounts

HOW TO APPLY The meetings of the Board of Directors of 3i Trustee Company Limited are held approximately every three months

WHO TO APPLY TO Company Secretary's Office, The 3i Charitable Trust, 3i plc, 91 Waterloo Road, London SE1 8XP *Tel* 0171-928 3131 *Fax* 0171-928 0058

CC NO 1014277   **ESTABLISHED** 1988

∎ Timperley Educational Foundation

WHAT IS FUNDED The advancement of education

WHAT IS NOT FUNDED Upper age limit 21

WHO CAN BENEFIT Individuals and organisations

WHERE FUNDING CAN BE GIVEN The Ecclesiastical Parish of Christ Church, Timperley

TYPE OF GRANT One-off and recurring

FINANCES
- Year 1996
- Grants £3,300
- Income £10,512

TRUSTEES D Camplejohn, T A K Seller, Rev J Sutton, S J Taylor, P Turner

HOW TO APPLY To the Correspondent in writing: application forms issued by headteachers to those going to university have to be submitted by end of August. Primary schools within the Parish can write with details

WHO TO APPLY TO P Turner, Clerk, Timperley Educational Foundation, 103 Sylvan Avenue, Timperley, Altrincham, Cheshire WA15 6AD *Tel* 0161-969 3919

CC NO 1018845   **ESTABLISHED** 1993

··

■United Merseyside Trust

WHAT IS FUNDED To promote, further or support any charitable purpose in the area Where Funding Can Be Given

WHO CAN BENEFIT There are no restrictions on the age; professional and economic group; family situation; religion and culture; and social circumstances of; or disease or medical condition suffered by, the beneficiaries

WHERE FUNDING CAN BE GIVEN Merseyside county

TYPE OF GRANT Core costs. Funding is available for more than three years

RANGE OF GRANTS £100–£1,000

FINANCES
- Year 1997
- Income £65,754
- Grants £65,158

PUBLICATIONS (1997–98 summary report-Merseyside area)

NOTES Small grants given to local charities benefiting local people. Local committees decide for each borough

HOW TO APPLY Please send accounts and sae. Applications must be received before the end of the calendar year

WHO TO APPLY TO John Pritchard, Administrator, United Merseyside Trust, c/o United Trusts, PO Box 14, 8 Nelson Road, Liverpool L69 7AA *Tel* 0151-709 8252

CC NO 701910 **ESTABLISHED** 1989

··

■United Trusts

WHAT IS FUNDED General charitable purposes. Distribution decisions are made by work place charity committees or local trust committees

WHAT IS NOT FUNDED The donor's committees decide what is not funded

WHO CAN BENEFIT Neighbourhood-based community projects tend to be major recipients. There are no restrictions on the age; professional and economic group; family situation; religion and culture; and social circumstances of; or disease or medical condition suffered by, the beneficiaries

WHERE FUNDING CAN BE GIVEN UK, at present mainly North West England

FINANCES
- Year 1996–97
- Income £382,000
- Grants £295,000

TRUSTEES Up to twenty people elected by members

HOW TO APPLY Applications should be made to the Secretary of the local United Trust Fund or Workplace Trust concerned. Applications from charities in Merseyside may be made either direct to the Trust Chairman or to John Pritchard, the Administrator

WHO TO APPLY TO Fred Freeman, Chairman and Hon Director, United Trusts, PO Box 14, 8 Nelson Road, Edge Hill, Liverpool L69 7AA *Tel* 0151-709 8252

CC NO 327579 **ESTABLISHED** 1987

■The Vaux Group Foundation

WHAT IS FUNDED The Trust funds communities and organisations where the company operates. Particularly charities working in the fields of: housing associations; sheltered accomodation; information technology and computers; personnel and human resource services; infrastructure development; charity or voluntary umbrella bodies; architecture; combined arts; visual arts; opera companies and opera groups; theatrical companies and theatre groups; health facilities and buildings; conservation; animal facilities and services; schools and colleges; bursaries and fees; community issues; and various community facilities and services

WHAT IS NOT FUNDED Individuals. National appeals unless there is a local bias towards a Group trading

WHO CAN BENEFIT Small, local groups, local and regional charitable organisations and some national organisations benefiting: children; young adults; older people; actors and entertainment professionals; at risk groups; carers; disabled people; those disadvantaged by poverty; gays and lesbians; those living in rural areas; victims of abuse, crime and domestic violence

WHERE FUNDING CAN BE GIVEN North East and North West England and Yorkshire

SAMPLE GRANTS £15,000 to Durham County Foundation for community issues
£10,000 to Diana, Princess of Wales Memorial Fund for community issues
£75,000 to Midland Enterprise Fund for community issues
£7,000 to Manchester University
£5,000 to Hotel and Catering Benevolent Association
£5,000 to Hospitality Training Foundation
£2,500 to Manor Training and Resource Centre for community issues
£2,500 to Prince's Youth Business Trust for youth appeal
£2,000 to South Yorkshire Foundation for community issues
£2,000 to NE Civic Trust for community issues

FINANCES
- Year 1995–96
- Income £36,478
- Grants £127,000

TRUSTEES William P Catesby, Frank Nicholson, Sir Paul Nicholson, Christopher Storey, Neal Gossage

HOW TO APPLY To the address under Who To Apply To in writing

WHO TO APPLY TO Hilary Florek, Administrator, The Vaux Group Foundation, Vaux Group plc, The Brewery, Sunderland SR1 3AN *Tel* 0191-567 6277 *Fax* 0191-514 2488
Web Site http://www.vaux.group.co.uk

CC NO 802636   **ESTABLISHED** 1988

■The Verdin Trust Fund

WHAT IS FUNDED Most of the Trust's funds are given in the form of prizes to Young Farmers Associations and local schools

WHO CAN BENEFIT Students, schools and Young Farmers Association. Local hospitals and voluntary services

WHERE FUNDING CAN BE GIVEN Mid-Cheshire

TYPE OF GRANT One-off and recurring. Annual prizes to schools and Young Farmers Association. Small grants to students towards expenses of course fees

SAMPLE GRANTS £175 to Cheshire County Federation of Young Farmers for prize fund (annual grant)
£155 to Winsford Verdin High School for prize fund (annual grant)
£115 to Sir John Deanes College for prize fund (annual grant)
£115 to Leftwich High School for prize fund (annual grant)
£100 to an individual, grant towards course fees
£100 to Leighton Hospital Scanner Appeal
£75 to Northwich Victoria Infirmary for patients fund (annual grant)
£50 to an individual, grant towards course fees

FINANCES
- Year 1994–95
- Income £2,200
- Grants £1,800

TRUSTEES A G Cross, N C D Marsh, Major P G Verdin, Ms J A Williams

HOW TO APPLY To the Correspondent in writing

WHO TO APPLY TO R Forster, Secretary, The Verdin Trust Fund, Roma, 115 Shipbrook Road, Rudheath, Northwich, Cheshire CW9 7HG *Tel* 01606 74301

CC NO 221295   **ESTABLISHED** 1890

Does the trust you have chosen match your needs? Haphazard applications waste postage and time

191

■The Ward Blenkinsop Trust

WHAT IS FUNDED General charitable purposes with emphasis on support for medical research

WHAT IS NOT FUNDED No grants to individuals

WHO CAN BENEFIT Mainly research foundations and charitable organisations. There are no restrictions on the age; professional and economic group; family situation; religion and culture; and social circumstances of; or disease or medical condition suffered by, the beneficiaries

WHERE FUNDING CAN BE GIVEN UK. Special interest in the Merseyside area

TYPE OF GRANT Mainly cash

SAMPLE GRANTS £36,650 to Cheshire County Council for youth arts initiative
£25,000 to Chatterbridge Cancer Research Fund for cancer research
£16,400 to Royal Academy of Dancing for special needs programme
£10,000 to St Mary's (Horsham) Restoration Appeal
£8,000 to The CLOD Ensemble
£5,000 to International Spinal Research Trust
£5,000 to Stephen Park Trust
£5,000 to Father Roger Charter Mission
£5,000 to Manchester Youth Theatre
£5,000 to British Sports Association for the Disabled

FINANCES
- Year 1997
- Grants £244,935
- Income £246,511

TRUSTEES J H Awdry, A M Blenkinsop, T R Tilling

HOW TO APPLY In writing from charitable organisations, not individuals

WHO TO APPLY TO J H Awdry, The Ward Blenkinsop Trust, Broxbury, Codmore Hill, Pulborough, West Sussex RH20 2HY

CC NO 265449   **ESTABLISHED** 1972

■Warrington Animal Welfare

WHAT IS FUNDED To relieve the suffering of pet animals who are in need of care and attention. In particular, by assisting with the cost of neutering and treatment of sick and injured animals, and by rehoming unwanted animals

WHO CAN BENEFIT Animals

WHERE FUNDING CAN BE GIVEN Borough of Warrington and surrounding districts

SAMPLE GRANTS £8,101 for veterinary treatment cost
£180 for dog food
£125 for dog convalescence boarding fees

FINANCES
- Year 1995–96
- Grants £8,708
- Income £9,620

WHO TO APPLY TO R Valerie Dabbs, Warrington Animal Welfare, 393 Warrington Road, Glazebury, Warrington, Cheshire WA3 5NY

CC NO 1057149   **ESTABLISHED** 1996

■Warrington Church of England Educational Trust

WHAT IS FUNDED Educational purposes in the area Where Funding Can Be Given, including repairs to school buildings

WHO CAN BENEFIT Schools benefiting children and young adults

WHERE FUNDING CAN BE GIVEN Warrington

FINANCES
- Year 1996
- Grants £32,358
- Income £46,157

TRUSTEES J O Colling (Chairman), J B Naylor (Treasurer)

HOW TO APPLY To the address under Who To Apply To in writing

WHO TO APPLY TO John Naylor, Law Clerk, Warrington Church of England Educational Trust, Ridgway Greenall, 21 Palmyra Square, Warrington, Cheshire WA1 1BW

CC NO 511469   **ESTABLISHED** 1952

■Mrs Waterhouse Charitable Trust (440)

WHAT IS FUNDED General charitable purposes based in, or with branches in, Lancashire

WHAT IS NOT FUNDED No grants to individuals, or for expeditions or scholarships

WHO CAN BENEFIT Registered charities only. There are no restrictions on the age; professional and economic group; family situation; religion and culture; and social circumstances of; or disease or medical condition suffered by, the beneficiaries

WHERE FUNDING CAN BE GIVEN UK, but preference for Lancashire

TYPE OF GRANT Cash grants, mostly recurring. Occasional large grants for capital purposes

RANGE OF GRANTS £1,000–£5,000; typical grant £2,000–£5,000

FINANCES
- Year 1997
- Income £282,901
- Grants £291,000

TRUSTEES D H Dunn, Mrs I Dunn

HOW TO APPLY In writing. See below for further details

WHO TO APPLY TO D H Dunn, Correspondent, Mrs Waterhouse Charitable Trust, 25 Clitheroe Road, Whalley, Clitheroe BB7 9AD

CC NO 261685   **ESTABLISHED** 1967

Commentary

In 1967 Mrs Elsbeth Waterhouse set up a family trust with the main objective of providing funds on a regular basis to augment the income of charities to enable them to maintain and improve their services. The Trust has continued to carry out these objectives since the death of Mrs Waterhouse in 1992, and the present Trustees are her nephew D H Dunn and his wife. A limited number of more substantial grants may be made in order that organisations can finance charitable projects of a capital nature. Donations are mainly given to organisations based in, or with branches in, the Lancashire area. However, applications from other parts of the UK may be considered.

Apart from favouring local projects, the Trustees place no restrictions on the types of project they are prepared to consider, except for those set out above. The accounts for the year 1996–97 show that 66 charities received a total of £291,000 in grants, the largest being £50,000 to BHRV Health Care NHS Trust. The grants list indicates that medical charities were favoured, particularly medical research, but many environmental organisations also benefited.

Most of the grants awarded are recurrent from year to year. Loans will not be considered.

There are no application forms or formal guidelines. Applicants are recommended to submit a brief description of their charity's aims and objects and, if available, a copy of their latest accounts. Applications can be made at any time during the year, but grants are normally made in March following a review during January/February. Telephone calls are discouraged. The Trustees usually award most of the grants towards the end of the financial year, in February and March, but money may be given throughout the year. The Trust does not have a formal assessment procedure

SAMPLE GRANTS
The top ten grants made in 1997 were:
£50,000 to BHRV Health Care NHS Trust
£25,000 to National Trust Lake District Appeal
£10,000 to Royal Society for the Protection of Birds
£10,000 to Christie Hospital NHS Trust
£10,000 to Super Scan Appeal

£10,000 to Derian House
£6,000 to Friends of Chernobyl's Children
£5,000 to East Lancashire Hospice Fund
£5,000 to NSPCC Blackburn Branch
£5,000 to Cancer Relief Macmillan Fund

■ The Wedge

WHAT IS FUNDED The Trust makes grants only to organisations undertaking play and youth work in Merseyside. It prefers to support small local organisations rather than large or national bodies. Grants are made towards playscheme running costs, play equipment, day trips for playschemes

WHAT IS NOT FUNDED No grants to individuals. No grants are given for holidays, salaries, building costs or to religious organisations

WHO CAN BENEFIT Organisations benefiting children and young adults

WHERE FUNDING CAN BE GIVEN Liverpool

TYPE OF GRANT Grants to small local charities undertaking play and youth work. The Trust prefers to make a larger number of small grants rather than a few large grants. Grants are both single payment and recurrent

RANGE OF GRANTS £50–£500

FINANCES
- Year 1995
- Income £14,113
- Grants £17,500

TRUSTEES B Moores, A C McIntyre, A T Mcfarlane

HOW TO APPLY Applications should be in writing including a detailed budget and a copy of the latest available Accounts. Trustees meet quarterly

WHO TO APPLY TO A C McIntyre, The Wedge, South Moss House, Pasture Lane, Formby, Merseyside L37 0AP

CC NO 328382   **ESTABLISHED** 1988

■ The West Cumbria Charitable Trust

WHAT IS FUNDED Priority given to urban or rural regeneration, environmental improvements, benefits for children or young people, assistance for the elderly, funding for local projects

WHAT IS NOT FUNDED National charities based in West Cumbria, organisations based outside the area who wish to develop work in West Cumbria, organisations focusing on the unemployed or economic development

WHO CAN BENEFIT People living in West Cumbria whose groups meet Trust guidelines. All applications must have element of self help.

Charities benefiting people of all ages and living in both urban and rural areas will be considered

WHERE FUNDING CAN BE GIVEN West Cumbria

TYPE OF GRANT Generally small grants

RANGE OF GRANTS £200–£2,000

SAMPLE GRANTS £2,000 to West Cumbria Gym Club to renovation of derelict area for gym use
£1,530 to Bootle Village Hall for disabled toilets and showers
£1,250 to Turning Point, Workington for furniture for arts project
£1,200 to Netherhall School, Maryport for renovation and environmental work on yard
£1,120 to Cockermouth Mechanics Band towards new instruments
£1,023 to Distington Walled Garden for new polythene tunnel for charitable business
£1,000 to CHILD (Children's Holiday Initiative) for toys for children with learning disabilities
£1,000 to Greysouthen playing field for equipment for the play area
£1,000 to Brigham War Memorial Hall towards a new kitchen
£500 to Haverigg Guides for replacement camping equipment

FINANCES
- Year 1998
- Income £25,000
- Grants £17,000

TRUSTEES Rev J Baker, Mrs A Cunningham, Mrs B Ford, B Minto, Mrs H Scott, D Sibbit, Lady Ann Shuttleworth

NOTES Trustees meet in February and July

HOW TO APPLY Leaflet outlining Trust's aims and guidelines available from CVS, Border House, Whitehaven. The CVS will give help and advice to applicants if necessary. All applications to be made in writing

WHO TO APPLY TO Mrs H J Scott, The West Cumbria Charitable Trust, 148 Queen Street, Whitehaven, Cumbria CA28 7AZ

CC NO 1067621   **ESTABLISHED** 1998

■West Lancashire Masonic Educational Trust

WHAT IS FUNDED The relief of poverty and the advancement of education, especially special schools, by: (a) the assistance of such children of any age of freemasons in West Lancashire; (b) the assistance of any children whether or not children of a Freemason; and (c) making grants to other charities registered in England and operating in the same field or relief as the Trust

WHAT IS NOT FUNDED No grant are made for travel bursaries or expeditions

WHO CAN BENEFIT To benefit children, young adults, disabled people and those disadvantaged by poverty. Neighbourhood-based schemes, assistance to any organisation assisting children in educational and/or medical need

WHERE FUNDING CAN BE GIVEN Lancashire and surrounding counties

TYPE OF GRANT Project, capital, recurring costs and one-off. Funding is available for up to and over three years

SAMPLE GRANTS £160,000 to 1997 Festival Masonic Trust for Girls and Boys for maintenance and education
£45,111 to the Royal School for the Blind, Liverpool to provide a mobile training unit

FINANCES
- Year 1997–98
- Income £80,554
- Grants £205,000

TRUSTEES C P Wright, K E Moxley, T Hudson

HOW TO APPLY Guideline are issued by the Trust. A copy of the applicant's constitution, annual report, and income and expenditure accounts are required. All applications will be acknowledged

WHO TO APPLY TO Hon Secretary, West Lancashire Masonic Educational Trust, Masonic Hall, 22 Hope Street, Liverpool L1 9BY *Tel* 0151-709 2458 *Fax* 0151-709 6864

CC NO 526574   **ESTABLISHED** 1855

■The Westminster Foundation (168)

WHAT IS FUNDED General charitable purposes at the discretion of the Trustees. There is emphasis on welfare, the Church, conservation, youth and medicine

WHAT IS NOT FUNDED No grants to individuals, 'holiday' charities, student expeditions, nor research projects. The arts and arts/education budget is fully committed until at least 2004

WHO CAN BENEFIT Registered charities benefiting children, young adults and older people, ex-service and service people, homeless people, and those living in rural areas

WHERE FUNDING CAN BE GIVEN The North West of England with the emphasis on rural areas, and Central London

TYPE OF GRANT Usually one-off, but any type considered at the discretion of the Trustees

FINANCES
- Year 1997
- Income £1,478,981
- Grants £1,083,610

TRUSTEES The Duke of Westminster, OBE, TD, DL (Chairman), J H M Newsum, B A J Radcliffe

HOW TO APPLY To the Secretary of the Foundation in writing, enclosing an up to date set of accounts, together with a brief history of the project to date and the current need

WHO TO APPLY TO J E Hok, Secretary to the Foundation, The Westminster Foundation, 53 Davies Street, London W1Y 1FH

CC NO 267618   **ESTABLISHED** 1974

Commentary

The Westminster Foundation was founded in 1974 by the Fifth Duke of Westminster, the father of the present Duke.

The Foundation supports a number of different programmes within its broad objectives. The social and welfare programme supports a wide range of organisations, many of them community based, covering areas such as the alleviation of homelessness, the sick and the elderly, children (especially disadvantaged children), people with a range of disabilities and people affected by drug and alcohol misuse. The Trust also runs a number of smaller programmes including: the Church programme, conservation programme, youth programme, and medicine programme. The Foundation also runs arts and education programmes, both of which are fully committed until 2004.

The funding policies of the Foundation are subject to change, although there are not likely to be any major changes in the above categories. However, the Trustees anticipate that they will be giving fewer but larger grants in the future and that they will become more active in addressing more of the needs in rural areas. The Foundation will continue to focus upon Central London and North West England, especially Cheshire and rural Lancashire.

The Foundation does not replace statutory funding which a government body has a duty to provide, but will consider funding a project which is not covered by statutory responsibility. The Foundation does co-fund, and may promise money to a worthy organisation in order to encourage matching funding. However, it is unlikely to involve itself in formal partnership funding. The Foundation is willing to consider any type of grant necessary to the needs of an organisation, but is very unlikely to make loans. The Foundation recognises the value of core funding grants.

Applications should be made briefly in writing to the Secretary and should include a brief history of the project to date, details of the current need and up-to-date accounts. All applications are acknowledged. The Secretary then filters the applications, getting rid of those that are outside of the Foundation's remit. The remainder of the appeals are considered at one of the Trustees' four annual meetings. Some of these applicants will then be visited and their projects' viability assessed. Only successful appeals will receive further correspondence. Once a grant has been given, the Foundation checks very carefully that it is applied for the purpose it was gifted. Grants that are being made over a period of more than a year are visited, and reports are requested on the projects

SAMPLE GRANTS
The top ten grants given in 1997 were:
£80,000 to the Soil Association
£57,000 to Treloar Trust
£55,000 to Royal United Services Institute for Defence Studies
£50,000 to Chester Cathedral Development Trust
£50,000 to Hooke Park College (the Parnham Trust)
£35,000 to Wye College
£33,000 to Forum for the Future
£30,000 to Centrepoint Soho
£30,000 to the Passage Day Centre
£27,000 to the University of Liverpool Veterinary Faculty

■ Westmorland Charity Concerts Society

WHAT IS FUNDED General charitable purposes

WHERE FUNDING CAN BE GIVEN South Cumbria

TYPE OF GRANT Recurring, core costs and one-off

SAMPLE GRANTS £2,375 to British Heart Foundation
£2,375 to Cystic Fibrosis

FINANCES
- Year 1994–95
- Income £8,224
- Grants £4,750

TRUSTEES Appointed annually (eight Trustees): five from Lakeland Sinfonia Concert Society, two from Westmorland Music Council and one from Rotary Club of Kendal

WHO TO APPLY TO S O'Connor, Westmorland Charity Concerts Society, High Meadows, Oxenholme Lane, Natland, Kendal, Cumbria LA9 7QH *Tel* 01539 720888

CC NO 1027338   **ESTABLISHED** 1993

■ The Wethered Bequest

WHAT IS FUNDED The elderly and the arts, including support for students. Prefer modest projects for which a relatively small grant would be of significant value

WHAT IS NOT FUNDED No very large projects

WHERE FUNDING CAN BE GIVEN Merseyside

TYPE OF GRANT Normally one-off, but occasionally by installments

SAMPLE GRANTS £4,000 to the Royal Liverpool Philharmonic Society
£3,000 to Royal Liverpool Philharmonic concert
£1,000 to Royal Liverpool Philharmonic Youth Choir
£500 to KIND
£500 to Liverpool Student Community Action
£500 to Liverpool Women's Hospital Art Project
£300 to Chapel Bell Tower restoration

FINANCES
- Year 1996–97
- Income £7,008
- Grants £7,779

TRUSTEES Gordon Lindsay, Ms Carol Mason

HOW TO APPLY To the Correspondent in writing

WHO TO APPLY TO Cuff Roberts, Trustees Solicitors, The Wethered Bequest, 100 Old Hall Street, Liverpool L3 9TD *Tel* 0151-227 4181 *Fax* 0151-227 2584

CC NO 700195 **ESTABLISHED** 1988

■ Norman Whiteley Trust

WHAT IS FUNDED To help evangelical Christian causes primarily

WHAT IS NOT FUNDED No grants made in response to general appeals from large national organisations nor to smaller bodies working in areas other than those set out above

WHO CAN BENEFIT Christian charities. Organisations benefiting Christians and Evangelists

WHERE FUNDING CAN BE GIVEN Cumbria only

TYPE OF GRANT One-off, recurrent, capital, running costs

FINANCES
- Year 1997
- Income £144,000
- Grants £101,000

TRUSTEES Mrs B M Whiteley, P Whiteley, W Thomas, J Ratcliff, D Dixon

HOW TO APPLY In writing only – no telephone calls

WHO TO APPLY TO D Foster, Secretary, Norman Whiteley Trust, Fallbarrow, Windermere, Cumbria LA23 3DL

CC NO 226445 **ESTABLISHED** 1963

■ Wigan Town Relief in Need Charity

WHAT IS FUNDED The advancement of welfare

WHO CAN BENEFIT Organisations and individuals within the Wigan boundary

WHERE FUNDING CAN BE GIVEN The former County Borough of Wigan

TYPE OF GRANT Core costs, recurring costs and one-off

FINANCES
- Year 1996
- Income £7,600

HOW TO APPLY To the Correspondent in writing

WHO TO APPLY TO G Shepherd, Clerk, Wigan Town Relief in Need Charity, Moot Hall Chambers, 8 Wallgate, Wigan, Lancashire WN1 1JE *Tel* 01942 241522 *Fax* 01942 212247

CC NO 248976 **ESTABLISHED** 1979

■ The Charles Wilson Trust

WHAT IS FUNDED To further any movement likely to promote union amongst Christian sects. To advance true religion locally by preference

WHO CAN BENEFIT Christians

WHERE FUNDING CAN BE GIVEN Crewe

SAMPLE GRANTS £1,000 to families under stress
£625 to Wilson Scout Group

FINANCES
- Year 1996
- Income £9,571
- Grants £1,625

WHO TO APPLY TO Cyril H Carrier, The Charles Wilson Trust, 367 Hungerford Road, Crewe, Cheshire CW1 5EZ

CC NO 260457 **ESTABLISHED** 1970

■ The Windle United Charity

WHAT IS FUNDED General charitable purposes

WHO CAN BENEFIT Individuals and local organisations

WHERE FUNDING CAN BE GIVEN The Ancient Township of Windle

SAMPLE GRANTS £2,500 to Age Concern
£2,500 to St Helens and Knowsley Hospice
£600 to individuals

FINANCES
- Year 1996
- Income £3,690

TRUSTEES Mrs M P Fraser, J May, J Stead, J C Tyrer, A Whiteside, W J Woodcock

HOW TO APPLY To the Correspondent in writing

WHO TO APPLY TO Clerk to the Trustees, The Windle United Charity, Messrs Haygrath Jones, 8 Hardshaw Street, St Helens WA10 1RE

CC NO 1041793   **ESTABLISHED** 1994

■ W Wing Yip and Brothers Charitable Trust

WHAT IS FUNDED Chinese organisations, especially educational. Relief of poverty, Chinese students, education of Chinese children living in the area Where Funding Can Be Given

WHO CAN BENEFIT Chinese organisations benefiting: children, young adults, students and those disadvantaged by poverty

WHERE FUNDING CAN BE GIVEN Birmingham, Manchester, Croydon and Cricklewood

TYPE OF GRANT One-off, project and start-up costs. Funding for up to two years will be considered

RANGE OF GRANTS £50–£1,900; typical £250

FINANCES
- Year 1996–97
- Grants £7,200
- Income £139,102

TRUSTEES R A Brittain, D M King, G Y Yap, L S Yap, W Wing Yip

HOW TO APPLY To the address under Who To Apply To in writing

WHO TO APPLY TO R A Brittain, Trustee, W Wing Yip and Brothers Charitable Trust, 375 Nechells Park Road, Nechells, Birmingham B7 5NT *Tel* 0121-327 6618

CC NO 326999   **ESTABLISHED** 1986

■ The Winwick Educational Foundation

WHAT IS FUNDED Education, especially in the form of grants to schools

WHAT IS NOT FUNDED Beneficiaries must be under the age of 25

WHO CAN BENEFIT Local schools, some individuals

WHERE FUNDING CAN BE GIVEN The ecclesiastical parishes of Winwick, Newton St Peter's, Newton All Saints, Emmanuel Wargrave, St John's Earlestown, Lowton St Luke's and Lowton St Mary's

FINANCES
- Year 1996
- Income £4,817

TRUSTEES G D Maines, R G Davies, D Miles, John D Parr, T Chisnall, Mrs A C Atherton, Rev

R G Lewis, Mrs Bessie Griffin, Rev Graham Keegan

HOW TO APPLY To the Correspondent in writing

WHO TO APPLY TO J B Naylor, Clerk, The Winwick Educational Foundation, Ridgway Greenall Solicitors, 21 Palmyra Square, Warrington, Cheshire WA1 1BW *Tel* 01925 654221 *Fax* 01925 416527 *E-mail* law@ridgway.co.uk

CC NO 526499   **ESTABLISHED** 1968

■ The Leslie and Renee Woolf Charitable Trust

WHAT IS FUNDED To benefit Jewish and medical welfare causes in the Beneficial Area

WHO CAN BENEFIT Individuals and institutions

WHERE FUNDING CAN BE GIVEN UK, especially Manchester

FINANCES
- Year 1994–95
- Grants £45,000
- Income £11,400

HOW TO APPLY To the Correspondent in writing

WHO TO APPLY TO D A Woolf, Trustee, Leslie and Renee Woolf Charitable Trust, 27 Daylesford Road, Cheadle, Cheshire SK8 1LE

CC NO 1001685   **ESTABLISHED** 1991

■ The Woolton Charitable Trust

WHAT IS FUNDED The current policy of the Trustees is to make one-off grants to Liverpool based charities and charities specialising in research into blindness and other sight disabilities

WHAT IS NOT FUNDED No grants to non-registered charities

WHO CAN BENEFIT Registered charities benefiting medical professionals, research workers and those suffering sight loss and blindness

WHERE FUNDING CAN BE GIVEN Merseyside

TYPE OF GRANT One-off or annual

RANGE OF GRANTS £100–£2000

FINANCES
- Year 1997
- Grants £20,185
- Income £24,423

TRUSTEES Rt Hon Simon Frederick, Third Earl of Woolton, Ms J Sandeman-Allen

HOW TO APPLY Applications for grants can be submitted at any time, and suitable applications are then forwarded to the Trustees for their approval

WHO TO APPLY TO The Trustees of the Woolton Charitable Trust, c/o Nigel Packer & Company, 3rd Floor, Royal Liver Building, Pier Head, Liverpool L3 1JH

CC NO 209931   **ESTABLISHED** 1959

■World Friendship

WHAT IS FUNDED To advance education among people in need of financial assistance

WHO CAN BENEFIT Individuals and institutions

WHERE FUNDING CAN BE GIVEN Diocese of Liverpool

TYPE OF GRANT Recurring

FINANCES
- Year 1994–95   • Income £8,154

TRUSTEES F A Broadbent, J E Jones

WHO TO APPLY TO R Arden, World Friendship, Eamon Arden and Co, Church House, 1 Hanover Street, Liverpool L1 3DW

CC NO 513643   **ESTABLISHED** 1983

■Wyre Animal Welfare

WHAT IS FUNDED The Trust supports the rehousing of homeless animals and gives financial assistance to low income families to neuter and spay animals

WHO CAN BENEFIT Individuals or families, animal welfare organisations. All individuals and families must be on income support

WHERE FUNDING CAN BE GIVEN UK with preferences to Lancashire, and if funds are sufficient, overseas

TYPE OF GRANT Very small grants, eg for OAP's vets fees, a few to animal charities, and medical fees for animal rescue. Running costs are considered

RANGE OF GRANTS £200–£250

FINANCES
- Year 1997   • Income £16,283
- Grants £650

TRUSTEES Mrs Evans, R A Dodd, Mrs Brown

NOTES Majority of income spent on running costs, ie pet food, veterinary fees, cleaning, etc

HOW TO APPLY In person at the Wyre Animal Welfare Shop, otherwise in writing

WHO TO APPLY TO R A Dodd, Wyre Animal Welfare, 87 Poulton Road, Fleetwood, Lancashire FY7 6TQ

CC NO 1025042   **ESTABLISHED** 1993

■The Yorkshire Bank Charitable Trust

WHAT IS FUNDED Charities considered for support include those engaged in youth work, facilities for the less able-bodied and mentally disabled, counselling and community work in depressed areas, with some support also being given for education and for the arts. The Trustees would be unlikely to make more than one donation within any 12 month period

WHAT IS NOT FUNDED Applications from individuals, including students, are ineligible. No grants made in response to general appeals from national organisations

WHO CAN BENEFIT Registered charities benefiting: children and young adults; at risk groups; disabled people; those disadvantaged by poverty; socially isolated people and those involved in the arts

WHERE FUNDING CAN BE GIVEN Within the area covered by branches of the Bank, ie in England from north of the Thames Valley to Newcastle upon Tyne

TYPE OF GRANT Usually one-off for a specific project or part of a project

FINANCES
- Year 1996   • Income £240,439
- Grants £122,357

TRUSTEES D T Gallagher, O P Vanzuyden, C Herbert

HOW TO APPLY At any time. Applications should include relevant details of the need the intended project is designed to meet

WHO TO APPLY TO Executive Secretary, The Yorkshire Bank Charitable Trust, Yorkshire Bank plc, 20 Merrion Way, Leeds, West Yorkshire LS2 8NZ

CC NO 326269   **ESTABLISHED** 1982

■Youth and the Community Trust

WHAT IS FUNDED To encourage and develop voluntary service work by young people in the community of the City of Manchester

WHO CAN BENEFIT Individuals and institutions

WHERE FUNDING CAN BE GIVEN City of Manchester

TYPE OF GRANT Recurring

FINANCES
- Year 1995–96
- Income £8,929

WHO TO APPLY TO City Treasurer, Youth and the Community Trust, City Treasurers Department, PO Box 314, Town Hall, Manchester M60 2JR

CC NO 246283   **ESTABLISHED** 1966

Does the trust you have chosen match your needs? Haphazard applications waste postage and time

199